NEW YORK CONTEMPORARY ART GALLERIES

THE COMPLETE ANNUAL GUIDE

RENÉE PHILLIPS

Manhattan Arts
INTERNATIONAL

200 East 72 Street, Suite 26-L, New York, NY 10021
T: (212) 472-1660   F: (212) 794-0324
E: info@ManhattanArts.com   W: www.ManhattanArts.com

Quantity Discount Prices are Available.
Book Buyers: Please Contact Bert Geller

NEW YORK CONTEMPORARY ART GALLERIES
THE ONLY COMPREHENSIVE RESOURCE OF ITS KIND

Published by Manhattan Arts International
200 East 72 Street, Suite 26L, New York, NY 10021
T: (212) 472-1660   F: (212) 794-0324
E: info@ManhattanArts.com   W: www.ManhattanArts.com

Manhattan Arts International also publishes *Manhattan Arts International Magazine online* and *Success Now! The Artrepreneur Newsletter For Fine Artists*. It is the publisher of *Presentation Power Tools For Fine Artists, Creating Success: The Artist's Complete Guide to Freedom & Prosperity,* and *Success Now! The Motivational Guide.*

First Edition: 1995
Second Printing: 1995
Third Printing: 1996
Second Edition: 1997
Third Edition: 1998
Second Printing: 1998
Third Printing: 1999
Fourth Edition: 2000
Second Printing: 2001
Fifth Edition: 2002

Cover design by David Arsenault and Rolf Saint-Agnes.

NEW YORK CONTEMPORARY ART GALLERIES

Library of Congress ISSN 1081-8847
ISBN 0-9646358-8-7
Fifth Edition

I lovingly dedicate this book to
the memory of my sister
Selene Brown
for the love and creativity
she generously shared.

NEW YORK CONTEMPORARY ART GALLERIES

"It's manna from heaven. For anybody interested in the workings of the art world and the mysteries of the gallery system." **Edward Rubin, *New Art Examiner***

"No journal better serves the aspiring artist or the tourist confounded by surfeit." **Ivan Karp, Owner & Director, O.K. Harris Works of Art**

"What an accomplishment amassing all the information, but even more of a feat getting the information from dealers in New York. I know others have tried but were unsuccessful." **Caroll Michels, author, *How to Survive and Prosper as an Artist***

"An honest and comprehensive resource." **Cornelia Seckel, *Art Times***

"Indispensable in locating galleries and artists." **Marlena Greene, Curator**

"The scope to personal access to the New York Art World." **Donna Cameron, Artist, Writer, Filmmaker. Faculty, School of Visual Arts**

"Search no further. This landmark directory is the only sensible guide to NY galleries. Packed with vital information and detailed listings, it makes for easy and inspiring reading." **Elizabeth Exler, *Journal of the Print World***

"While the guide is aimed principally at artists, it's useful for collectors, art consultants and enthusiasts." ***National Sculpture Society***

"My 'Bible' to the Art World." **Melissa Wolf, Executive Director, Women's Studio Center**

"Everything you ever wanted to know about New York galleries but were afraid to ask." **Louis Vega, Editor, *Talent in Motion***

"I love it. It's really concise and up-to-date. It puts the New York artworld in a nutshell." **Rupert Goldsworthy, Chelsea, New York gallery owner**

"By far the best resource for any artist trying to de-mystify the New York gallery scene." **Marianne McNamara, Artist, editor, *Westside Arts Coalition News***

"This book is the only comprehensive resource of its kind. It is invaluable to any artist seeking to gain access to NYC's galleries. This book helps artists better market their work by demystifying the process of applying to and being selected by NYC galleries." **Matthew Deleget, Artist and Program Officer, Visual Artist Information Hotline, New York Foundation for the Arts**

"For collectors seeking out the undiscovered." **Robert Persky, *The Photograph Collector***

It's the ultimate roadmap to New York Galleries." **Melissa Christiano, Artist and Teacher, Williams College**

"This helps artists in their professional relationships with galleries." **Regina Stewart, Artist, Executive Director, New York Artists Equity Association**

"The New York Art World can be a jungle... and this book can be your chart into unexplored territory." **Robert Kameczura, *Chicago Artists' News***

"Very helpful in clarifying the manner in which galleries function." **Dr. Alastair Granville-Jackson, Ed.D., FRSA, Artist**

"NYC art history is being made and *New York Contemporary Art Galleries* is recording it." ***The Artist's Proof*, NYAEA**

"Renée Phillips makes sense of the art world." **Perri Colley, *Our Town***

"I wish there was a similar book like this in London, England to help find galleries." **Lamis Khamis, Artist, England**

"A very valuable tool for artists." **Dan Concholar, Director, Art Information Center**

"Indispensable in our search for venues for our ideas." **Denise Iacovone, Artist, Co-founder, Coalition of Creative Artists**

"The service you provide is essential." **John Amato, Synchronicity Fine Arts**

ACKNOWLEDGMENTS

New York Contemporary Art Galleries would not exist without the tenacity of many talented artists, curators and dealers throughout the world who have encouraged me to demystify the New York City gallery system. I am grateful for every art enthusiast and art professional whose curiosity and diverse interests were the catalysts for creating the first edition of this book in 1995 and the reason for its perpetuity. To every individual who has accepted my counseling, attended my seminars, and subscribed to Manhattan Arts International and Success Now! For Artists, I am enormously appreciative for your interest and participation.

My gratitude goes to all of you who enthusiastically endorsed this book from the beginning including Donna Cameron, Dan Concholar, Matthew Deleget, Elizabeth Exler, Lynne Friedman, Rupert Goldsworthy, Marlena Greene, Sandra Indig, Ivan C. Karp, Caroll Michels, Rosemarie Montague, Robert Persky, Edward Rubin, Cornelia Seckel, Regina Stewart, and Melissa Wolf, among many others.

Accolades go to Gerri Buchanan and Kris Vagner for their tenacious research and editorial assistance. They helped me investigate every corner of the five boroughs to bring many new galleries and alternative spaces to this edition. My warm appreciation goes to David Arsenault, an outstanding fine artist who redesigned the cover of this edition and the previous edition. Credit also goes to Rolf Saint-Agnes for the initial design in 1995.

My gratitude goes to everyone who purchased all previous editions of New York Contemporary Art Galleries and encouraged your friends, colleagues and students to buy copies, as well as those who placed advance orders for this edition. The successful distribution of the first four editions is attributed to professional word-of-mouth, in addition to the support of the Museum of Modern Art, Amazon.com, Barnes & Noble Bookstore, BarnsandNoble.com, Rizzoli Bookstore, Borders Books, New York Artists Equity Association, O.K. Harris Works of Art, Sam Flax Art Store and many other suppliers of the book, including hundreds of libraries, universities, art schools and art organizations across the country.

During the creation of this book I had the pleasure of communicating with more than 1,000 gallery owners, curators, directors, private dealers and artists. Their friendly cooperation in completing our questionnaire by phone, fax, and email helped to make this otherwise arduous task a wonderful adventure. I look forward to working with them on many future editions of New York Contemporary Art Galleries. Our conversations inspired many ideas for panel discussions and articles that will appear on www.ManhattanArts.com, and in future books.

My loving appreciation is extended to my mother Elyse Green for her unwavering confidence in me, my special brother Pete for his legal expertise, my Aunt Sharon, for her guiding light, and my precious nephews and nieces, Michael, Jason, Cheri and Vanessa, for their joyful presence and their love for art. And many thanks to all of my loved ones, and invaluable friends and clients for their extraordinary patience while I worked on this project.

RENÉE PHILLIPS

"Renée sounds the clarion call for self-empowerment
and is the voice to the artist of the 21st century."
Bernard Olshan, Artist, National Academy Museum

Renée Phillips is the author of all five editions of *New York Contemporary Art Galleries*, hailed by the art community as the only comprehensive resource of its kind. She is the author of all three editions of *Presentation Power Tools For Fine Artists* and *Success Now! For Artists: A Motivational Guide For The Artrepreneur.* Her most recent book is *Creating Success: The Artist's Complete Guide to Freedom & Prosperity.* She is founder and Editor-in-Chief of *Manhattan Arts International* magazine (1983-2000), now an E-zine at www.ManhattanArts.com. She is Editor-in-Chief of *Success Now! The Artrepreneur Newsletter.* She is also a member of the distinguished International Association of Art Critics.

She is founder and director of Manhattan Arts International, an organization dedicated to fostering relationships between artists and other members of the art community and art enthusiasts. As a pioneer in her field as a career advisor and coach to artists and agents from around the world she provides direction, specific strategies and resources in the areas of marketing, publicity and promotion.

Her highly attended motivational seminars have been held at many universities and art institutions including Marymount Manhattan College, City College, Heckscher Museum, and Columbia University. She is a guest speaker for such organizations as New York Foundation for the Arts, American Society of Contemporary Artists, Teacher's College Association, and Artists Talk on Art. Each month she conducts a workshop "How to Sell Your Art" for The Learning Annex in New York, NY. She also served as a faculty member of Marymount Manhattan College for which she gave tours to galleries and artist's studios and a series of Artist and Business seminars.

For her contributions to the Arts she has been awarded citations from two NYC mayors. She was featured in *New York Newsday* as a "Community Leader." She has been listed in numerous directories such as *Who's Who in America, Who's Who in American Art*, and *Community Leaders of the World.* Articles about her have appeared in *The New York Times, Crain's New York Business,* and *Our Town.*

Articles she has written have appeared in many publications nationwide, including *The Artist's Proof*, a publication of New York Artists Equity Association, an artist advocacy organization, in which she held a position on the Board of Directors. She is currently on the Advisory Boards of several art institutions.

Ms. Phillips has juried and curated more than 50 multi-media art exhibitions in art centers, corporate venues and galleries, including the National Arts Club, Lincoln Center, and First Women's Bank, among others, many of which received national TV and international print coverage. She organized the "*Manhattan Arts* Debate," the only political debate in NYC's history to concentrate solely on the arts.

Renée Phillips studied art at the Art Students League in New York, NY. As a professional artist she had many solo and group exhibitions. Her work is included in many private and public collections including Mr. and Mrs. Corwin of Panasonic, Merrill Lynch and Chase Manhattan Bank.

INTRODUCTION

The historical influence and current role of New York City's galleries and museums are indisputable. Without them the City would not have achieved the status as a global leader intellectually, creatively and commercially. This city attracts, influences, exhibits and sells artwork by artists from all continents in staggering numbers, thereby enhancing its multi-cultural vitality. In tiny rooms and giant lofts we find a colorful compendium of art movements and techniques, and every-visual-thing from Traditional to New Media, Outsider to Conceptual, Self-Taught to Site-Specific, Latin-American to Russian, Vintage to Video, and Minimal to Pop.

"AN HONEST AND COMPREHENSIVE RESOURCE"

Since 1995, *New York Contemporary Art Galleries* has been recording the activities of New York City's exhibition venues. It has been praised by members of the art community as the only comprehensive resource of its kind. We personally contacted each gallery to obtain the information directly, and there was no fee for them to be listed, which is why Cornelia Seckel, Publisher of *Art Times,* describes it as "an honest and comprehensive resource."

Expanded, updated and revised, the Fifth Edition of *New York Contemporary Art Galleries* includes more than 1,000 profiles. It is an all-inclusive directory of commercial and non-profit galleries, mainstream and alternative exhibition venues, private dealers, curators, corporate art consultants, museums and artists' studios that exhibit contemporary art which, for the purpose of this book, has been defined as art that has been created since World War II. Most of them show contemporary art exclusively; others focus on art from earlier periods and include contemporary art. This information is indicated in the individual gallery listings.

"IT PUTS THE NEW YORK ART WORLD IN A NUTSHELL"

The breadth and scope of *New York Contemporary Art Galleries* has been designed to inform and inspire the reader, whether you are an avid collector seeking out the undiscovered, or an artist in search of exhibition opportunities. Rupert Goldsworthy, Chelsea gallery owner, stated: "It puts the New York art world in a nutshell."

This book brings you behind the scenes to meet esteemed art dealers, many of whom who have impacted the course of art history by establishing new artists and movements. Equally significant, the book introduces you to younger dealers who are breaking with tradition and are revolutionizing the way art is exhibited and sold. It will be fascinating to follow them and save every edition of *New York Contemporary Art Galleries* for its treasure trove of historical information.

New York has always been the center of the American art world, but it replaced Paris as the capital of the international art market during the time between World War II and the opening of the renowned Leo Castelli's gallery in 1957. The City's own school, Abstract Expressionism, and members such as Jackson Pollack, were lifted to the status of global leaders. Since then, its dominant position has unchanged.

This edition portrays New York's eclectic art scene and its power to change the city's complexion. It reveals the burgeoning migration of artists and dealers to Chelsea and its environs and those in Brooklyn and Queens who are developing new artistic communities. The increase of artist studios and artist-run galleries reflects an increase of "artrepreneurship." And, multi-cultural alternative spaces are here to stay.

New York City's diverse neighborhoods are juxtaposed in a kaleidoscope of harmonies and contrasts, from Tribeca to Harlem, from SoHo to Williamsburg, and from Chelsea to the Upper East Side.

Each region invites exploration, made simple by the arrangement of chapters:

- Tribeca/Lower Manhattan
- SoHo
- Lower East Side/East Village/Greenwich Village/West Village/Union Square/Gramercy Park
- Chelsea/South Chelsea/Meat Packing District
- Midtown (30-59 Street)
- Uptown (60-above)
- The Outer Boroughs: Brooklyn/Bronx/Queens/Staten Island

Each entry includes such information as:

- Name of gallery
- Address
- Telephone
- Fax
- Email
- Web site
- Owner
- Director
- Background
- Year established
- Hours
- Admission fees
- Gallery size
- Description of work shown
- Prices, Markets, Collectors
- Number of artists represented and their origins
- Five artists and their media
- Focus/Mission
- Number of annual solo and group exhibitions
- Publications in which the galleries advertise
- Artist selection process
- Materials, requirements and fees requested from artists
- Response time
- Additional information such as special programs and services

"FOR ANYONE INTERESTED IN THE MYSTERIES OF THE GALLERY SYSTEM"

Not all exhibition venues and galleries operate in the same manner. This book clearly illustrates: What is the educational and/or professional background of the gallery owner? For what purpose was the institution established? Which dealers represent famous artists' estates? Which galleries are owned and operated by artist members? These questions and more are revealed in this book, in an easy-to-read, concise style. Edward Rubin, NYC art critic and writer for the *New Art Examiner* claimed this book is: "For anyone interested in the workings of the art world and the mysteries of the gallery system."

"FOR COLLECTORS SEEKING OUT THE UNDISCOVERED"

Among the many living legends who appear in this book are Ileana Sonnabend, Paula Cooper, Robert Miller, Holly Solomon, and Larry Gagosian. Ivan C. Karp, known as the Sage of SoHo was once assistant to Leo Castelli before opening his own gallery O.K. Harris Works of Art in 1969. It paved the way for SoHo to become the landmark district it remains today. Karp's 10,000 sq. ft., museum-like gallery, located at 383 West Broadway, is open to the public during exhibition installations, in order to "help people uncover the mystery of the arts."

You will find many more art dealers eager to assist and educate every one who expresses interest in learning about art. Whether you are a neophyte or advanced collector, you will find art in all styles, media and price ranges to suit your needs. I hope this book will encourage you to visit the hundreds of exciting and diversified NYC galleries that are free and open to the public in addition to the world's foremost museums. I hope the experience will expand your appreciation for the styles with which you are already familiar, and inspire you to explore and embrace new artistic expressions. Relax and enjoy the journey of discovering tomorrow's mainstream art stars.

"IT IS INVALUABLE TO ANY VISUAL ARTIST"

For an artist the task of comprehending NYC's myriad exhibition spaces can be overwhelming. This book is a tool to save time and money in your search for exposure, recognition and income – to give you more time to devote to your creative process. It sheds light on a complex subject that has been plagued by secrecy and myths due to a lack of concrete, factual information – until now. Whether you are an art student or an established artist, this book will demystify the gallery system. As Matthew Deleget, Program Officer of the New York Foundation for the Arts, stated: "It is invaluable to any visual artist seeking to gain access to NYC's galleries."

Since the First Edition of *New York Contemporary Art Galleries* was published in 1995, many artists from around the world have reported success stories from using it. This new, expanded edition is packed with more than 1,000 listings. There are numerous opportunities that are available to artists, whatever your style, age, career level, or origin. The detailed profiles serve to empower you with essential information including the dealers' professional background, their focus/mission, their methods of selecting artists, direction on how and when to approach them, and any gallery fees and other requirements. Its aim is to help you take the first step to establish rapport and build partnerships with key individuals in the art world.

Please know that all of the information contained in this directory is subject to change; the charm of New York City is its constant state of flux. Our vigorous efforts to obtain, confirm, and update the information persisted until the final hours before press time, in fact, we included a list of some new and noteworthy galleries that came to our attention hours before press time.

If you should find any of the information contained in this book to be incorrect or incomplete please notify us by mail or email. If you represent a gallery or are a private dealer that is not included, please let us know.

There is no charge to be included in this book.

HOW TO BREAK INTO NEW YORK GALLERIES

If you are an artist seeking NYC gallery representation you are aware that hundreds of thousands of other artists from around the globe are competing against you. Although many of you find the idea of approaching New York galleries an intimidating prospect many galleries enjoy discovering new artists and contributing to their growing reputations. You can imagine, however, the abundance of unsolicited materials, visits, phone calls and emails they receive from artists trying to get their attention. Overwhelmed by stacks of materials, much of which is sent without knowledge of the gallery's artistic direction, you can understand why throughout this book you read their plea that artists familiarize themselves with their exhibitions before approaching them.

To learn who, how, and when to approach and to best promote and market your work, you are invited to attend my workshops and lectures that I present throughout the U.S. "How to Sell Your Art" formerly known as "How to Break Into New York Galleries" is a comprehensive, three-hour workshop I developed for The Learning Annex in New York City. Artists from around the world have attended it and walked away with more of an understanding of how the gallery system operates.

My advice is after you have made your list of prospects that look appropriate in this book, visit the galleries in person before submitting any materials. View several exhibitions in the desired galleries, speak to the personnel, attend the opening receptions, and network within the art community. Become acquainted with the artists affiliated with the galleries that interest you because dealers often rely on their recommendations. If you cannot travel to NYC visit the galleries' websites and also become acquainted with them through art periodicals in print and on the Internet.

In addition to honing your technical skills and creative vision I stress the importance of preparing the best quality presentation materials possible. Throughout this book you will notice the galleries request materials with SASE (self-addressed, stamped envelope). If you want your materials returned enclose one with sufficient postage. Enclose a cover letter directed to the person in charge. In addition to slides you may want to send photographs, laser, or other color copies of your work for them to retain for future access. Some galleries accept photo CDs. A color brochure or catalogue will also suffice. There are printers listed in the Resource section of this book. You will also find an order form for *Presentation Power Tools For Fine Artists*, another book of ours that helps artists prepare all of the necessary documents for a polished professional approach to dealers, collectors and critics.

HELP ART PROFESSIONALS TO BECOME SELF-SUFFICIENT

For more than 20 years I have been a professional advisor and coach to artists and agents worldwide of all career levels, styles and media. As founder and director of Manhattan Arts International our mission is to help art professionals become self-sufficient "Artrepreneurs". Our web site www.ManhattanArts.com contains an art magazine, resources, artist's and agent's profiles and juried competitions. We invite you to join us there and at our workshops to share, exchange and develop relationships.

I wish you success in all of your creative endeavors and I look forward to hearing about them! Please email me at Renee@ManhattanArts.com.

Renee Phillips

TABLE OF CONTENTS

NEW YORK CONTEMPORARY ART GALLERIES

REVISED & EXPANDED FIFTH EDITION

We've added dozens of NEW profiles in this edition.
We welcome them all and wish them longevity.

A Ramona
Philip Alan
Maurice Arlos
Art at Format
ArtLink
Axis
June Bateman
Bitforms
Camhy Studio
Canada
Chambers
Chappell
Chung-Cheng
CJG Projects
Coda
Ethan Cohen
Cook
Cooper Classics
Corning
Carol Cravin
Cricket Hill
Dumbo Arts Center
Exhibit A
Eye Beam
Eye Storm
Fresh Art
Fuse
Galapagos Art Space
Galerie Le Provence
Goliath
The Half King

Susan L. Halper
Here
International Print
    Center
Irish Arts Center
Priska Juschka
Klotz/Sirmon
Leo Koenig
Krasdale
Patricia Laligant
Latin Collector
LFL
Joe & Emily Lowe
Maccarone
Marvelli
Messineo Wyman
    Projects
Manhattan Arts
    International
Gail Martin
Kagan Martos
Ariel Meyerowitz
Yossi Milo
Murray Guy
James Austin Murray
Jessica Murray Projects
North Star
125 Maiden Lane
Opera
The Parlor
Octavio Paz

Portraits and
    Painting
Project
Progressive Art at
    the Well
Riva
Rivington Arms
Russek
Russian American
    Cultural Center
Rx Art
Savacou
Kenny Schachter
Scholten Japanese
Paul Sharpe
    Contemporary
Sound Sculpture Studio
St. George
Studio Annex
Studio 18
Sugar Hill Arts Center
Dominic
    Taglialatella
Talwar
James Francis Trezza
Van de Weghe
Verlaine
And many others!

WHAT IS CONTEMPORARY?

*For the purpose of this book the word Contemporary
encompasses art work created since World War II.*

That meaning includes all styles and all media.

You'll find them all in this book.

TRIBECA
& LOWER MANHATTAN

PAUL SHARPE CONTEMPORARY
"Founded on the premise that the artist comes first and is the *raison d'etre* of the art world. The gallery is designed as a salon rather than a white box."

ADELPHI UNIVERSITY MANHATTAN CENTER
75 Varick St., 2nd floor, 10013. **TEL:** (516) 877-4460.
F: (212) 431-5161. **W:** www.adelphi.edu
Open: Mon.-Fri. 9-5. **Year established:** 1988.
Owner: Adelphi University. **Director:** Professor Richard Vaux.
Work shown: Painting, drawing, prints and photography.
Work by: Exhibitions have featured Richard Vaux: paintings and drawings; Carl Eckhoff: paintings; Jock Anderson: paintings; and Nik Davidopoulous: photography/mixed media; among others.
Annual exhibitions: 3 solo/ 2 group. **Advertising:** *Gallery Guide.*
Focus/Mission: To show professional art and Adelphi University alumni in various styles.
Selection process: Exhibitions are arranged on an invitational basis. All artists are selected from professional referrals and materials submitted to the gallery. Artists should mail slides, biography, resumé and SASE. **Response time:** 1 month.

AMOS ENO
59 Franklin St., 10013. **T:** (212) 226-5342.
F: (212) 343-1271. **E:** amoseno@bway.net
Open: Wed.-Sat. 11-6. **Size:** 900 sq. ft.
Year established: 1974. **Director:** Deborah de Bruin.
Owner: Artist members. Non-profit cooperative gallery.
Work shown: All styles and media. **Annual exhibitions:** 13 solo/3 group.
Markets: Individual, corporate, and museum. **Prices:** $500 and up.
Artists represented: 25. Ages: 30-60. New York based, national, and international artists. 35% of the artists are in museum collections.
Focus/Mission: To provide alternative, non-profit resources for fine artists. The gallery also presents readings and music events.

Selection process: Members meet bi-monthly to review artists' materials.
Response time: 1month. Artists are encouraged to visit the gallery to look at the members' work before making an appointment. Information may be sent to out-of-state artists. Artists should request application information.
Fees: Members are required to pay monthly dues and provide minimal help with gallery duties. Artists are responsible for their exhibition expenses.

APEX ART C.P.

291 Church St., 10013.
F: (212) 431-4447.
W: www.apexart.org
Year established: 1994.
Founder/Director: Steven Rand.
Work shown: Varied styles and media.
TEL: (212) 431-5270.
E: info@apexart.org
Open: Tues.-Sat. 11-6.
Owner: Non-profit organization.
Assistant Director: Heather Felty.
Annual exhibitions: 8.
Advertising: *Artforum, Documents* and *Gallery Guide.*
Focus/Mission: This is a non-profit, curator-driven exhibition space. We invite guest curators to assemble shows; we do not interfere in their decision process.
Selection process: All works are selected by guest curators. Exhibition proposals are accepted in Jan. and Feb. Call for information.
Additional information: Each show is accompanied by a full-color, museum-quality brochure containing reproductions of the works and an essay by the curator.

MAURICE ARLOS

85 Franklin St., (between Church and Broadway), 10013.
T: 965-5466.
E: priapos@att.net
Open: Mon.-Sat. 11-6.
F: (212) 965-5468.
W: www.mauricearlos.com
Year established: 2001.
Owner/Director: Maurice Arlos, who has an extensive business background and extensive art interests.
Work shown: Non-academic Figurative art. Painting, sculpture, work on paper.
Artists represented: 6, from the U.S.
Work by: Claude Carone: painting; Deborah Masters: sculpture; Thaddeus Raddel: painting; Kyle Staver: painting; and Chuck Dowdish; painting; among others. **Prices:** $200-15,000.
Annual exhibitions: 10.
Advertising: *Gallery Guide.*

ART GALLERY AT 55 BROAD STREET

55 Broad St., 10004.
F: (212) 422-0711.
W: www.artvault.com
Year established: 2000.
T: (212) 825-2059.
E: stliferart@aol.com
Open: Mon.-Fri. 9-5.
Size: 4,000 sq. ft.
Curator: Jane St. Lifer, Owner/Director of St. Lifer Fine Art, Inc.
Work shown: Contemporary art in all media.
Annual exhibitions: 4.
Focus/Mission: To present the work of mature to the public and to enhance the growing reputation of the cultural arts in the neighborhood.
Selection process: Artists should mail slides, photographs, resumé and SASE.
Response time: 1 month.
Additional information: Jane St. Lifer is also an art appraiser.

ART FOR MEDIA

9 White St., 4th floor, 10013.　　**T:** 423-0607.
E: mediaart@att.net　　**W:** www.artformedia.com
Open: By appointment.　　**Contact:** Laurie Friedman and Elenor Trifon.
Work shown: Painting, drawing, sculpture and photography by Contemporary artists. Art for Media rents and sells art for film, TV, commercials, photo shoots and to corporations.

ART IN GENERAL

79 Walker St., 10013.　　**T:** (212) 219-0473.
F: (212) 219-0511.　　**E:** info@artingeneral.org
W: www.artingeneral.org　　**Artists represented:** 220.
Open: Tues.-Sat. 12-6; Closed mid-July through Sept. 1.
Year established: 1981.　　**Size:** 3,500 sq. ft.
Owner: Non-profit organization sponsored by the NEA, NY State Council on the Arts, other public foundations, and individuals.
Director: Holly Block.　　**Assistant Director:** Catherine Ruello.
Work shown: All styles and all media including video and installations. The program consists of primarily group thematic exhibitions.
Focus/Mission: To focus on the development of contemporary art that is often under-represented in larger museum and commercial gallery structures. To present work by emerging artists, with a strong representation of women and artists who are developing a new direction. To present artwork in a broad cultural context, addressing key issues related to art-making and to timely social and political concerns. To remain accessible as a forum for which artists' work in a range of media and at varying stages of development may be reviewed.
Selection process: A panel consisting of 10 artists reviews work on a quarterly basis. Artists should send SASE and request an application form.
Additional information: Exhibiting artists receive an honorarium. There are no exhibition fees and no gallery commission is taken on sales.

ART PROJECTS INTERNATIONAL (A.P.I.)

429 Greenwich St., 10013.　　**T:** (212) 343-2599.
F: (212) 343-2499.　　**E:** api@artprojects.com
W: www.artprojects.com　　**Open:** By appointment.
Year established: 1993.　　**Size:** 1,500 sq. ft.
Owner/Director: Jung Lee Sanders, background in museum experience.
Work shown: Contemporary art, with a focus on works by leading contemporary artists from Asia.　　**Markets:** Individual, corporate, and museum.
Artists represented: 8. 80% of the artists are in museum collections.
Work by: Pouran Jinchi: painting; Jian-Jun Zhang: mixed-media; Il Lee: works on paper; Gwenn Thomas: photo-emulsion on linen; and Yeong Gill Kim: acrylic on canvas, and works on paper; among others.
Collectors: National Museum of Modern Art (Seoul, Korea), Parish Art Museum, and Fukuoka City Art Museum, Japan.
Annual exhibitions: 2 solo/2 group. **Advertising:** *Art in America* and *ARTnews*.
Focus/Mission: To enhance cultural dialogue and facilitate the international exchange of ideas among artists, art professionals, scholars, collectors, and the art viewing public. To bring the work of Asian artists to NYC and the work of western contemporary artists to Asia.　　*continued*

Selection process: 60% of the artists are selected from referrals, 15% are selected from slides, and 35% from museum exhibitions and publications. Artists should mail 10 slides, resumé and SASE. We review materials quarterly. **Response time:** 3 months. Artists are expected to pay for framing their work.

THE ART SHOWCASE AT THE BOND MARKET

40 Broad St., 12th floor, 10004.　　**T:** (212) 440-9418.
Open: By appointment.　　**Director:** Susan Cusumano.
Work shown: Contemporary paintings and work on paper.
Work by: Bari Goodman; Suejin Jo; Pam Chin Lee; Younghee Choi Martin; and Vry Roussin; among others.
Focus/Mission: This is an alternative space that presents semi-annual exhibitions in a corporate setting.

ASIAN AMERICAN ARTS CENTRE

26 Bowery, 10013.　　**T:** (212) 233-2154.
F: (212) 766-1287.　　**E:** aaartsctr@aol.com
W: www.artspiral.org　　**Size:** 1,200 sq. ft.
Open: Tues.-Fri. 12-6, Sat. 4-6; Summer: call for hours.
Year established: 1974.　　**Director:** Robert Lee, art history background.
Work shown: All styles and media. **Annual exhibitions:** 5 group.
Artists represented: 1,000, in the slide archive. They are Asian artists or artists whose work is significantly influenced by Asian culture, regardless of race.
Focus/Mission: To increase public visibility and knowledge of contemporary Asian American artists. The Centre administers numerous programs, seminars, workshops, presentations, performances, and publications.
Selection process: All artists are selected from slides sent to the Centre. Artists should mail 20 slides, biography, resumé. The Centre will keep materials in the archives. They will not be returned. **Response time:** 2-3 weeks.
Requirements: Artists are required to make arrangements to transport their art.

A TASTE OF ART

147 Duane St., 10013.　　**T:** (212) 964-5493.
F: (212) 964-2671.　　**E:** info@atasteofart.com
Open: Mon.-Fri. 12-8, Sat. 12-6.　Closed in August.
Year established: 2001.　　**Annual exhibitions:** 10.
Owner: Lawrence Asseraf, a lawyer for 15 years, and collector for 25 years.
Work shown: Contemporary art in all media including video.
Work by: Izak: illustration; DeSaiz: painting; Dietrich Ian Lafferty: photography and mixed media; and David Taylor: photography; among others.
Prices: $950-12,000.
Selection process: Artists should send slides, photographs, resumé, and SASE.

AVERY ON BOND

2 Bond St., 10012.　　**T:** (212) 614-1492.
F: (212) 614-1494.　　**E:** averyonbond@aol.com
Open: Mon.-Sat. 11-7, Sun 12-6　**Year established:** 1995.　**Size:** 2,500 sq. ft.
Owner: Rick Avery, antique dealer and art collector.
Focus/Mission: I choose artwork that I love. It fits into the ambiance of my antique and furniture store and gallery and helps to create a sense of home.

Selection process: 50% of the artists are selected from professional referrals, 50% from art seen in exhibitions or artists' studios. We are not looking for new artists.

BRIDGEWATER FINE ARTS

78 Leonard St., 10013.   **T:** (917) 406-3644.
E: bwfinearts@aol.com   **W:** www.bridgewaterfinearts.com
Open: By appointment.   **Year established:** 1984.
Owners: Paul Bridgewater: gallery owner for 24 years
Director: Lynn Park.   **Work shown:** Predominantly Representational painting, sculpture, drawing and photography.
Artists represented: 20-30.   **Ages:** 30-70.

➤ **Work by:** Steven Skollar: paintings; Norm Magnusson: painting; Torkil Gudnason: photography; and Iris El Ayoubi: collage on paper; among others.
Prices: $500-15,000.   **Collectors:** Prudential, Philip Johnson Art Museum, and the Print Collections of Cornell and Yale.
Annual exhibitions: 8 solo/2 group.
Advertising: *Gallery Guide, Art in America* and *ARTnews*.
Focus/Mission: To champion representational art with an academic bent – quite solid and painterly work with a contemporary twist.
Selection process: Unsolicited slides are accepted with SASE but their return is uncertain. **Requirements:** Artists should have a unique vision that is balanced with technical talent. Artists are expected to pay for framing and transportation.

HAL BROM

90 West Broadway, 10007.   **T:** (212) 732-6196.
Open: By appointment.   **Year established:** 1976.
Owner: Hal Brom.   **Director:** Ric Oquita.
Work shown: American and European Contemporary painting, drawing, sculpture, and photography.
Work by: Mike Bidlo; Andre Cadere; Rosemarie Castoro; Roger Cutforth; Luis Frangella; and Keith Haring; among others.

CANADA

55-59 Chrystie St., 10002.   **T:** (212) 925-4631.
W: www.canadabasement.com   **Year Established:** 2001.
Size: 3,000 sq. ft.   **Work shown:** Contemporary art in all media.
Director: Suzanne Butler; background: private art dealer.
Artists represented: 10; Origins: International.

➤ **Work by:** Anke Weyer: painting; Aaron Brewer: sculpture; Wallace Whitney: painting; Sarah Braman: sculpture; and Robin Peck: sculpture.
Annual exhibitions: 10.   **Advertising:** *Mix Magazine*.

CAPELUTO ARTS

443 Greenwich St., Studio 6F, 10013   **T:** (212) 219-8287.
F: (212) 219-1048.   **W:** www.capelutoarts.com
E: CapelutoArts@aol.com   **Open:** By appointment.
Directors: Wendy Capeluto and Jamie Kohen.
Work shown: Fine contemporary ceramics by artists from all origins.

continued

Work by: Shinman Yamada; Jissei Omine; and Frank Boyden; among others.
Focus/Mission: To give potters a venue to represent their work as an artform. Focusing primarily on wood-fired ceramic art, this gallery is one of merely a few galleries featuring works by potters from all over the world.
Additional information: The gallery is run by a mother and daughter team.

ETHAN COHEN FINE ARTS

37 Walker St., 10013.
T: (212) 625-1250.
F: (212) 274-1518.
E: ethancohen@ecfa.com
W: www.artnet.com/ecohen.html
Artists represented: 5.
Open: Tues.-Fri. 12-6, Sat. 12-5, and by appointment.
Year established: 2000.
Owner/Director: Ethan Cohen.
Work shown: Contemporary Chinese art of emerging and established artists.
Work by: Shi Chong: oil painting; Qiu Zhijie: ink painting, photography, video, and installation; Lin Tianmiao: photography and installation; Wu Shan Zhuan: conceptual installation and painting; and Lin Yi Lin: performance, photography, video and installation; among others.
Selection process: The gallery reviews portfolios monthly. A sampling of color copies of the work, resumé and SASE is adequate, however artists may also send slides and/or photographs.

RENEE FOTOUHI FINE ART

315 Church St., 10013.
T: (212) 431-1304.
F: (212) 431-7462.
Open: By appointment.
Owner: Renée Fotouhi.
Work shown: Contemporary and Modern art in all media.
Work by: Miró; Warhol; Basquiat; Lichtenstein; and Rivera; among others.

FRANKLIN FURNACE ARCHIVE

45 John St., Suite 611, 10038.
T: (212) 766-2606.
F: (212) 766-2740.
E: mail@franklinfurnace.org
W: www.franklinfurnace.org
Year established: 1976.
Owner: Non-profit organization.
Founding Director: Martha Wilson.
Administrator: Harley Spiller.
Program Coordinator: Tiffany Ludwig.
Work shown: Netcast performance art.
Focus/Mission: The Franklin Furnace is no longer performing as an art exhibition space. This is an in-your-face arts organization that has transformed into a production entity in order to place artists before broader audiences and by electronic mediums on the Internet. Its history has been to present artists from diverse racial and ethnic groups, female artists, gay, lesbian and bisexual artists, artists from different regions of the nation and the world, and artists who have political, social, religious, or moral outlooks who may challenge those of mainstream American culture.
Selection process: Artists should visit the web site to obtain information.
Deadline for artist's proposals: April 1.

HENRY STREET SETTLEMENT

*"To celebrate the arts and arts education
with the diverse population of the Lower East Side.
Many of our exhibitions are socially conscious
and all are focused on the intersection
of community, culture, and the arts."*

HENRY STREET SETTLEMENT

Abrons Arts Center, 466 Grand St., 10002.   **T:** (212) 598-0400.
F: (212) 505-8329.   **W:** www.henrystreetarts.org
Size: 3,000 sq. ft.   **Open:** Tues.-Sat. 12-6. Closed in August.
Owner: Non-profit organization.   **Year established:** 1893.
Visual Art Director: Susan Fleminger.
Gallery Coordinator: Kirstin Broussard.
Work shown: Contemporary art in all media.
Work by: Contemporary artists are shown through curated group exhibitions in the main gallery. Solo photography exhibitions are held in the Culpeper Gallery by the on the entrance level.
Annual exhibitions: 5 group/ 8 solo photography.
Focus/Mission: To celebrate the arts and arts education with the diverse population of the Lower East Side. Many of our exhibitions are socially conscious and all are focused on the intersection of community, culture, and the arts.
Selection process: For group thematic shows: curators may send proposals to the gallery with slides, biographies and a SASE. For one-person photography shows artists should request an application by mail with a SASE.
Additional information: We offer an Artist-in-Residence Workspace Program (Artists should send SASE for application), an extensive studio art instructional program, an Arts-in-Education program (workshops by professional artists and arts educators are implemented in classrooms from pre-kindergarten through high school in public schools throughout NYC), and a gallery education program.

JACOB JAVITS FEDERAL BUILDING LOBBY

26 Federal Plaza, 10278.   **T:** (212) 264-9290.
F: (212) 264-3857.   **E:** michelle.phillips@tsa.tov
Open: Mon.-Fri. 8-5.
Contacts: Building Managers, General Services Administration: David Segermeister and Kirkland Smith.
Building Operating Assistant: Michele Phillips.
Work shown: Contemporary painting, photography, drawing, sculpture, craft.
Annual exhibitions: 12.
Selection process: Artists should approach the Building Managers anytime by calling for information about the space availability. Exhibiting artists must be members of a non-profit organization. They must obtain a permit for the "Use of Space in Public Buildings and Grounds." No controversial topics or subjects of nudity.

STEVEN KASHER

54 North Moore St., 10013. **T:** (212) 966-3978.
F: (212) 226-1485. **E:** kashers@idt.net
Open: By appointment. **Size:** 1,500 sq. ft.
Year established: 1997. **Owner/Director:** Steven Kasher.
Work shown: Contemporary and vintage photography by artists from all origins.
Markets: Individual, corporate, museum.
Prices: $50-1,000,000.
Work by: Eugene Richards; The Burns Collection of medical and historical photographs; Wingate Paine: vintage prints, 1965-1966, from *The Mirror of Venus*; Vintage Soviet photographs by Alpert, Langman, Petrusov, and others; and Vintage Hollywood, Vaudeville and Broadway portraits and theatricals.
Advertising: *Photography in NY.*
Focus/Mission: To show Vintage and Contemporary photography of social and historical importance.
Selection process: 80% of the artists are selected from professional referrals, 20% from art seen in exhibitions, publications and artists' studios.

HAL KATZEN

459 Washington St., 10013. **T/F:** (212) 925-9777.
E: hkatzen916@aol.com **W:** www.katzen.com
Size: 1,800 sq. ft.
Open: Tues.-Sat. 10-6 and by appointment.
Year established: 1987. **Owner/Director:** Hal Katzen.
Work shown: Contemporary and Modern American and European paintings, sculpture, works on paper, and prints. Resale secondary market.
Work by: The estate of Lila Katzen. Also work by Romare Bearden; Robert Motherwell; Hans Hoffmann; Sam Francis; Pablo Picasso; and Henry Moore; among others.
Collectors: Metropolitan, Philip Morris, and Cleveland Museum.
Selection process: We are currently not looking for new artists.

THE KNITTING FACTORY

74 Leonard St., 10013. **T:** (212) 219-3006.
F: (212) 219-3401. **W:** www.knittingfactory.com
Open: Daily. Call for hours. **Director:** Michael Dorf.
Year established: 1987. **Owner:** This is a live performance
space/music club featuring performance art, multi-media, and video art.
Selection process: Artists should send videos, CDs, slides, and other materials with SASE to Booking Agent. **Response time:** 2 months or longer.

LEO KOENIG

249 Center St., 10013. **T:** (212) 334-9255.
E: leokoenig@hotmail.com **Open:** Tues.-Sat. 10-6.
Year established: 1999.
Owner: Leo Koenig. **Director:** Elizabeth Balog.
Work Shown: Contemporary painting.
Artists represented: 12.
Work by: Aidas Barelkis; Bill Saylor; Jeff Elrod; Dorben Kichler; and Lisa Ruyter; among others.

LATIN COLLECTOR

153 Hudson Street, 10013.   **T:** (212) 334-7813.
F: (212) 334-7830.   **W:** www.latincollector.com
E: info@latincollector.com   **Open:** Mon.-Fri. 10-6, Sat. and Sun. 1-6.
Year established: 2001.   **Size:** 5,000 sq. ft.
Owner: Frederico Seve, owner of a gallery in Rio De Janeiro, Brazil.
Work Shown: Latin American art in all media and styles.
Artists represented: 12.
Work by: Tony Bechara: painting; Pin Morales: painting; Edgar Negret: sculpture; Tatiana Parcero: photography; Claudia Jaguaribe: photography; and Andre Cypriano: photography; among others.
Annual exhibitions: 8-10.
Selection process: Artists should send slides, photographs, biography, resumé and SASE.

LOFT LAWYERS

145 Hudson St., 10013.   **T:** (212) 431-7267.
F: (212) 431-7312.   **Open:** 9:30-5, or by appointment.
Year established: 1986.   **Size:** 2,500 sq. ft.
Owner/Director: John Upton, lawyer. **Assistant Director:** Joel Siegel.
Work shown: Primarily painting; some sculpture.
Prices: $500-5,000.   **Annual exhibitions:** 3 solo.
Focus/Mission: "We are a law office that likes to show progressive art."
Selection process: Artists are selected from slides sent to the office. Artists should send approximately 12 slides with SASE. **Response time:** 1 month. There are no exhibition fees and no gallery commission.

MACCARONE

45 Canal St., 2nd + 3rd floor, 10002. **T:** (212) 431-4977.
F: (212) 965-5262.   **E:** kitchen@maccarone.net
W: www.maccarone.net   **Open:** Wed. – Sun. 10-6.
Year established: 2001.
Director: Michele Maccarone, former director of Luhring Augustine.
Work shown: Emerging, international, contemporary art. Primarily multimedia, sculpture, video, drawing.
Work by: Christoph Buchel; Christian Jankowski; Claudia and Julia Muller; Olav Westphalen; and Mike Bouchet; among others.
Prices: $1,000 - $150,000.   **Annual exhibitions:** 6
Focus/Mission: To bring together American and European artists and present museum quality, site-specific installations in the gallery.

MELA FOUNDATION, INC.

275 Church St., 3rd floor, 10013.   **T:** (212) 925-8270.
F: (212) 226-7802.   **W:** www.virtulink.com/mela/main.htm
Open: Thurs. and Sat. 2-midnight; Summer: call for hours.
Admission: $4.   **Year established:** 1985.
Size: 1,400 sq. ft.
Owner: Mela Foundation, a not-for-profit interdisciplinary arts organization. This is a Sound and Light Environment exhibition space.
Artistic Directors: La Monte Young and Marian Zazeela.   *continued*

— **Work by:** La Monte Young; Marian Zazeela; and Pandit Pran Nath.
Focus/Mission: To encourage creative work in the fields of music, the visual arts, and other media, to explore the applications of advanced technologies to artistic expression, and to present major contemporary works and extended duration art installations that eliminate the boundaries between artistic disciplines. The Foundation is also devoted to the development and maintenance of extensive archives documenting the work of some of the central figures in the world of contemporary art.
Additional information: Books and recordings focusing on the works of LaMonte Young, Marian Zazeela, Pandit Pran Nath and other artists may be purchased.

JAMES AUSTIN MURRAY STUDIOS

59 Franklin St., 10013.
W: www.jimmurraystudios.com
Year established: 1998.
T: (212) 965-8692.
Open: By appointment.
Size: 600 sq. ft.
Work shown: Abstraction with figurative elements, mixed media on canvas.
Prices: $200-8,000.
Advertising: *Gallery Guide*.
Annual exhibitions: 3.

NY LAW SCHOOL: SHEPARD & RUTH K. BROAD STUDENT CENTER

47 Worth St., 10013.
Open: Daily 10-7.
T: (212) 431-2100.
Year established: 1993.
Work shown: All styles and media.
Selection process: Exhibitions are coordinated with Organization of Independent Artists. Contact O.I.A.: (212) 219-9213.

123 WATTS

123 Watts, 10013.
F: (212) 274-1726.
W: www.123watts.com
appointment.
Owner: Barbara Berzack.
T: (212) 219-8339.
E: gallery@123watts.com
Open: Tues.- Sat. 12-6, Mon. by
Year established: 1994.
Director: Josee Bienvenu.
Work shown: Contemporary art and avant-garde from the 1920s -60s.
Markets: Individual and corporate. **Prices:** $400-120,000.
Artists represented: 15, from U.S., France, Germany, Latin America, and Japan.
— **Work by:** Marco Maggi: drawing; Stafan McClure; Hans Bellmer: photography, drawings and sculpture; Gary Gissler: drawing and painting; among others.
Annual exhibitions: 4 solo/3 group.
Advertising: *Gallery Guide* and *Photography in NY*.
Selection process: 60% of the artists are selected from professional referrals, 10% from slides sent to the gallery, and 30% from art seen in exhibitions or artists' studios. Artists should mail slides, photographs, biography, resumé, and SASE. Artists' materials are reviewed every week. Call for information before submitting materials. **Response time:** Months.

125 MAIDEN LANE

125 Maiden Lane, 10038.
F: (212) 206-6114.
Year established: 2000.
T: (212) 202-6060.
Open: Mon.-Fri. 9-5.
Owner: Time Equities, Inc.

Curator: Linda Cross.   **Annual exhibitions:** 4.

Work shown: Sculpture by outstanding contemporary artists exploring a variety of approaches and materials.

Selection process: Artists should call Larry Gillig (212) 206-6060.

ORGANIZATION OF INDEPENDENT ARTISTS (O.I.A.)

19 Hudson St., Room 402, 10013. **T:** (212) 219-9213.
F: (212) 219-9216.   **E:** org.ind.artists@worldnet.net
W: www.oiaonline.net   **Open:** Tues.- Fri. 1-5.
Year established: 1976.   **Owner:** Non-profit organization.
Program Director: Nadini Richardson. **Membership Director:** Pam Cooper.
Work shown: All styles and media.

Focus/Mission: To provide public spaces for exhibitions throughout New York. The gallery maintains a slide registry available to curators, art professionals, artists and others. O.I.A. also publishes a newsletter and conducts slide viewings. O.I.A. conducts two annual Curators Workshops and one annual juried Salon Exhibition.

Selection process: Send SASE for membership information.

CHERYL PELAVIN FINE ART

13 Jay St., 10013.   **T:** (212) 925-9424.
F: (212) 431-3037.   **E:** cpelavin@aol.com
W: www.cherylpelavin.com   **Open:** Tues.-Sat 11-6
Year established: 1981.   **Owner/Director:** Cheryl Pelavin, an artist with more than 20 years experience as a collaborator and art dealer.

Work shown: Paintings and unique works on paper by contemporary artists.

Markets: Individual, corporate, and museum. **Prices:** $750-20,500.

Artists represented: Mostly North America. All artists are in museum collections.

Work by: Katherine Bowling: monotypes; Gregory Crane: paintings and monotypes; Daisy Craddock: paintings and works on paper; Valentina Dubasky, paintings and monoprints; and Donna Sharrett: assemblage; among others.

Collectors: Champion Paper Collection, J.P. Morgan, U.P.S. Int., and Prudential.

Annual exhibitions: 6-8.   **Advertising:** *Gallery Guide.*

Focus/Mission: To publish the work of young and mid-career artists and exhibit both their works on paper and paintings.

Selection process: 50% of the artists are selected from professional referrals, and 50% are selected from art seen in exhibitions and artists' studios. Artists should send slides, biography and SASE. **Response time:** 6 months.

PESCEPALLA DOCKS

345 Greenwich St., 10013.   **T:** (212) 625-3148.
F: (212) 625-0957.   **E:** ppd@pescepalla.com
W: www.pescepalla.com
Open: Tues.-Sat. 12-7, Sun. 12-5. Closed in August.
Year established: 1999   **Size:** 2,400 sq. ft.
Owners/Directors: Guido & Francesca Zwicker, former choreographers.
Manager: Judy Melinger.

continued

Work shown: A variety of original one-of-a-kind objects in all media including ceramic sculpture, special furniture and paintings. **Annual exhibitions:** 6.
Prices: $50-8,000. All major credit cards are accepted.
Selection process: Artists should send slides, photographs, biography, artist's statement, prices, SASE, and reason why their art is suited for this gallery.
Response time: 1 month.
Additional information: The owners also have a gallery in Italy where many of the items are created.

RUSSIAN AMERICAN CULTURAL CENTER

55 John St., 10038.
E: khidart@aol.com
Open: Tues.-Fri. 12-5.
Year established: 1998.
T: (212) 744-5168.
W: www.russianamericanculture.com
Director: Regina Khidekel.
Work shown: Contemporary Russian, American and Eastern European art.
Origins: Russian, American-Russian and American artists.
Annual exhibitions: 8-10 solo/1-2 group.
Focus/Mission: To create a support network. To preserve cultural heritage and foster ongoing creative development through multi-dimensional cultural and educational activities and international exchange. The Center has an artist career development program and presents large projects.
Selection process: We are currently not looking for new artists.

RHONDA SCHALLER STUDIO

59 Franklin St., 10013.
E: rlsstudio@earthlink.net
Open: By appointment.
T: (212) 226-0166.
W: www.koop.dartmouth.edu
Size: 800 sq. ft.
Markets: Individual, corporate, museum.
Work shown: Postmodernist sculpture, drawings and prose; visceral elements, and found objects.

PAUL SHARPE CONTEMPORARY

86 Walker St., 6th floor, 10013.
W: www.artware-software.com/psca
Open: Wed. 12-8, Thurs.-Sat. 12-6, and by appointment.
Year established: 2001.
T/F: (646) 613-1252.
Size: 1,500 sq. ft.
Owner/Director: Paul Sharpe, previously worked at the Whitney Museum.
Work shown: Contemporary art, with a tendency toward abstraction.
Artists represented: 20, international.
Work by: Linda Cummings: photography; Katy Martin: painting; Anton Christian: painting; Fairfax Dorn: painting; Anthony Cotsisas: photography, among others.
Prices: $500-50,000.
Advertising: *Gallery Guide.*
Annual exhibitions: 16 solo.
Focus/Mission: PSCA is founded on the premise that the artist comes first and is the *raison d'etre* of the art world. The role of the gallerist is to nurture creative accomplishment and to cultivate the collectors and curators who can sustain the artists. The gallery itself is meant to encourage a dialogue in issues in art today and is designed as a salon rather than a white box. The concept is to create a space where artists and art lovers can congregate and enjoy fine contemporary art.

Selection process: Artists should mail slides, photographs, resumé and SASE. Response time: 1 month.
Additional information: The gallery hosts fund-raising events for non-profit organizations in addition to book signing events.

JANE ST. LIFER FINE ARTS

11 Hanover Square, #703, 10005. **T:** (212) 825-2059.
F: (212) 422-0711. **E:** stliferart@aol.com
W: www.artregister.com **Open:** By appointment.
Year established: 1989. **Owner/Director:** Jane St. Lifer.
Work shown: 19th and 20th century artists' exhibition posters.
Work by: Georges Braque; Bernard Buffet; Marc Chagall; Jean Cocteau; and David Hockney; among others.
Additional information: Jane St. Lifer is also an art appraiser.

STUDIO 18

18 Warren St., 10007. **T:** (212) 385-6734.
Open: Thurs.-Sat. 1-6. **Owner/Director:** Franz Friedrich.
Year established: 2001. **Work shown:** All media, toward Abstraction and Minimal with occasional Realism. The gallery was previously the studio of painter Frances Heathering.
Work by: Frances Heathering: painting; Joe Barnes; painting; Joyce Rezendes: painting; BobWitz: painting and sculpture; and Fumio Yoshimura: sculpture.
Prices: $300-35,00. **Advertising:** Gallery Guide.

SYNAGOGUE FOR THE ARTS

49 White St., 10013. **T:** (212) 966-7141.
F: (212) 966-4968. **W:** www.civiccentersynagogue.org
Open: Mon.-Thurs.1-5, Tues. 1-7; Summer: Call for hours.
Year established: 1994. **Size:** 3,000 sq. ft.
Work shown: All styles and media by artists of all ages and origins.
Annual exhibitions: 6-8. **Advertising:** Gallery Guide.
Focus/Mission: To be an alternative space and exhibit a diversity of work and styles of emerging and established artists in a multi-purposed community setting.
Selection process: All artists are selected from slides and other materials sent to the gallery. We review artists' materials in the Spring and the Fall. Send SASE to the Gallery Committee to obtain the exhibition guidelines, and then submit slides, biography, resumé and SASE. **Response time:** 8-12 months. There is a $200 stipend granted by the Synagogue per show to apply toward exhibition expenses. **Requirements:** No subjects of nudity.

JAN WEISS

68 Laight St., 6th floor, 10013. **T:** (212) 925-7313.
Open: By appointment. **Year established:** 1989. **Size:** 1,200 sq. ft.
Owner/Director: Jan Weiss.
Work shown: Contemporary art. American, European and Australian art; especially Urban Aboriginal Australian art.
Work by: Sally Morgan: painting and prints; Bronwyn Bancroft: painting; Karen Casey: painting and installation; and Lin Onus: painting.
Selection process: We are currently not looking for new artists.

WORLD FINANCIAL CENTER COURTYARD

220 Vesey St., 10281.
F: (212) 945-3392.
W: www.worldfinancialcenter.com
Year established: 1988.
Work shown: All styles and media.

T: (212) 945-0505.
E: wfcae@wfprop.com
Open: Tues.-Fri. 11-6, Sat. and Sun. 12-5.
Size: 10,000 sq. ft.

Focus/Mission: The gallery has an international focus, and collaborates with cultural institutions in the U.S. and abroad. Exhibitions have included contemporary art from Russia, Mexico, and New York.

Selection process: Exhibitions are arranged in collaboration with cultural institutions. Artists should not contact the gallery directly.

CAN'T FIND YOUR FAVORITE GALLERY?

If your favorite NYC gallery or private dealer
is not listed in this edition,
please send us its name, address, telephone,
email and web site.
We will add it to the next edition.
There is no charge to be listed.

Mail to the attention of
New York Contemporary Art Galleries,
c/o Manhattan Arts International
or send us the information via email
to NYCAG@ManhattanArts.com

SOHO

O.K. HARRIS
**"The gallery functions much like a museum.
The gallery's main concern is to show
the most significant art work of our time.
In its choice of works to be exhibited
it demonstrates no prejudice
as to the style or materials employed."**

ABSOLUTE ASIA
180 Varick St., 10014.   **T:** (212) 627-1950.   **F:** (212) 627-4090.
E: info@absoluteasia.com   **W:** www.absoluteasia.com
Open: Mon.-Fri. 9-6.   **Year established:** 1994.
Size: 800 sq. ft.   **Owner:** Ken Fish, a Southeast Asia specialist.
Work shown: Traditional and contemporary art of Asia. Painting, photography and traditional crafts. 80% of the artists shown are in museum collections.
Work by: Nguyen Tu Nghiem: gouache on paper; Hoang Dang Nhuan: gouache on paper; Dang Xuan Hoa: painting; Tran Khanh Chuong: painting; and Cindy Ho: photography; among others.   **Annual exhibitions:** 2 solo/2 group.
Focus/Mission: To expand awareness of Asian art and culture.
Selection process: Artists should mail 4 slides and SASE. Artists must have a prominent involvement in either traditional or contemporary art forms of Asia.

ACE
275 Hudson St., 10013.   **T:** (212) 255-5599.
F: (212) 255-5799   **Open:** Tues.-Sat. 10-6.
Year established: 1994.   **Owner/Director:** Douglas Chrismas.
Work shown: Contemporary, Abstract, Minimal and Conceptual art.
Work by: Emerging and established U.S. and international artists.
Selection process: We are currently not seeking new artists.

AGORA
415 Broadway, 10012.   **T:** (212) 226-4406.
F: (212) 966-4380.   **E:** AG@agora-gallery.com
W: www.agora-gallery.com   **Open:** Tues.-Sat 12-6.
Work shown: All styles and media. **Markets:** Individual and corporate.
Selection process: Artists should send 10 slides and SASE.
Response time: 3 weeks.
Fees: Artists should expect to pay exhibition and promotion expenses.

A.I.R.

40 Wooster St., 2nd floor, 10013. **T:** (212) 966-0799.
F: (212) 941-7508. **E:** director@airnyc.org
W: www.airnyc.org **Year established:** 1972.
Director: Dena Muller. **Open:** Tue.-Sat. 11-6. Closed late July-Aug.
Owner: Non-profit women's cooperative gallery.
Work shown: Contemporary art in all media by women artists.
Artists represented: 35. All ages and origins. 85% are in museum collections.
Collectors: Metropolitan, MoMA, Whitney, and Guggenheim museums.
Focus/Mission: To advance the status of women artists by exhibiting diverse work of the highest quality. To provide leadership and a sense of community to women artists.
Annual exhibitions: 20 solo/2 group. **Advertising:** *Gallery Guide.*
Selection process: To apply for membership artists should mail 10-20 slides, resumé and SASE to AIR Gallery.
Fees: Artist members pay membership and exhibition fees.

BROOKE ALEXANDER EDITIONS

59 Wooster St., 10012. **T:** (212) 925-4338.
F: (212) 941-9565. **E:** brookealex@earthlink.net
Open: Tues.-Sat. 10-6 and by appointment.
Year established: 1968. **Owner:** Brooke Alexander.
Director: Michelle Quinn **Work shown:** Contemporary art and editions.
Artists represented: Predominantly American and European contemporary artists. All of the artists are in museum collections.
Annual exhibitions: 3 solo/7 group. **Advertising:** *Artforum* and *On Paper.*
Collectors: MoMA, Metropolitan, Whitney, and New York Public Library.
Selection process: Artists should call for current viewing policy.

THE ALTERNATIVE MUSEUM

32 West 82 St., 10024. **T:** (212) 966-4444.
E: altmuseum@aol.com **W:** www.alternativemuseum.org
Year established: 1975. **President:** Geno Rodriguez.
Owner: Non-profit organization. This is an electronic museum.
Work shown: Scanned images, digitized video / audio reproductions of artwork.
Focus/Mission: To show artists of all racial, economic and gender backgrounds. To bring the arts into a more interactive relationship with the broadest segment of society. To provide a professional showcase for artists, leadership with an "artist's" perspective within the museum profession, and an atmosphere wherein ideas can be presented and challenged. The Museum is an evolving institution, which changes with the needs of society.
Selection process: Artists should call or email and request information.

AMBASSADOR

114 Spring St., 10012. **T:** (212) 431-9431. **F:** (212) 431-8123.
W: www.ambassadorgalleries.com **Year established:** 1988.
Owner: Eleanor Miner. **Assistant Director:** Maggi Hausman.
Open: Mon.-Thurs. 10-6, Fri. 10-7, Sat. 11-6, Sun.12-6, evenings by appointment.

Work shown: Impressionist, Realist, Modern and celebrity paintings, lithographs, and sculpture.

Markets: Individual and corporate. **Prices:** $1,000-30,000.

Artists represented: 14 male/6 female. 20% are in museum collections.

— **Work by:** Tarkay: paintings, lithographs, watercolors; Bruno Zupan: paintings, lithographs, watercolors; Roy Fairchild: lithographs and drawings; and celebrity artists such as Jerry Garcia and Tony Curtis; among others.

Annual exhibitions: 8-10 solo.

Advertising: *Architectural Digest, ARTnews, The New York Times,* and radio.

Focus/Mission: To offer a broad range of well-priced, exceptional quality art.

Selection process: 10% of the artists are selected from referrals, 50% from slides sent to the gallery, and 40% from art seen in exhibitions or artist studios. Artists should mail slides, photos, resumé, prices, and SASE.

Response time: 2 months.

AMERICAN FINE ARTS

22 Wooster St., 10013.   **T:** (212) 941-0401.   **F:** (212) 274-8706.

Open: Tues.-Sat. 12-6.   **Year established:** 1988.

Size: 1,000 sq. ft.   **Owner:** Colin de Land.

Director: Christine Tsvetanov.   **Assistant Director:** Daniel McDonald.

Work shown: Conceptual art in all media.

Markets: Individual, corporate and museum. **Prices:** $100-100,000.

Artists represented: 50% male/50% female. **Origins:** U.S., Europe, and Japan. 50% of the artists are in museum collections. **Annual exhibitions:** 10.

— **Work by:** Mark Dion: sculpture; Andrea Fraser: photography; Alex Bag: photography; Peter Fend: alternative fuel sources and text; and Art Club 2000; among others.

AMERICAN PRIMITIVE

594 Broadway, #205, 10012.   **T:** (212) 966-1530.   **F:** (212) 343-0272.

Year established: 1978.   **Size:** 2,800 sq. ft.

Open: Mon.-Sat. 11-6, Summer Tues.-Fri. 11-6.

Owner/Director: Aarne Anton, owner of a company that produces bases and displays for art.   **Assistant Director:** Tina Anton.

Work shown: American Self-taught, Outsider and Folk Art in all media.

Artists represented: 15, mostly from the U.S. 50% are in museum collections.

Markets: Individual, corporate, museum. **Prices:** $100-100,000.

— **Work by:** Raymond Materson: pictures sewn from the threads of his unraveled socks; Robert Sholties: paintings, visionary images by a self-taught surrealist; Sam Gant: paintings combining word and images (lacking hearing and speech, his art is his communication); and Jimmy Lee Sudduth: paintings made with clay and found materials which invoke his rural roots; among others.

Annual exhibitions: 4 solo/4 group.   **Advertising:** *Gallery Guide, Art in America, Antiques and Arts Weekly, Raw Vision,* and *Folk Art Magazine.*

Focus/Mission: To exhibit self-taught artists working outside of the mainstream of academic art.

Selection process: 15% of artists are selected from referrals, 15% from slides and other materials sent to the gallery, and 15% from art is seen in exhibitions, and the rest of the artists are selected from other sources. Artists should send slides, photos, biography, and SASE to gallery. **Response time:** 1-2 weeks.

ANIMAZING

474 Broome St., 10013.   **T:** (212) 226-7374.
F: (212) 226-7428.   **W:** www.animazing.com
Year established: 1986.   **Size:** 1,500 sq. ft.
Owners: Heidi Leigh and Nick Leone.   **Director:** Nick Leone.
Open: Mon.-Sat. 10-7, Sun.11-6; Summer: Fri. 10-8, Sat. 10-8, Sun. 11-7.
Work shown: Vintage and Contemporary Animation art, fine art and craft. This is NYC's only licensed Disney Gallery. It handles Drawings and Cels (original and limited editions) from all studios including Hanna Barbera, Nickelodeon, Fox, Peanuts, and artist Chuck Jones.   **Prices:** $20-20,000.
Collectors: Jim Carey, Michael Jackson, Whoopie Goldberg, David Letterman, and Steven Speilberg.
Annual exhibitions: 5 solo/4 group. **Advertising:** *Guest Informant, Gallery Guide, Animation, New York* magazine, and trade publications.
Focus/Mission: The owners are collectors and love what they do. Their focus is on finding remarkable original vintage art.
Selection process: Artists must be working in the industry. They should call Nick Leone for an appointment.
Additional information: The gallery presents book signings and special events.

ANTIQUARIUS

484 Broome St., 10013.   **T:** (212) 343-0311.
F: (212) 343-0849.   **W:** www.antiquarius2000.com
Open: Mon.-Fri. 10-7. Sat: 11-7. Sun. 12-6.
Work shown: Antique Tribal and European furniture, African tribal rugs and contemporary vegetal dyed rugs. Also ceramic, terra cotta and wooden bowels and other decorative items from around the world.
Additional information: The owners are also importers and wholesalers.

APOGEE

Call for new location.   **T:** (212) 674-1991.
W: www.petergee.com   **Year established:** 1964.
Owner/Director: Peter Gee.
Work Shown: Contemporary art prints and painting by NY artists.
Prices: $1,500 - $40,000.   **Annual Exhibitions:** 4.

ARCADIA

51 Greene St., 10013.   **T:** (212) 965-1387.
F: (212) 965-8638   **E:** arcadiafa@aol.com
W: www.arcadiafinearts.com   **Year established:** 2001.
Open: Mon.-Fri. 10-6, Sat.-Sun. 11-6.
Owner/Director: Steven Diamant, has 15 years experience in other galleries.
Work shown: Contemporary realism. Figurative, landscapes, and still lifes. Paintings, sketches and prints.   **Artists represented:** 30, from all origins.
Work by: Malcolm Liepke; Ron Hicks; Francis Livingston; Robert Liberace; and Robert La Duke; among others.
Annual exhibitions: 10.   **Advertising:** *US Artists* and *Art & Antiques*.
Focus/Mission: To show the best representational work possible.
Selection process: Artists should mail slides, transparencies, photographs, resumé and SASE. **Response time:** 1 month.

ART ALLIANCE

98 Greene St., 2nd floor, 10012. **T:** (212) 274-1704.   **F:** (212) 274-1682.
E: artallny@aol.com   **Open:** By appointment.
Year established: 1989.   **Size:** 1,200 sq. ft.
Owner/Director: Leah Poller, graduate of Ecole Nationale Superieure de Beaux Arts, Paris. She is an international curator for museums and other art institutions.
Assistant Director: Michelle Biton.
Work shown: Realism by Latin, South American and African artists. Painting, work on paper, and sculpture.
Artists represented: 12-20 from all origins. 80% male/20% female. **Ages:** 35-75. 90% of the artists are in museum collections.
Work by: G. Matthiesen: sculptor using found objects and live body casting to reinvent social archetypes; Bernardo Torrens: Spanish Realist, figurative work in the tradition of Ingres; Jose Luis Corella: Spanish Realist, figurative work; Mario Murua: co-founder of Magic Image art movement, raucous Expressionist; and Dino Valls: Spanish Realist; among others.
Collectors: Alitalia Airlines, MoMA, Boca Raton, FL, and Santiago Art Museum.
Markets: 70% individual, 20% corporate, 10% museum. **Prices:** $375-150,000.
Advertising: *Gallery Guide* and *Nexus*.
Focus/Mission: To serve as an agent and/or gallery for mid and late career foreign artists desiring U.S. market and critical acceptance. To continue long term, in-depth representation of the same artist, with an emphasis on career building, museum presence, and historical contribution.
Selection process: Artists should call before mailing 10-20 slides, resumé, and SASE. **Requirements:** Artists should have made major contributions in their home country and have total commitment to history (art) in the making.
Additional information: This is a very unconventional, intimate viewing space, with a one-on-one relationship with collectors. Leah Poller organizes "Salon" evenings by invitation which bring international, creative talents together with art lovers, critics and members of the business world. The gallery's traveling exhibition program is available upon request.

ART AT FORMAT

50 Wooster St., 10013.   **T:** (212) 941-7995.
E: art4format@aol.com   **Year established:** 1999.
Owner/Director: Sany Mariquez.
Open: Mon.-Thurs. 10-7, Fri. 10-6, Sat.10-6, Sun. 12-5.
Work shown: Contemporary Brazilian artists. This is a high end furniture store.
Work by: Newman Schutze; Felipe Senatore; Estela Sandrini; and Clovis Junior; among others.   **Annual exhibitions:** 6-8.
Focus/Mission: To promote Brazilian artists new to New York City.
Selection process: Email or mail photographs or slides with resumé and SASE.

ARTISTS SPACE

38 Greene St., 10012.   **T:** (212) 226-3970.
F: (212) 966-1434.   **W:** www.artistsspace.org
Open: Tues.-Sat 11-6.   **Year established:** 1973.
Owner: Non-profit organization.   **Director:** Barbara Hunt.
Work shown: All styles and media. **Annual exhibitions:** 15.
Advertising: *Gallery Guide*.

continued

Focus/Mission: To serve as a laboratory for the development of new work, and specifically the work of under-recognized or emerging artists. It also maintains a slide registry consisting of 4,000 artists available for viewing.

Selection process: Artists should call or visit the web site for information.

ATELIER INTERNATIONAL ART GROUP

594 Broadway, Suite 305, 10012. **T:** (212) 431-0630. **F:** (212) 431-0224.
E: atelierart@aol.com **W:** www.atelierart.com
Open: Tues.-Sat. 12-6. **Size:** 1,000 sq. ft.
Year established: 1997. **Owner/Director:** Carole Jones: MA, DePaul University, Chicago, IL, followed by more than 14 years in the gallery business.
Work shown: Contemporary eclectic art. Mixed media, painting and sculpture.
Markets: Individual, corporate, and museum.
Annual exhibitions: 9 solo/3 group. **Prices:** $1,000-200,000.
Artists represented: 10, from Asia, Europe, and North and South America. 50% male/50% female. 90% are in museum collections.
Work by: Fernando Feuerheisen: Abstract Classical, mixed media on canvas; Laurie Wohl: Classical, mixed media on canvas; Weileng Zhao: Abstract Classical, mixed media on canvas; Charlotte Segal: Abstract Classical, mixed media on canvas; and Jeffrey Perren: Abstract Classical, mixed media oil, steel, and fire; among others.
Advertising: *Gallery Guide, SoHo magazine,* and *New York Times Today.*
Focus/Mission: It is committed to emerging artists that have a sense of Classical with a Contemporary image that reaches to the educational and spiritual being of its constituency. The artists are passionate in the way they live, paint and sculpt.
Selection process: 50% of the artists are selected from professional referrals, 50% from slides and other materials sent to the gallery. Artists should mail slides, photographs, biography, resumé, artist's statement, prices and SASE. Artists should call for an appointment. We review artists' materials when time permits.
Response time: 6-12 months. **Requirements:** Commitment.
Additional information: The gallery presents events of not-for-profit arts projects, performances, readings, and discussions.
Fees: Artists should be prepared to pay exhibition-related expenses.

ATLANTIC

40 Wooster, 4th floor, 10013. **T:** (212) 219-3183.
E: atlantic@metconnect.com **W:** www.atlantic.artshost.com
Open: Tues.-Sat 12-6; closed Aug. **Year established:** 1974.
Size: 2,000 sq. ft. **President:** Carol Hamman.
Vice-President: Nancy Balliett. **Owner:** Atlantic Gallery Artists League. Non-profit cooperative gallery.
Work shown: All styles of original paintings, prints and sculpture. No crafts.
Artists represented: 35 members. 35% male/65% female. All ages. All origins. 50% of the artists are in museum collections.
Work by: Leah K. Tomaino; Nancy Balliett; Sally Brody; and John Hawkins; among others. **Annual exhibitions:** 12.
Markets: Individual and corporate. **Prices:** $150-8,000.
Collectors: Arthur Anderson Accountants, IBM, and Texaco.
Focus/Mission: To promote emerging and established artists from the U.S.

Selection process: Artists are selected from slides sent to the gallery. Slides and original art are reviewed once a month. Artists should come into the gallery personally or send materials and artwork with SASE. **Response time:** 1 month. **Fees:** $85 per month membership. Artists are expected to pay for their own exhibition expenses. The gallery charges 10% commission on sales.

AXELLE FINE ARTS

148 Spring St., 10012.   **T:** (212) 226-2262.
F: (212) 226-1339.   **E:** desk@axelle.com
W: www.axelle.com   **Open:** Daily 11-7.
Year established: 1997.   **Owner:** Bertrand N. Delacroix, art publisher.
Director: Tad Talarek.   **Size:** 5,000 sq. ft.

Work shown: Contemporary European art with a French accent. Original oils and limited edition prints. **Artists represented:** 7 from France. 50% male/female.
Work shown: Oil paintings and limited edition prints.
Work by: Michel Delacroix: Naif artist; André Bourrié: Modern Impressionist; Fabienne Delacroix: Naif artist; Elisabeth Estivalet: Modern landscapist; and Jean-Daniel Bouvard: Modern artist; among others.
Advertising: *Art and Antiques.*
Selection process: All artists are selected from art seen in exhibitions, publications and artists' studios. Artists should mail photographs with SASE.
Response time: 1 month.

JUNE BATEMAN

560 Broadway, Suite 309, 10012.   **T:** (212) 925-7951.
E: batemandavis@aol.com   **W:** www.junebateman.com
Year established: 2000.   **Artists represented**: 15.

Owner/Director: June Bateman, former art director in Film.
Work shown: 20th and 21st Century Fine Art Photography.
Work by: Amy Arbus; Elio Sciol; Jeff Harris; Eun Suk Joo; and Joan Almond; among others.

BELENKY

151 Wooster St., 10012.   **T:** 1-800-SOHOGEMS and (212) 674-4548.
F: (212) 674-6551.   **W:** www.belenky.com
Open: Tues.-Sat. 10:30-6, Sun. 12-6.
Directors: Lucette Bloomgarden and Seth Bloomgarden.
Work shown: Exclusive designs in diamond, ruby, emerald and sapphire jewelry by the world's top designers including Steven Kretchmer and Michael Good.
Focus/Mission: To show exciting established as well as emerging artists.

BENEDETTI

52 Prince St., 10012.   **T:** (212) 226-2238.
F: (212) 431-8106.   **E:** fineart@benedetti.com
W: www.benedetti.com   **Open:** Daily, 11-6.
Year established: 1989.   **Size:** 7,000 sq. ft.
Director: Charles Huller. **Owners**: Charles Huller and Bettina Caiola:
art historians, and consultants to galleries and private collectors.
Work shown: All styles and media by American and European artists.

continued

Artists represented: 10 male/5 female. **Ages**: 30-97. All of the artists are in museum collections.

Work by: Erte: bronzes; Anthony Quinn: mixed media and originals; Wilkinson: acrylics; Frederick Hart: acrylics; and Felix de Weldon: bronzes; among others.
Collectors: Metropolitan, Smithsonian, The White House, and The Vatican.
Markets: Individual, corporate, and museum.
Prices: $3,000-150,000. **Annual exhibitions:** 2 solo/1group.
Focus/Mission: To specialize in art that is beautiful and important. We have an unlimited exchange program. We assist clients in liquidating and/or trading works.
Selection process: Artists are selected from exhibitions, referrals, slides sent to the gallery and publications. Artists should call for an appointment. Artists should send slides, photos, biography, resumé, and SASE.

PETER BLUM

99 Wooster St., 10012.   **T:** (212) 343-0441.
F: (212) 343-0523.   **E:** pblum@nyct.net
W: artnet.com/peterblum   **Size:** 1,300 sq. ft.
Year established: 1994.
Open: Tues.-Fri. 10-6, Sat 11-6. Closed in August.
Owner/Director: Peter Blum, publisher of limited edition prints.
Work shown: Neo Expressionism, Minimalism, Post Modernism and Conceptual prints, books, drawings, paintings, sculpture and photographs.
Work by: Louise Bourgeois: prints, drawings and books; David Rabinowitch: prints, drawings, sculpture and books; James Turrel: prints and books; and Helmut Federle: paintings, drawings, prints and books; among others.
Collectors: MoMA and Whitney.
Annual exhibitions: 4 –6. **Advertising:** *Art in America* and *Gallery Guide*.
Selection process: Artists are selected from exhibitions and publications. Artists should familiarize themselves with the gallery before approaching it. They should send 20 slides, resumé, SASE and cover letter.
Requirements: Artists should create exceptional works of art that are not hindered by time or fashion.

BONINO

48 Great Jones St., 10012.   **T:** (212) 598-4262.
F: (212) 982-2842.   **Open:** By appointment.
Year established: 1963.   **Owner/Director:** Fernanda Bonino.
Work shown: Contemporary Italian and Latin American paintings and sculpture.

JANET BORDEN

560 Broadway, 10012.   **T:** (212) 431-0166.
F: (212) 274-1679.   **E:** jborden@dorsai.org
W: www.janetbordeninc.com   **Open:** Tues.-Sat. 11-5.
Year established: 1988.   **Size:** 1,700 sq. ft.
Owner/Director: Janet Borden.
Work shown: Contemporary photography.
Artists represented: 12. All origins. All artists are in museum collections.
Work by: Tina Barney; Jan Groover; Sandy Skoglund; and Neil Winoker.
Collectors: MoMA, George Eastman House, L.A. County Museum, and Metropolitan. **Prices:** $500-20,000.

FRANKLIN BOWLES

431 West Broadway, 10012. T: (212) 226-1616.
F: (212) 226-3131. W: www.franklinbowlesgallery.com
E: pcarter@franklinbowlesgallery.com Open: Mon.-Sun. 11-7.
Owner: Franklin Bowles. Director: Phebe Carter.
Year established: 1971 in San Francisco, 1990 in New York.
Work shown: Mixed media. Artists represented: 10, from U.S. and Europe.
Work by: Pierre-Marie Brisson: mixed media, contemporary fresco with primitive renderings; Claude Lazar: Cinematic Realist: nostalgic interiors in oil on canvas; Yuri Kuper: found objects in assemblages; and Lev Meshberg: still life and landscape paintings that are a homage to his memories. Also 20th Century Master graphics by Chagall, Picasso, and Matisse among others.
Advertising: *Gallery Guide* and *SoHo NY*.
Selection process: Artists should mail slides, photos, biography, resumé, prices, and SASE.

BROOME STREET

498 Broome St., 10013. T/F: (212) 941-0130.
E: reginas@anny.org W: www.anny.org
Open: Tues.-Sun. 11-6. Size: 1,400 sq. ft.
Year established: 1991. Owner: New York Artists Equity Association,
a non-profit membership and arts advocacy organization.
Work shown: All styles and media. Prices: All ranges.
Focus/Mission: To enable emerging artists of all ages to have a space to introduce their work and talent.
Selection process: The gallery is available for exhibitions on a rental basis to individual artists and arts organizations. Call for availability 6 mo-1 year in advance. Submit a written proposal and resumé. For a one-person show include at least 10 slides or photos; for a group show include two from each exhibitor.
Additional information: The exhibition space is also available for seminars and meetings after 6 pm. New York Artists Equity Association (NYAEA) also offers membership to artists and affiliates. Call or write for membership application.

SPENCER BROWNSTONE

39 Wooster St., 10013. T: (212) 334-3455.
F: (212) 274-1157. E: sbgsoho@aol.com
W: www.sbrownstonegallery.com Open: Tues.-Sat. 11-6.
Size: 4,500 sq. ft. Year established: 1994.
Owner/Director: Spencer Brownstone.
Assistant Director: Lorraine Hussenot.
Work shown: Contemporary painting, photography, installation, sculpture, video.
Artists represented: At least 8.
Work by: Phil Bower: painting; Rebecca Quaytman: painting; Jordan Tinker, painting and sculpture; Kelly Lamb; Olivier Mosset; James Rielly; Jeffrey Sturges; and Edwin Zwakman; among others. Prices: $1,000-50,000.
Collectors: The Tate, The Saatchi Collection, Metropolitan, and MoMA.
Annual exhibitions: 6-10 solo/1-3 group.
Advertising: *Artforum, Art Press, Art in America,* and *Frieze.*

continued

Selection process: 30% of the artists are selected from professional referrals, 10% from slides sent to the gallery, and 60% from art seen in exhibitions or artists' studios. Artists should mail slides, photos, biography, resumé and prices. No calls, please. The gallery reviews materials monthly. **Response time:** Up to 6 months.
Requirements: Artists who want to be represented by the gallery should have a full biography, resumé, transparencies, museums and important collections.

CALDWELL SNYDER

451 West Broadway, 10012.   **T:** (212) 387-0208.
F: (212) 387-0717.   **W:** www.caldwellsnyder.com
Open: Daily 11-7, Sun. 11-6:30.   **Size:** 1,650 sq. ft.
Owners: Oliver Caldwell and Susan Snyder. **Director:** Karen Schneidman.
Year established: 1995. This Fine Art Publishing Company was founded in 1990.
Work shown: Figurative, Fauvist, Expressionist painting; mixed media; and sculpture.
Artists represented: 8 from Europe and North America. 60% male/40% female. 60% of the artists are in museum collections.
Work by: Thomas Pradzynski: "Urban Realism" historic street scenes, allegorical, acrylics on canvas, and serigraphs; Manel Anoro: Fauve-Expressionist, oil on canvas, serigraphs, stone lithographs, and acrylic on paper; Regina Saura: collage elements balanced with strong color and geometry, mixed media on canvas, and mixed media monoprints; and Maria Luisa Campoy: sculpture; among others. **Prices:** $2,000-50,000.
Annual exhibitions: 8 solo/1 group.
Advertising: *Gallery Guide, ARTnews,* and *Architectural Digest.*
Focus/Mission: To represent both emerging and established artists primarily from Europe and new to American collectors. To educate our clientele. To provide many different media and a good price range in order to work with new as well as seasoned collectors. We are known for the high quality of our artwork and staff.
Selection process: 75% of the artists are selected from professional referrals, 25% from art seen in exhibitions or artists' studios. Artists should submit slides, photos, biography, resumé and prices with SASE. **Response time:** 3-6 months.
Additional information: The gallery will, at its discretion, place installations of art in lobbies, office buildings, restaurants and store windows, free of charge.

JACQUES CARCANAGUES

106 Spring St., 10012.   **T:** (212) 925-8110.
F: (212) 925-8112.   **E:** rcn@interport.net
Open: Daily 11:30-7.
Work shown: Collectibles, antiques, handicrafts and folk art from India, Nepal, Afghanistan, Thailand, China, Tibet, Korea, Philippines and South America. Tribal and ethnic silver, jewelry, textiles, furniture, clothing and ritual objects.
Additional information: The owners are direct importers.

CLAUDIA CARR: WORKS ON PAPER

478 West Broadway, 2nd floor, 10012. **T:** (212) 673-5518.
F: (212) 673-0123.   **E:** caludiacarr@erols.com
Open: By appointment only.   **Year established:** 1996.
Owner: Claudia Carr, former painter, curator, and art educator.
Work shown: A range of styles of exclusively work on paper, and photography.

Artists represented: 6 male/ 6 female.
Work by: Jenny Okun: architectural photographs; Garth Evans: drawings, prints and watercolors; Larry Poons: monotypes; Aaron Siskind: photographs; and Eleanore Mikus: paper fold and work on paper; among others.
Markets: Individual, corporate, and museum. **Prices:** $300-8,000.
Collectors: Barry I. Friedman, Lawrence Weschler, Kathryn Staley, and Elizabeth Darhansoff. **Annual exhibitions:** 6 solo/ 2 group.
Advertising: *On Paper, Gallery Guide, Art in America* and *Review*.
Focus/Mission: To show all aspects of works on paper and photography.
Selection process: 85% of the artists are selected from professional referrals, 5% from slides sent to the gallery, and 10% from art seen in exhibitions or artists studios. Artists should mail slides, photographs, resumé, prices and SASE.
Response time: 2 months.
Requirements: Artists must have professionalism and commitment. Artists are expected to pay for framing and some advertising.

EDWARD CARTER

560 Broadway, 4th floor, 10012.   **T:** (212) 966-1933.
Year established: 1999.   **Open:** Tues.-Sat. 10-6, Thurs. 10-8.
Owner: Edward Carter.   **Background:** Collector.
Work shown: A large inventory of Ansel Adams' photography in addition to the work of other major landscape photographers.
Work by: Ansel Adams; James Alinder; Lucienne Bloch; Christopher Burkett; Robert Glenn Cetchum; among others. **Annual exhibitions:** 12.
Additional information: The gallery has three other locations in Aspen, CO; Gualala, CA and Lewis, DE.

CAST IRON

159 Mercer St., 4th floor, 10012.   **T:** (212) 274-8624.
F: (212) 925-0342.   **W:** www.castirongallery.com
Open: Tues.-Sat. 12-6.   **Year established:** 1990.
Size: 3,500 sq. ft.   **Owner:** Fusako Ohta.
Director: Himiko Joseph.   **Prices:** $300-30,000.
Annual exhibitions: 15.   **Advertising:** *Gallery Guide*.
Work shown: Contemporary fine art by international artists.
Selection process: Artists should submit slides, resumé, and SASE.

CAVIN-MORRIS

560 Broadway, #405B, 10012.   **T:** (212) 226-3768.
F: (212) 226-0155.   **Open:** Tues.-Fri. 10-6, Sat 11-6.
E: mysteries@aol.com   **W:** www.artnet.com/cavinmorris.html
Size: 3,000 sq. ft.   **Year established:** 1980.
Owners/Directors: Shari Cavin and Randall Morris.
Work shown: Contemporary Self-taught, Visionary, and Tribal Art in all media.
Artists represented: 25 or more. 50% male/female. **Ages:** 20-90. 30% of the artists are represented in museum collections.
Work by: Brian Rutenberg: paintings; Chelo Amezcua: drawings; Bessie Harvey: sculpture; and Jon Serl: paintings; among others.
Collectors: Herbert Waide Hemphill Jr. and Amr Shaker Collection.

continued

Prices: $100-30,000. **Annual exhibitions:** 6 solo/4 group.
Advertising: *Gallery Guide* and *Folk Art Magazine*.
Focus/Mission: The gallery exhibits art that is not usually shown in the mainstream: self-taught produced by Old Masters and artists from the New Wave.
Selection process: 80% of the artists are selected from slides sent to the gallery. Artists should approach the gallery anytime and deliver slides with SASE.

CERES

584-588 Broadway, #306, 10012.   **T/F:** (212) 226-4725.
E: ceresgallery@earthlink.net   **W:** www.ceresgallery.org
Open: Tues.-Sat. 11-6.   **Year established:** 1983.
Owners: Non-profit cooperative gallery.
Co-Presidents: Francine Perlman and Bonnie Martinez.
Work shown: All styles and media by women artists from all origins.
Markets: Individual, corporate, and museum.
Prices: $75-6,000.   **Artists represented:** 50.
Work by: Christina Biaggi: painting; Roseanne Backstedt: painting; Stefany Benson: painting and construction, Carol Goebel: sculpture; and Judy Hoffman: 2- and 3-dimensional work using artist-made paper; among others.
Annual exhibitions: 27.   **Advertising:** *Gallery Guide*.
Focus/Mission: This is a feminist gallery which serves as a supportive base for a diversity of artistic and political views.
Selection process: Members are voted into the gallery at membership meetings, held the first Tuesday each month. Artists should request an application.
Fees: Full membership: $110/month. Affiliate membership: $60/month. National Full Membership: $200/mo. Each member is entitled to a 3-week, one-person exhibition every two and ½ years. There are also group shows. There is no gallery commission charged on sales.
Additional information: The gallery's programs include music, dance and poetry.

C.F.M.

112 Greene St., 10012.   **T:** (212) 966-3864.
F: (212) 226-1041.   **E:** cfmg@mindspring.com
W: www.cfmgallery.com   **Open:** Mon-Sat 11-6, Sun. 12-6.
Year established: 1984.   **Size:** 3,000 sq. ft.
Owner/Director: Neil P. Zukerman, previously a private dealer.
Work shown: Figurative Surrealism, and Symbolism specializing in Leonor Fini and Salvador Dali. All media with an emphasis on painting and sculpture.
Artists represented: 10-20. 50% male/50% female. **Origins:** Europe and U.S.
Work by: Salvador Dali; Leonor Fini; Anne Bachelier; and Frederick Hart.
Prices: Up to $600,000. **Markets:** 90% individual, 5% corporate, 5% museum.
Annual exhibitions: 6 solo/2 group.
Advertising: *Sunstorm Fine Arts, Art Business News, Where, & Guest Informant*.
Focus/Mission: A people-friendly gallery, which welcomes everyone from art students to serious collectors. It is a gallery with a point of view.
Selection process: Artists should send slides or photos and SASE. No calls, please. Personal visits to the gallery are encouraged for the artist to understand the focus and sensibility exhibited. **Requirements:** Artwork must demonstrate superb technique, dramatic vision and beauty to match the gallery's sensibility. No exhibition fees. Sculptors may have to assist with transportation expenses.

THE DRAWING CENTER

"To provide opportunities for emerging and under-recognized artists, to demonstrate the significance and diversity of drawings throughout history, and to stimulate public dialogue on issues of art and culture."

T. F. CHEN CULTURAL CENTER

250 Lafayette St., 10012.　　　T: (212) 941-9296.
F: (212) 966-5285.　　　E: chen@tfchen.org
W: www.tfchen.org　　　Open: Tues.-Sat. 11-6, by appointment only.
Year established: 1996.　　　Size: 20,000 sq. ft.; 4 floors exhibition space.
Owner: The T.F. Chen Cultural Center. Directors: Lucia Chen and Ped Chen.
Work by: Dr. T. F. Chen: Neo-Iconography paintings and original graphics which employ "cultural" images (icons) of East and West, past and present, to create pictures bearing a message and beauty.
Markets: Individual, corporate, and museum. Prices: $500-1 million.
Focus/Mission: To serve as an international cultural exchange.

CHILDREN'S MUSEUM OF THE ARTS, SOHO

182 Lafayette St., 10013.　　　T: (212) 274-0986.
F: (212) 274-1776.　　　W: www.cmny.org
Admission: $5.　　　Open: Wed. 12-7, Thurs.-Sun. 12-5.
Director: Evelyn Rossetti.
Year established: 1989 in another NYC location, 1998 in this location.
Work shown: There is an international, children's art collection, with changing themes. The museum also exhibits the work of adult artists whose work relates to those specific themes. The museum also contains commissioned installations by professional artists. Annual exhibitions: 2-3.
Focus/Mission: This is a hands-on museum designed for children from 18 months to 10 years. It has various work spaces where children can explore different media.
Selection process: Artists should send proposals to Elizabeth Reiss.
Additional information: Workshops for children of different ages are held throughout the day in addition to scheduled classes and a drop-in program for toddlers and preschoolers.

CINQUE

560 Broadway, 5th floor, 10012.　　　T: (212) 966-3464.
Open: Tues.-Sat 1-6.　　　Year established: 1969.
Founders: Romare Bearden, Ernest Crichlow, and Norman Lewis.
Owner: Non-profit gallery.　　　Director: Ruth Jett.
Focus/Mission: To assist the growth and development of minority artists.
Additional information: In addition to its exhibitions the gallery also sponsors educational outreach programs, lectures/seminars and a wide range of other programs and services.

CORPORATE ART ASSOCIATES

578 Broadway, Suite 106, 10012.   **T:** (212) 941-9685.
F: (212) 925-3449.   **E:** caajc@prodigy.net
Open: Mon.-Fri. 11-6.
Owner/President: James Cavello, art consultant, appraiser and collector for over 20 years.
Executive Director: Margarite Almeida, international art consultant.
Work shown: All media.   **Markets:** Corporate, residential, institutions.
Work by: Ben Freeman; Francis Hines; Brad Howe; Karen Mulqueen; and Tim White; among others.
Focus/Mission: To offer advising, research, buying and selling modern and contemporary art for private and corporate collections and site-specific architectural projects. To offer appraisal, design, placement, installation, curatorial and exhibition services.
Selection process: Artists should mail slides or photographs of new work in a theme format, biography, resumé, prices, and SASE. Response time: 4-6 weeks.
Additional information: James Cavello also co-owns of Westwood Gallery.

CHARLES COWLES

74 Grand St., 10013.   **T:** (212) 925-3500.
F: (212) 925-3501.   **W:** www.cowlesgallery.com
Open: Tues.-Sat. 10-6.   **Year established:** 1980.
Owner: Charles Cowles.   **Director:** Michael Sweney.
Associate Director: Dennis Christie.
Work shown: Contemporary and Modern painting, work on paper and sculpture.
Artists represented: 20+.
Work by: Vernon Fisher; Al Souza; Beatrice Caracciolo; and Darren Waterston; among others.
Advertising: *Artforum, Art in America, ARTnews,* and *Gallery Guide, The New York Times,* and *New York Observer.*
Selection process: We are currently not looking for new artists.

CODA

472 Broome St., 10013.   **T:** (212) 334-0407.
E: codaart@aol.com   **W:** www.codagalleryny.com
Open: Mon.-Wed.10-6, Thurs.-Sat. 10-7, and Sun. 12-6.
Year established: 2000.   **Owners/Directors:** Connie and David Katz.
Director: Virginia Martin.
Work shown: Contemporary painting, sculpture and glass.
Artists represented: 150; mostly American, some international.
Work by: David Dornan: painting; Peter Burega: painting; Vladimir Cora: painting; John Kennedy: sculpture; and Jamie Perry: painting; among others.
Prices: $200 - $30,000.   **Annual exhibitions:** 6
Advertising: *Gallery Guide* and *New York Magazine.*
Selection Process: Artists should send slides, photos, resumé, and SASE.
Response time: 1-2 months.
Additional information: The gallery also has branches in California and Utah.

CROSBY PAINTING STUDIO

31 Crosby St., 10013. **T:** (212) 941-5045.
Open: By appointment. **Year established:** 1992.
Owner/Director: Minerva Durham.
Work shown: Contemporary figurative art in all media.
Annual exhibitions: 11.
Focus/Mission: To promote Figurative study with daily Figure painting workshops offered at reasonable prices. To encourage appreciation for the work of underexposed figurative artists.
Selection process: Artists who participate in the painting workshops are shown in the group exhibitions. Artists should expect to pay some exhibition expenses.

DACTYL FOUNDATION FOR THE ARTS AND HUMANITIES

64 Grand St., 10013. **T:** (212) 219-2344.
F: (212) 226-7320. **E:** email@dactyl.org
W: www.dactyl.org **Year established:** 1996.
Open: Tues.-Sat. 1-6 during exhibitions, and by appointment.
Directors: Victoria N. Alexander (literary and visual theory), Neil Grayson (visual art), and Patrick Markey (theater and film).
Work shown: Contemporary drawing and painting.
Focus/Mission: To encourage the view that there is a place for artistic intention even in a world without telos. Our programs are designed to develop an aesthetic that is informed by science, history and philosophy and that takes into consideration both the intellectual and intuitive responses to art.
Selection process: Artists should submit slides, resumé, and SASE anytime.
Additional information: The Foundation offers $3,000 awards to writers for essays in Literary and Visual Theory, provides a Theater and Film/Video Screening Room for writers, and sponsors Readings, Panel Discussions, Lectures and Acoustic Concerts.

DEITCH PROJECTS

76 Grand St., 10013. **T:** (212) 343-7300.
F: (212) 343-2954. **E:** email@deitch.com
Open: Tues.-Sat. 12-6. **Year established:** 1996.
Size: 3,000 sq. ft. **Directors**: Suzanne Geiss, Elizabeth Schwartz.
Owner: Jeffrey Deitch, curator, art dealer, art advisor.
Work shown: Mixed media. Installations by international emerging artists. We also represent the estate of Keith Haring.
Artists represented: 5-10. 50% male/female.
Work by: Vanessa Beecroft: video and photographs based on performances; Mariko Mori: photographs and video; Ghada Amer: embroidery on canvas; and Kurt Kauper: portrait painting; among others.
Annual exhibitions: 10 solo/ 2 group. **Advertising:** *Flash Art* and *Artforum*.

MARY DELAHOYD

426 Broome St., 10013. **T:** (212) 219-2111.
Owner/Director: Mary Delahoyd, art historian, and curator.
Work shown: All styles and media. **Size:** 700 sq. ft.
Open: Sat.1-6, and by appointment; Summer: By appointment.

continued

Artists represented: 8.
Work by: Adele Ursone: paintings; John L. Murphy: photographs and paintings; Jim Olsen: paintings and drawings; John Turturro: mixed media; Sandra Payne: mixed media; and Tony Whitfield: fine art and furniture; among others.
Annual exhibitions: 5 solo/1 group. **Advertising:** *Gallery Guide.*
Focus/Mission: To exhibit the work of a small group of artists, each of whom charts a distinct territory for creative expression.

CECILIA DE TORRES

140 Greene St., 10012.　　　**T:** (212) 431-5869.
F: (212) 343-0235.　　　**W:** www.ceciliadetorres.com
Open: Tues.-Sat. 12-6.　July: Call for hours.　Closed in August.
Year established: 1993.　　　**Owner:** Cecilia De Torres.
Background: Internationally recognized authority on Torres-García, writer, critic, curator, author of the catalogue raisonné of Torres-García.
Director: Dan Pollack.
Work shown: Constructivist and Geometric Abstraction in all media.
Markets: Individual, corporate and museum. **Annual exhibitions:** 3-4.
Artists represented: 24.　**Origins:** North America, South America and Europe. 80% are in museum collections.
Work by: Joaquín Torres-García, Modernist master of Constructivism, creator of the School of the South; and Julio Alpuy, sculptor and painter, disciple of Torres-García; among others. Contemporary artists include Costa; Buzio; and Chilindron; among others.
Focus/Mission: Dedicated to the wider dissemination of knowledge and appreciation for Torres-García, his students and their legacy. The School of the South (1943-1962) was the most significant art community of its time in Latin America. It combined avant-garde European movements with the iconography of the Indo American cultures to create a new art tradition for the Americas, based on Torres-García's theories of "Constructive Universalism."
Selection process: All artists are selected from professional referrals.

DFN

176 Franklin St. 10013.　　　**T:** (212) 334-3400.
F: (212) 965-0263.　　　**W:** www.dfngallery.com
Open: Tues.-Sat. 10-6.　　　**Year established:** 1996.
Size: 5,000 sq. ft.　　　**Owner:** Richard L. Davidman.
Director: Heidi Kujac.　　　**Work shown:** Contemporary art in all media.
Prices: Up to $25,000.
Work by: Tula Telfair: paintings; Sue Grossman: charcoal drawings; Thomas Birkner: paintings; and Jacqueline Gourevitch: paintings; among others.
Selection process: Artists should mail slides, resumé, and SASE.
Response time: 4-6 weeks.

DIA CENTER FOR THE ARTS: BROKEN KILOMETER

393 West Broadway, 10012.　　　**T:** (212) 925-9397.
F: (212) 627-1455.　　　**W:** www.diacenter.org
Year established: 1979.　　　**Open:** Wed.-Sun. 12-6.　Closed 3-3:30.
Director: Michael Govan.　　　**Assistant Director:** Stephen Dewhurst.

Work shown: Single long-term installation "500 Brass Rods. The Broken Kilometer" by Walter DeMaria.
Selection process: We are currently not looking for new artists.

DIA CENTER FOR THE ARTS: NEW YORK EARTH ROOM

141 Wooster St., 2nd floor, 10012.   **T:** (212) 473-8072.
W: www.diacenter.org   **Open:** Wed. -Sun 12-6; Summer: closed.
Year established: 1977.   **Size:** 3,600 sq. ft. loft.
Director: Michael Govan.   **Assistant Director:** Stephen Dewhurst.
Work shown: Single long term installation of "Interior Earth Sculpture" by Walter DiMaria.
Selection process: We are not looking for new artists.

DIEU DONNÉ PAPERMILL

433 Broome St., 10013.   **T:** (212) 226-0573.
F: (212) 226-6088.   **E:** info@papermaking.org
W: www.papermaking.org   **Open:** Wed.-Sat. 12-6.
Year established: 1994.   **Director:** Mina Takahashi.
Work shown: Art in, or dealing with, handmade paper by artists from all origins.
Work by: Bart Wasserman; Lesley Dill; Chuck Close; and William Anastasi; among others; all paper works and paper editions.
Advertising: *Gallery Guide.* **Prices:** $25-25,000.
Focus/Mission: To advance and promote the art of hand papermaking. The curatorial focus is on works made in/with handmade paper.
Selection process: Artists in exhibitions are selected by Dieu Donne Peppermill.

THE DRAWING CENTER

35 Wooster St., 10013.   **T:** (212) 219-2166.
F: (212) 966-2976.   **W:** www.drawingcenter.org
Year established: 1977.   **Size:** 2,600 sq. ft.
Owner: Non-profit institution.   **Director:** Catherine de Zegher.
Open: Tues.- Fri. 10-6, Sat. 11-6; Closed in August.
Work shown: All styles of unique work on paper, wall drawings, and drawing installations.
Focus/Mission: To focus solely on the exhibition of drawings, both contemporary and historical. To provide opportunities for emerging and under-recognized artists, to demonstrate the significance and diversity of drawings throughout history, and to stimulate public dialogue on issues of art and culture.
Annual exhibitions: 2 special and/or historical and 4 contemporary.
Selection process: Most artists are selected from The Viewing Program. We review slides on an on-going basis. Artists should send slides, photos, resumé, artist's statement, and SASE. **Response time:** 6 weeks.
Additional information: Exhibiting artists receive an honorarium. The Drawing Center presents public events, symposia, and town meetings. It maintains a slide registry of unaffiliated artists who create works on paper, and who are invited to keep slides on file in the registry.

ARTIST REGISTRIES

Several organizations maintain artist slide registries that are available for viewing by appointment. They include the Organization of Independent Artists, The Drawing Center, Artists Space, and Leslie-Lohman Gay Art Foundation, among others.

EGIZIO'S PROJECT

596 Broadway, Suite 406, 10012. **T:** (212) 226-8537.
F: (212) 226 4561. **E:** EgizioP@aol.com
W: www.egiziosproject.com **Open:** Tues.-Sat. 12 - 6 and by appointment.
Year established: 1998. **Size:** 1,200 sq. ft.
Owner/Director: Egizio Panetti, background: architecture and art historian, curator, art dealer. **Work shown:** Various art in all media.
Artists represented: 12. **Prices:** $600-16,000.
Annual exhibitions: 9.
Work by: Marzia Gandini, oil on canvas; Grimanesa Amoros, mixed media; Sylvia Plachy, photography; and James Jorio, acrylic or oil on canvas; among others.
Focus/Mission: Quality, concept, and presentation.
Selection process: Artists are selected from materials mailed to the gallery and from meeting the artist and making studio visits. Artists should mail slides and/or photographs with SASE. **Response time:** 4-6 weeks.

EIGHTH FLOOR ARTISTS

473 Broadway, 7th floor, 10012. **T:** (212) 274-8993.
F: (212) 226-3400. **W:** www.nyartsmagazine.com
Open: Tues.-Sat. 10-6.
Year established: 1994. **Size:** 2,000 sq. ft.
Owner/Director: Abraham Lubelski, artist and collector.
Work shown: All styles, mixed media. **Prices:** $500-10,000.
Artists represented: 34. All origins. 50% male/female. 50% are in museum collections. **Annual exhibitions:** 8 solo/12 group.
Advertising: *NY SoHo Arts Magazine* and *NY SoHo Listing and Map.*
Focus/Mission: To offer an alternative and to be flexible and adaptive in working closely with artists as curators and organizers.
Selection process: We review artists materials every Thurs., Fri., and Sat.
Response time: 1 week. **Requirements:** Artists should be highly self-motivated.

EL-BAZ

77 Mercer St., 10012. **T:** (212) 966-7282.
F: (212) 966-8285. **Open:** By appointment.
Year established: 1982. **Size:** 1,800 sq. ft.
Owner/Director: Jacob El-Baz, background: professional photographer with expertise in the publishing of graphics and posters.
Director: Deborah Lynn Davis.
Work by: Michael Eisenman: mixed media; Nissan Engel: mixed media; Jacob El-Baz: photography; among others. **Prices:** $500-5,000.
Advertising: *New York Times, Gallery Guide,* and *Photography in New York.*

Focus/Mission: To show quality work with wide ranging appeal.

Selection process: 40% of the artists are selected from profession referrals, 50% from slides sent to the gallery, and 10% from art seen in exhibitions or artists studios. Artists should call the gallery for an appointment.

THE ENCHANTED FOREST

85 Mercer St., 10012. **T:** (212) 925-6677.
Open: Mon.-Sat 11-7, Sun 12-6. **Year established:** 1989.
Owner: David Wallace. **Manager:** Agnieszka Potoczek
Work shown: Traditional hand blown glass, tapestries, optical toys, wooden boxes and pottery.
Artists represented: 715. **Ages:** 14-85. **Origins:** All, mostly American.
Work by: Shelley Knapp: kaleidoscopes; Arlynne Miller: jewelry; Glenn Straub: kaleidoscopes; Rebecca Stewart: glass blown art; Leda Lee: jewelry; among others. **Prices:** $20-10,000.
Selection process: We are constantly looking for objects that delight the eye and satisfy the soul. Artists should mail slides and samples. No walk-ins, please.

ENTRÉE LIBRE

110 Wooster St., 10012. **T:** (212) 431-5279.
F: (212) 431-7399. **E:** entreelibre@compuserve.com
Year established: 1992. **Size:** 1,300 sq. ft.
Open: Mon.-Fri. 11-6, Sat., Sun. 12-6.
Owners: Paula Lajaunie and Richard Widmaier-Picasso.
Work shown: Contemporary design for interiors specializing in the highest quality textiles, rugs, and sculptural furniture from around the world by emerging as well as established artists.
Prices: $1,000-22,000. **Artists represented:** 8.
Work by: Marcel Zelmanovitch: paintings translated into hand-woven carpets, John Kennedy: bronze sculpture; Aris Paganakis: lighting; and Jonathan Cohen: fine furniture; among others.
Annual exhibitions: There are no exhibitions, but the work changes constantly.
Selection process: Artists should mail or deliver slides with SASE. We are always interested in seeing new work.

ELEANOR ETTINGER

119 Spring St., 10012. **T:** (212) 925-7474.
F: (212) 925-7734. **E:** eegallery@aol.com
W: www.eegallery.com **Size:** 15,000 sq. ft.
Year established: 1975. **Open:** Mon.-Fri. 10-6, Sat. 11-6, Sun. 12-6.
Owner/Director: Eleanor Ettinger, dealer and printmaker.
Work shown: Representational genre paintings, watercolors and original lithographs.
Markets: Individual, corporate and museum. **Prices:** $500-500,000
Artists represented: 15. **Ages:** 32-65. **Origins:** U.S., Asia, and Europe.
Work by: Malcolm T. Liepke: classically inspired figurative work; Frank Arcuri: traditional still life reminiscent of the Dutch School; Kenton Nelson: idealized urban and suburban landscapes painted in almost a hyper reality of heroic imagery; and Norman Rockwell: America's most beloved artist and historian; among others. *continued*

Work by: Malcolm T. Liepke: classically inspired figurative work; Frank Arcuri: traditional still life reminiscent of the Dutch School; Kenton Nelson: idealized urban and suburban landscapes painted in almost a hyper reality of heroic imagery; and Norman Rockwell: America's most beloved artist and historian; among others.

Collectors: Hirshhorn, Brooklyn Museum, Metropolitan, and The White House.

Annual exhibitions: 4 solo/8 continual group.

Advertising: *ARTnews, Gallery Guide, Art and Auction, Architectural Digest* and *Art and Antiques.*

Focus/Mission: To represent contemporary works in the representational genre by artists of technical accomplishment and merit.

Selection process: 50% of the artists are selected from professional referrals, and 50% are selected from slides sent to the gallery. Artists should mail SASE, slides, biography, and prices.

Requirements: Representational work that is technically proficient with an emotional appeal.

EXHIBIT A

160 Mercer St., 10012.
F: (212) 343-0795.
W: www.artnet.com
Year established: 1998.

T: (212) 343-0230.
E: exhibitasoho@aol.com
Open: Tues.- Sat. 12-6.
Owner/ Director: Greg Smith. Background: Art publisher, artist, gallery owner, lawyer and professional tennis player.

Assistant Director: Mercedes Vicente.

Work shown: Contemporary art in all media. **Artists represented:** 5.

Work by: Serena Bocchino: painting; Yoko Motomiya: installation and prints; Greg Leshe: video and photography; Richard Mock: painting and prints; and Robert Edison Fylton, Jr.: photography and sculpture; among others.

Prices: $1,000-20,000. **Annual exhibitions:** 8.

Focus/Mission: This gallery projects art that translates well into multiples, projects and practical applications.

Selection process: We are currently not looking for new artists.

EXIT ART/THE FIRST WORLD

548 Broadway, 10012.
F: (212) 925-2928.
W: www.exitart.org

T: (212) 966-7745.
E: exitart@interport.net
Year established: 1982.

Owner: Non-profit organization.

Open: Tues.-Thurs. 10-6, Fri. 10-8, Sat. 11-8, Sun. 12-6.

Founders/Directors: Papo Colo and Jeanette Ingberman.

Work shown: Contemporary art in all media including performance and multi-media.

Focus/Mission: To be dedicated to transcultural, multi-disciplinary explorations of contemporary art issues. To organize and present experimental and historical projects exploring the diversity of contemporary culture in the visual arts, theater, design, film and video.

Size: 17,000 sq. ft. **Advertising:** *Gallery Guide.*

Selection process: We have an open review policy. Artists should send 10-20 slides, resumé, and artist's statement, and SASE to "Slide Review." We also accept videos and CDs. **Response time:** 2 months.

EYE STORM

60 Mercer St., 10012.
W: www.eyestorm.com
Year established: 1999.
T: (212) 226-1000
E: newyork.gallery@eyestorm.com
Owner: Eyestorm.com, an internet company.
Work shown: Contemporary prints and photographs.
Annual exhibitions: 10.

S.E. FEINMAN FINE ARTS, LTD

448 Broome St., 10013.
F: (212) 431-6495.
Size: 1,250 sq. ft.
T: (212) 431-6820.
Year established: 1993.
Open: Tues., Thurs.- Sat. 11-6, and Wed. 11-3; Closed last 2 weeks in August.
Owner: Stephen Feinman, gallery owner for 30 years and former President of Multiple Editions.
Work shown: Contemporary art.
Assistant Director: Thaddeus Cutler.
Prices: $250-15,000.
Artists represented: 16 male/4 female. Ages: 28-60. 25% of the artists are in museum collections.
Work by: Felix Sherman: painting; Miljenko Bengez: painting; Mikio Watanabe: mezzotint; Johnny Friedlaender: aquatint; Andre Masson: works on paper; and Nick Kosuicuk: oil on masonite; among others.
Annual exhibitions: 4 solo.
Advertising: *The New York Times*.
Markets: 95% private and 5% corporate.
Selection process: The gallery looks at new artists' slides and requests a minimum of 15. Artists should approach the gallery Tues. and Thurs. 12-5.
Response time: 2 weeks.
Requirements: Artists must have quality work and the ability to communicate with our personnel.

RONALD FELDMAN

31 Mercer St., 10013.
F: (212) 941-1536.
T: (212) 226-3232.
Open: Mon..-Sat. 10-6; Summer by appointment.
Year established: 1971.
Size: 4,000 sq. ft.
Owner/Director: Ronald Feldman; attorney.
Work shown: All media.
Artists represented: 35.
Work by: Joseph Beuys: installation, drawings, and sculpture; Ida Applebroog: painting/installation; Arakawa and Madeline Gins: painting/constructed environmental; and Hannah Wilke: sculpture, photography/video; among others.
Annual exhibitions: 6 solo/1 group.
Focus/Mission: To mount new exhibitions by artists who are concerned with social, scientific, and artistic ideas, often on a global scale.
Selection process: Artists should send cover letter, resumé, 1 sheet of slides, and SASE. Response time: Months.

MIMI FERZT

114 Prince St., 10012.
F: (212) 343-9469.
Year established: 1993.
Directors: Christine Sperber.
Artists represented: 20.
Open: Mon.-Fri. 10-6. Sat. 11-6. Sun. 11-6.

T: (212) 343-9377.
W: www.mimiferzt.com
Size: 2,200 sq. ft.

Work shown: 20th century Contemporary art of Russia and the former Soviet
Republics.
Work by: Mihail Chemiakin: monumental bronze sculpture, paintings, watercolors
and drawings; Zoya Frolova: mixed media paintings; Nikolai Makarov: mixed
media paintings; Dmitri Plavinsky: mixed media paintings, collage, drawings, and
installations; and Oscar Rabine: mixed media paintings; among others.
Annual exhibitions: 6 solo/5 group. Advertising: *The New York Times,
ARTnews, NY Observer, Art Forum,* and *Flash Art.*
Selection process: Artists should send cover letter, biography, slides or
photographs, and SASE. Response time: 2 months.

55 MERCER STREET

55 Mercer St., 10013.
Open: Tues.-Sat. 10-6.
Year established: 1969.

T: (212) 226-8513.

Owner: Artist members. Non-profit cooperative gallery.
Work shown: Contemporary art and installations, photography, painting,
sculpture and video. Prices: $400-20,000.
Size(s): 1,500 sq. ft. back, 1,100 sq. ft. front, plus a middle gallery.
Artists represented: 22 members. Ages: 30-60's. Origins: All. 80% of the
artists have won National Endowment for the Arts and Guggenheim Fellowships.
Work by: Ethelyn Honig; Joan Gardner; David Wooddell; Joy Walker; and Judy
Russell; among others.
Annual exhibitions: 24 solo/4 group. Shows run in 2 galleries simultaneously.
Focus/Mission: To offer opportunities to artists who find difficulty in other venues,
such as commercial galleries. Installations are encouraged.
Selection process: A committee of members reviews slides. The selection
committee changes annually. Artists should send slides, resumé and SASE.
Response time: 2 months.
Additional information: This is a cooperative gallery and members are eager to
also exhibit the work of non-members. Solo and group exhibitions are available.
Fees: Artists pay for their exhibition expenses.

450 BROADWAY

450 Broadway, 10013.
F: (212) 226-3400.
Open: Tues.-Sat. 1-6.
Year established: 1989.

T: (212) 941-5952.
W: www.nyartsmagazine.com
Size: 800 sq. ft.
Prices: $500-10,000.

Owner/Director: Abraham Lubelski, artist and collector.
Work shown: All styles, mixed media.
Artists represented: 34 from all origins. 50% are in museum collections.
Annual exhibitions: 8 solo; 12 group.
Advertising: *NY SoHo Arts Magazine, NY SoHo Listing and Map.*

Focus/Mission: To offer an alternative and to be flexible and adaptive in working closely with artists as curators and organizers.
Selection process: We review artists materials every Thurs., Fri., and Sat.
Response time: 1 week. **Requirements:** Artists should be highly self-motivated.
Fees: Artists should be prepared to pay promotion expenses.

FULCRUM

"To focus on artists that explore our relationship with the actual world through materials and the passage of time. The artists collaborate with nature. They are revolutionizing the way we think about art and nature."

FULCRUM

480 Broome St., 10013.
F: (212) 966-0962.
Year established: 1993.
T: (212) 966-6848.
Open: Tues.-Sat. 11-6, Sun.-Mon. 1-6.
Size: 6,000 sq. ft.
Owner/Director: Valerie M. Shakespeare; Background: Curator and sponsor of art projects through Actual Art Foundation, a not-for-profit organization.
Work shown: Actual art that focuses on the actuality of materials and how they change. All media, but mostly natural materials and the elements.
Artists represented: 7 male/6 female. **Ages:** 23-60. **Origins:** U.S., Japan, Russia, Europe, Bermuda, and Israel. 90% are in museum collections.
Work by: Dan Dempster: steel works and works from under water; Terry Fugate-Wilcox: earthquakes, lighting, gold lead, dust and rain; Alexia Nikov: patinaed metal leaf and metals; Nathan Slate Joseph: weathered metal collages; Gregg Degn: explosives; and Tony Reason: rust; among others.
Markets: Individual, corporate, and museum.
Collectors: MoMA, Guggenheim, Chase Manhattan, and Prudential.
Prices: $50-11,000.
Annual exhibitions: 8-10 solo/2 group. **Advertising:** *Gallery Guide.*
Focus/Mission: To focus on artists that explore our relationship with the actual world through materials and the passage of time. The artists collaborate with nature. They are revolutionizing the way we think about art and nature.
Selection process: 20% of the artists are selected from referrals, 40% from slides sent to the gallery, and 40% from art seen in exhibitions. Only artists whose work is "actual" should approach the gallery, on weekday mornings; or artists may mail slides, photos, biography, resumé, and SASE. **Response time:** 1 month.

LANCE FUNG

537 Broadway, 2nd floor, 10012.
F: (212) 431-3777.
Open: Tues.-Sat. 11-6.
Year established: 1995.
T: (212) 334-6242.
W: www.lancefunggallery.com
Size: 2,000 sq. ft.
Owner: Lance Fung.
Work shown: Conceptual, Minimal, Earth Art, and New Media Art. Photography, painting, sculpture, and video.
Markets: Individual, corporate, and museum. **Prices:** $1,000-200,000.

continued

Artists represented: 12. All artists are in museum collections.
Work by: Nam June Paik: video sculpture; Shigeko Kubota: Fluxus video artist, installation and sculpture; Robert Morrris: drawing; Gordon Matta-Clark: Conceptual earth artist, photography and sculpture; John Roloff: earth sculpture; among others.
Annual exhibitions: 6 solo/3 group.
Advertising: *Art in America, NY Arts magazine* and *Artforum*.
Selection process: All of the artists are selected from referrals. We are currently not seeking new artists.

GALLERY 456 at CHINESE AMERICAN ARTS COUNCIL

456 Broadway, 3rd floor, 10013.   **T:** (212) 431-9740.
F: (212) 431-9789.   **Open:** Daily 11-5.
Year established: 1972.   **Size:** 650 sq. ft.
Owner: Chinese American Arts Council.
Director: Alan Chow, Executive Director of Chinese American Arts Council.
Work shown: All styles and media by Asian artists. Western artists are occasionally included in group exhibitions. **Annual exhibitions:** 14.
Focus/Mission: The Chinese American Arts Council offers free services to emerging Asian artists.
Selection process: Artists should call and mail slides and resumé. A six-member committee selects the artists. **Response time:** 4-6 weeks.
Additional Information: This is the only not-for-profit Asian Gallery in SoHo.

GALLERY JUNO

568 Broadway, #604B, 10012.   **T:** (212) 431-1515.
F: (212) 431-1583.   **Open:** Tues.-Sat. 11-6.
Year established: 1992.   **Size:** 1,500 sq. ft.
Owner/Director: Junko Ishihara.
Work shown: Abstract to figurative painting, sculpture, and photography.
Markets: Corporate, private and museum. **Prices:** $1,000-5,000.
Artists represented: 20. 70% male/30% female. Ages: 25-60. All origins.
Work by: Pierre Jacquemon; Otto Mjannes; Kenneth McIndoe; among others.
Collectors: American Standards, Bank of Hiroshima, Sekido Kiko Manufacturing, and Dugan Advertising Agency.
Annual exhibitions: 6 solo/2 group. **Advertising:** *Gallery Guide* and *ARTnews*.
Focus/Mission: To present emerging artists from various backgrounds who are based in Modernism.
Selection process: Artists with work of a professional quality should send 20 slides, resumé, and SASE. **Response time:** Months.

GALLERY REVEL

96 Spring St., 10012.   **T:** (212) 925-0600.
F: (212) 431-6270.   **W:** www.gallery-revel.com
Year established: 1966.   **Size:** 6,100 sq. ft.
Owner: Corporation.   **Open:** Mon.-Fri. 9-6, Sat. 11-6, Sun. 12-5.
Work shown: Impressionist and Realist paintings and sculpture.
Artists represented: 12.

Work by: Yuri Dvornik: paintings; Guy Dessapt: paintings; Richard MacDonald: sculpture; Henry Peeters: paintings; and Wui Jian, paintings; among others. **Prices:** $1,500-30,000.
Selection process: Mail materials and SASE. **Response time:** Up to 6 months.

MONIQUE GOLDSTROM

560 Broadway, #303, 10012.   **T:** (212) 941-9175.
F: (212) 274-8650.   **W:** www.moniquegoldstrom.com
Open: Tues.-Sat. 11-6.   **Year established:** 1970.
Size: 2,000 sq. ft.
Owner: Monique Goldstrom. Background: Finance.
Work shown: Vintage and Contemporary photography, painting and sculpture.
Artists represented: 6. 75% are in museum collections.
Work by: Barbara Mensch; Mark Rowley; Bill Kane; Ken Stout; among others.
Collectors: MoMA, MoCA (L.A.), and Smithsonian. **Prices:** $100-unlimited.
Annual exhibitions: 10-12. **Advertising:** *Gallery Guide*; *The New York Times*.
Selection process: Artists are selected from referrals, slides sent to the gallery, exhibitions, and publications. The gallery reviews slides sent by mail at the end of January and end of July. Artists should include SASE. **Response time:** 1 month.

GRANT

7 Mercer St., 10013.   **T:** (212) 343-2919.
F: (212) 343-2973   **E:** grant@aol.com
W: www.grantgallery.com   **Year established:** 1998.
Open: Tues.-Sat. 11-7 and Sun. 12-6.
Owner/Director: Tatiana Grant, background: art consultant.
Work shown: Paintings and sculpture and some works on paper and prints.
Work by: Justin Love: acrylic and pastel; Dimitry Gerrman: bronze sculpture, Simon Pastukh: oil painting; and Vasily Kafanov: mixed media on canvas and works on paper; among others. **Prices:** $2,000-20,000.
Artists represented: 40. **Annual exhibitions:** 24.
Focus/Mission: To promote artists who are emerging in the American market, but are already well known in their respective countries.
Selection process: Artists are invited to submit slides, photographs, resumé, biography and SASE. **Response time:** 6 weeks.

HOWARD GREENBERG

120 Wooster St., 2nd floor, 10012. **T:** (212) 334-0010.
F: (212) 941-7479.   **W:** www.howardgreenberg.com
Open: Tues.-Sat. 10-6.   **Year established:** 1980.
Size: 2,500 sq. ft.   **Directors:** Tom Gitterman and Karen Marks.
Owner: Howard Greenberg. He has been a collector and dealer for over 20 years.
Work shown: Classic 20th century and Contemporary photography by American and European artists.
Work by: William Klein; Kenro Izu; Eikoh Hosoe; Andre Kertesz; Imogen Cunningham; and Ralph Eugene Meatyard; among others.
Collectors: MoMA, Metropolitan, San Francisco MoMA, and National Gallery.
Markets: 60% private, 20% corporate, 20% museum. **Prices:** $400-200,000.

continued

Focus/Mission: To show fine vintage and contemporary 19th and 20th century, American and European photographs. We specialize in both classic images and work that is integral to the history of photography.

Selection process: Artists are selected by referral only.

Additional information: The gallery is recognized as a pioneer in the areas of documentary and street photography from 1920-1960. It is well-known for its extensive collection of masterworks in the photography field.

STEPHEN HALLER

560 Broadway, 10012.
F: (212) 219-3246.
Open: Tues.-Sat. 10-6.

T: (212) 219-2500.
W: www.stephenhalergallery.com
Year established: 1969.

Owner/Director: Stephen Haller.

Work shown: Gestural Minimalism in paintings, sculpture, and works on paper.

Artists represented: Mid-career and emerging. 80% in museum collections.

Focus/Mission: Artists represented share a concern with the inner spirit of the work rather than the surface image. They are concerned with materials and the surfaces, or skins, that they can affect. The imagery tends to be minimal but filled with emotional gestures.

Annual exhibitions: 6-8 solo/2-4 group.

Advertising: *Gallery Guide, The New York Times* and *Review*.

Selection process: Most artists are selected from referrals by gallery artists and work seen in exhibitions. The gallery will only consider slides that are mailed with SASE and only interested in work that is aligned with the gallery's philosophy.

IT'S O.K. BEHIND THE SCENES

O.K. Harris Works of Art, founded by Ivan C. Karp in 1969, is a 10,000 sq. ft. gallery that functions much like a museum. But, unlike any museum or gallery, it remains open to the public during its exhibition installation process in order to "help people uncover the mystery of the arts."

O.K. HARRIS WORKS OF ART

383 West Broadway, 10012.
F: (212) 925-4797.
W: www.okharris.com
Size: 10,000 sq. ft.

T: (212) 431-3600.
E: okharris@okharris.com
Year established: 1969.
Gallery Manager: Suzanne Kreps.

Owner/Director: Ivan C. Karp. He was the Assistant Director, Leo Castelli Gallery, and art/film critic for *Village Voice*.

Open: Tues.-Sat. 10-6; Summer: Tues.-Fri.12-5.

Work shown: All styles and all media except prints. **Prices:** $200-150,000.

Artists represented: 60.

Work by: Clyde Lynds: sculpture/fiber optic; Muriel Castanis: sculpture; Ralph Goings: paintings; and Robert Bechtle: paintings.

Collectors: Metropolitan, MoMA, Whitney, and Pacific Telesis (San Francisco).

Annual exhibitions: 5 solo monthly (4 rooms) 1 group.

Advertising: *Gallery Guide*.

Focus/Mission: To exhibit mature and adventurous work by painters, sculptors, photographers and on occasion artifacts and collectibles worthy of esteem. The gallery maintains a complete photographic archive on its exhibitions from the time of its inception which is available to students and scholars without reservation. The gallery functions much like a museum. The gallery's main concern is to show the most significant art work of our time. In its choice of works to be exhibited it demonstrates no prejudice as to the style or materials employed.

Selection process: Artists are selected from slides sent to the gallery, from publications, and from exhibitions in alternative spaces. The gallery interviews up to 50 artist applicants in person and receives about 20 parcels of slides and photos in the mail each week, and visits the studios of those it considers to have works worthy of close inspection. Artists must enclose SASE with materials.

Additional information: The gallery remains open to the public during its exhibition installations in order to "help people uncover the mystery of the arts."

EMILY HARVEY

537 Broadway, 2nd floor, 10012.
T: (212) 925-7651.
F: (212) 966-0439.
E: ehgallery@earthlink.net
Open: By appointment.
Work by: Ay-O; Alain Arias-Misson; Geoff Hendricks; Carolee Schneermann; and Takako Saito; among others.
Advertising: *Gallery Guide.*

NANCY HOFFMAN

429 West Broadway, 10012.
T: (212) 966-6676.
F: (212) 334-5078.
W: www.nancyhoffmangallery.com
Year established: 1972.
Size: 4,500 sq. ft.
Open: Tues.-Sat. 10-6; July: Tues.-Sat. 10-5; August: Mon.-Fri. 10-5.
Owner: Nancy Hoffman, former director of Contemporary Art at French and Co. Member of the Art Dealers Association of America.
Director: Sique Spence.
Assistant Director: Christopher Watson.
Work shown: All styles of paintings, drawings, sculpture, and prints.
Artists represented: 25. 90% of the artists are in museum collections.
Work by: Joseph Raffael: watercolor; Carolyn Brady: watercolor; Don Eddy: paintings; Howard Buchwald; Ilan Averbuch; Viola Frey; Nicolas Africano: sculpture; and David Bierk: painting; among others. **Prices:** $500-100,000.
Annual exhibitions: 10 or more. **Advertising:** *The New York Times.*
Selection process: We look at new artists' slides almost every Thursday. Artists should leave slides in the gallery for review and pick them up later that day.

ILLUSTRATION HOUSE

96 Spring St., 7th floor, 10012.
T: (212) 966-9444.
F: (212) 966-9425.
W: www.illustration-house.com
Year established: 1971.
Size: 1,000 sq. ft.
Open: Mon.-Sat. 10-6 and by appointment.
Owners: Walt Reed and Roger Reed.
Members of the Appraisers Association of America.
Directors: Roger Reed and Fred Taraba. **Associate Director:** Lisa Green.
Work shown: Original illustration art in all media.
Artists represented: 85% male/15% female, from North America and Europe. 10% of the artists are in museum collections.

continued

Work by: Norman Rockwell: *Saturday Evening Post* covers, quintessential interpretations of 20th century Americana; J. C. Leyendecker: illustrator, *Saturday Evening Post* covers; Winsor McCay: cartoonist, creator of *Little Nemo In Slumberland* and *Dream of the Ravebit Fiend*; Howard Pyle: illustrator, Father of Modern Illustration and founder of the "Brandywine School"; among others.
Markets: Individual, corporate, museum. **Prices:** $500-250,000.
Annual exhibitions: 2 solo/varied group/ 2 annual auctions.
Advertising: *The New York Times, Art and Antiques,* and *Art and Auction.*
Focus/Mission: To present the fine art of illustration, spanning 100 years of American cultural history. We are the country's foremost dealer and archive for the sale and research of works intended for publication regardless of genre or media. **Selection process:** We are currently not looking for new artists.

IMAGES

580 Broadway, #204, 10012. **T:** (212) 219-8484.
F: (212) 219-9144. **Open:** By appointment.
Year established: 1992. **Size:** 1,000 sq. ft.
Owner/Director: Alan Spanier, an art consultant for over 20 years.
Market: Corporations, hotels, schools and hospitals. **Prices:** $500-10,000.
Work shown: All styles. Paintings, drawings, prints, sculpture, tapestries, photography, and ceramic.
Work by: Yale Epstein; George Anthoniesen; Susan Klebanov; Ruth Epstein; Charlotte Hinzman; Sharon Florin; and Alan Spanier; among others.
Focus/Mission: To show emotionally stimulating, beautiful, inspirational and pleasing art, regardless of the style or medium. To show art that a high proportion of the public will relate to in a positive way.
Selection process: Artists should send slides or photographs, resumé, prices, and SASE. We may elect to keep the materials on file and will contact the artist as soon as a need arises. Our consulting division sometimes sells works by artists who may not be our gallery artists. No calls or visits regarding submissions, please.
Requirements: Artists should have reached a level of technical expertise, so advanced that they progress within their own creative process, when they have found their core aesthetic.

MICHAEL INGBAR GALLERY OF ARCHITECTURAL ART

568 Broadway, 10012. **T:** (212) 334-1100.
F: (212) 334-9214. **E:** ingbargallery@aol.com
Year established: 1977. **Size:** 1,000 sq. ft.
Owner: Michael Ingbar. **Director:** Millicent Hathaway.
Open: Tues.-Sat. 12-6; Summer Mon.-Fri. 12-6.
Work shown: Art that depicts New York City buildings and structures in all media.
Artists represented: 130. 75% of the artists are in museum collections.
Work by: Richard Haas: paintings and prints; Roxie Munro: paintings; Judith Turner: black and white photography; Assunta Sera: oil on canvas; and Derek Reist: oil on canvas; among others.
Collectors: Metropolitan, MoMA, and Whitney museums. **Annual exhibitions:** 7.
Focus/Mission: To enhance people's perception of the beauty of New York City architecture via the fine arts and architectural renderings.

Selection process: 10% of the artists are selected from referrals, 50% from slides sent to gallery, 5% from exhibitions, 10% from publications. Artists should ascertain whether their art is appropriate before submitting slides, resumé and SASE.
Requirements: They must be professional and specialize in our subject matter.

SUSAN INGLETT

100 Wooster St., 2nd floor, 10012.   **T:** (212) 343-0573.
F: (212) 343-0574.   **Open:** Tues.-Sat. 11-6.
Year established: 1994.   **Size:** 1,000 sq. ft.
Owner/Director: Susan Inglett, director of Mary Boone Gallery, 1981-1990. She has been the publisher at I.C. Editions since 1990.
Work shown: Contemporary art in all media. **Artists represented:** 6.
Work by: Ed Ruscha; Peter Boynton; Andrea Zittel; Sheila Pepe; Allan McCollum and Terry Winters; among others.

ISE ART FOUNDATION

555 Broadway, 10012.   **T:** (212) 925-1649.
F: (212) 226-9362.   **Open:** Tues.-Sat. 12-6.
Year established: 1992.   **Size:** 1,600 sq. ft.
Owner: Non-profit organization.   **Director:** Shigeno Ichimura.
Work shown: Contemporary art in all media.
Annual exhibitions: 2 solo/4 group.
Selection process: 50% of the artists are selected from referrals, and 50% from slides. Artists should submit 20 slides, proposal, biography, artist's statement and SASE. **Response time:** Up to 1 year.

KAGAN MARTOS

515 Broadway, Suite 5BF, 10012.   **T:** (212) 343-4293
E: info@kaganmartos.com   **W:** www. kaganmartos.com
Open: Tues. – Sat. 11-6   **Year established:** 2000
Owners/Directors: Alona Kagan and Jose Martos, formerly private art dealers.
Work shown: Contemporary young and mid-career artists.
Artists represented: 8. International, mostly American.
Work by: Lyle Starr: painting; Lori Nix: photography; Randy Wray: painting; Bill Albertini: video, painting; Jean Christian Bourcart: photography; among others.
Prices: $500 - $10,000.
Advertising: *Frieze, Artforum, Flash Art, International Diary.*
Focus/Mission: Cutting edge contemporary conceptually based work.
Selection Process: Artists should send slides, resumé, and SASE.

KAVEHAZ CAFÉ

123 Mercer St., 10012.   **T:** (212) 343-0612.
F: (212) 343-0613.   **Open:** 7 days 10 am-12am.
Year established: 1995.   **Size:** 2,000 sq. ft.
Owner: Michael Yaacobi, formerly a civil engineer.
Work shown: Contemporary paintings. **Prices:** $500 and up.
Annual exhibitions: 11.   **Advertising:** *Gallery Guide.*
Focus/Mission: To give artists opportunities for exposure to the SoHo Art Community and the opportunity to sell their work.

continued

Selection process: 80% of artists are selected from professional referrals, 20% from slides sent to the gallery. Artists should mail slides, photos, resumé, SASE. **Response time:** 1 month.

BRONWYN KEENAN

3 Crosby St., 2nd floor, 10013.   **T:** (212) 431-5083.
F: (212) 431-3327.   **W:** www.artnewyork.com
Open: Tues.-Sat. 11-6.   **Year established:** 1995.
Size: 800 sq. ft.
Owner/Director: Bronwyn Keenan. He was a Christie's cataloger and appraiser, and the former director of Stephen Haller Gallery
Work shown: Contemporary video, painting, sculpture, and installation.
Artists represented: 5, from U.S., Holland, U.K., and Germany.
Work by: Reverend Ethan Acres; Nicole Carstens; Mary Esch; Mari Eastman; and Helen Garber; among others.
Markets: Individual and corporate.   **Prices:** $300-15,000.
Annual exhibitions: 10.   **Advertising:** *Artforum* and *Flash Art.*
Focus/Mission: To give emerging artists a forum to experiment and grow.
Selection process: 75% of the artists are selected from professional referrals, and 25% from art seen in exhibitions or artists studios. Artists should mail slides, biography and SASE to gallery.   **Response time:** 2 weeks.

JUNE KELLY

591 Broadway, 3rd floor, 10012.   **T:** (212) 226-1660.
F: (212) 226-2433.   **W:** www.junekellygallery.com
Year established: 1986.   **Size:** 3,000 sq. ft.
Open: Tues.-Sat. 11-6; July: Mon.-Fri. 11-6; closed in August.
Owner/Director: June Kelly. She was a private dealer in 19th and 20th century art and Romare Bearden's manager for 13 years.
Work shown: Abstract and Figurative paintings, sculpture and photography.
Artists represented: 15. **Origins:** North America and Europe.
Work by: Carmen Cicero: painting; Philemona Williamson: painting; Colin Chase: sculpture; Lisa C. Davis: mixed media; Jane Schneider: sculpture; Hughie Lee-Smith: painting; and Elizabeth Catlett: sculpture; among others.
Prices: $1,800-100,000. **Annual exhibitions:** 11 solo.
Advertising: *ARTnews, Art in America* and *The New York Times.*
Focus/Mission: To be a center of education, a place for exploration and a place where the rich beauty of the visual arts can be presented.
Selection process: The gallery reviews new artists' materials in April. Artists should mail slides or photos, resumé and SASE. No calls, please.
Requirements: Art must show a unique vision, art with poetry and spirituality, by artists who express their own vocabulary.

KENT

67 Prince St., 10012.   **T:** (212) 966-4500.
F: (212) 966-7820.   **W:** www.kentgallery.com
Open: Tues.-Sat. 12-6.   **Year established:** 1985.
Size: 2,500 sq. ft.
Owner/Director: Douglas Walla. He worked at Marlborough Gallery, 1976-1985.

Work shown: 20th Century Modern to Contemporary sculpture, drawings, paintings, and photography.

Artists represented: 5 male/ 5 female. Ages: 35-50. **Origins:** Predominantly Poland, Spain, Japan, Canada, and U.S. All artists are in museum collections.
Markets: 70% individual, and 30% museum. **Collectors:** Whitney, MoMA, Centre Pompedieu, and IVAM/Centre Julio Gonzalez, Spain.
Annual exhibitions: 4 solo.
Focus/Mission: To show historically viable Modern and Contemporary art with sound conceptual basis.
Selection process: All artists are selected from referrals. Artists should mail slides, resumé and SASE.

PHYLLIS KIND

136 Greene St., 10012.   **T:** (212) 925-1200.
F: (212) 941-7841.   **W:** www.phylliskindgallery.com
Owner: Phyllis Kind.   **Director:** Ron Jagger.
Year established: 1967.   **Size:** 2,750 sq. ft. total on two levels.
E: phylliskind@phylliskindgallery.com
Open: Tues.-Sat. 10-6; July Tues.-Fri. 10-6; August by appointment.
Work shown: Contemporary American and Russian paintings, sculpture, and work on paper, including American Self-taught, European, and Art Brut.
Artists represented: 25+. Most of them are in museum collections.
Work by: Alison Saar: sculpture; Mark Greenwold: painting; Robert Colescott: painting; and Martin Ramirez: works on paper; among others.
Annual exhibitions: 6-8.
Focus/Mission: We believe in the primary individuality of human creativity, which is never without reference to its time.
Selection process: Artists should mail or hand deliver slides, biography, and SASE. **Requirement:** Work must be unique and transformational.

MARTIN LAWRENCE

457 West Broadway, 10012.   **T:** (212) 995-8865.
F: (212) 353-3650.   **W:** www.martinlawrence.com
Year established: 1989.   **Director:** John Salvo.
Open: Daily 10-7; Summer: Mon.-Fri. 11-7, Fri. and Sat. 10-8.
Work shown: Pop, contemporary and modern masters. Original art, limited edition graphics, and sculpture.   **Artists represented:** 20.
Work by: Chagall; Picasso; Warhol; and Haring; among others.
Prices: $600-200,000. Major credit cards are accepted.
Advertising: *Gallery Guide, New York* and *The New York Times.*
Additional information: Martin Lawrence Galleries is an integrated publisher and retailer of limited editions and original art with galleries nationwide.

LEHMANN MAUPIN

39 Greene St., 10013.   **T:** (212) 965-0753.
F: (212) 965-0754.   **W:** www.artnet.com
Size: 3,500 sq. ft.   **Year established:** 1996.
Open: Tues.-Sat. 10-6. July: Tues.-Fri. 10-6. August by appointment.
Owners: Rachel Lehmann, former owner of Galerie Lehmann in Lausanne, Switzerland and David Maupin, former director of Metro Pictures.   *continued*

Work shown: Contemporary art in all media including video and film.
Markets: Individual, corporate, museum.
Focus/Mission: To provide artists and guest curators with an accommodating space for special projects, thematic group shows, collaborative or interdisciplinary projects, as well as solo exhibitions of new work or work from an artist's series.
Selection process: 50% of artists are selected from professional referrals, 50% from art seen in exhibitions or artists studios. We are currently not looking for new artists.

LEICA

670 Broadway, Suite 500, 10012. **T:** (212) 777-3051.
F: (212) 777-6960. **E:** leicaphoto@aol.com
Open: Tues.-Fri.11-6, Sat.12-6. **Year established:** 1994.
Size: 2,500 sq. ft.
On-site Owners/Directors: Rose and Jay Deutsch, former owners F.D.R. Gallery, collectors and dealers in photography, and Leica photographers.
Third Director: Roger Horn, President, Leica Camera (U.S.).
Work shown: Vintage and Contemporary photography. Photojournalism, documentary, and reportage, fine art photography.
Artists represented: 10. 50% male/female. All origins. 90% of the artists are in museum collections.
Work by: Leonard Freed, documentary; Ralph Gibson, fine art; Alex Webb, documentary and fine art; and Burk Uzzle, documentary and fine art; among others.
Collectors: Chrysler Museum, Boston Museum of Fine Art, International Center of Photography, and Library of Congress.
Markets: Individuals, corporate art purchasers, foundations, and museums.
Prices: $50-5,000. Major credit cards are accepted.
Annual exhibitions: 8. **Advertising:** *Photography in New York.*
Focus/Mission: To present exhibitions that reflect the Leica standards of excellence in photography.
Selection process: We look for contemporary photographers who work in the famous Leica tradition of Eisenstaedt, Cartier-Bresson, Haas and others.
Requirements: Most artists are part of Leica professional programs and/or working photojournalists.

LENNON, WEINBERG

560 Broadway, #308, 10012. **T:** (212) 941-0012.
F: (212) 941-0098. **E:** lennonweinberg@earthlink.net
Year established: 1988. **Size:** 3,000 sq. ft.
Open: Tues.-Sat.10-6; Summer: Tues.-Fri. 10-6.
Owner/Director: Jill Weinberg Adams.
Work shown: Varied styles of painting, sculpture, drawing, prints, and video.
Artists represented: 21 artists and 2 estates. Ages: 35-70. **Origins:** U.S. and Europe. All of the artists are in museum collections.
Work by: Catherine Murphy; Tony Berlant; Mary Lucier; Stephan Westfall; and Peter Soriano; among others. **Annual exhibitions:** 8.
Collectors: Metropolitan, MoMA, Art Institute of Chicago, and San Francisco Museum of Modern Art.
Selection process: We are not currently looking for new artists.

LESLIE-LOHMAN GAY ART FOUNDATION

127 B Prince St., 10012.   **T:** (212) 673-7007.
F: (212) 260-0363.   **E:** lldirector@earthlink.net
W: www.leslie-lohman.org   **Open:** Tues.-Sat. 1-6; closed in August.
Year established: 1990.   **Size:** 2,400 sq. ft.
Founders: Charles Leslie and J. Frederick Lohman.   **Director:** Wayne Snellen.
Work shown: Contemporary lesbian and gay erotic art, Figurative and Abstract art in all media.
Artists represented: All origins. 75% male/25% female.
Annual exhibitions: 5. **Advertising:** *HX* and *NEXT.*
Focus/Mission: As a non-profit institution, to preserve, protect and exhibit art that most likely would be hidden or destroyed due to prejudice and ignorance about the value and importance of lesbian and gay homoerotic art.
Selection process: 10% of the artists are selected from referrals, 80% from slides sent to the gallery, and 10% from art seen in exhibitions and artists studios. Artists should call for an appointment. Artists should mail slides, photos, biography, resumé, prices and SASE. **Response time:** 6-8 weeks.
Requirement: Art must be ready to hang.
Additional information: The Foundation has an archive and maintains files on lesbian and gay artists.

ABRAHAM LUBELSKI

473 Broadway, 7th floor, 10012.   **T:** (212) 274-8993.
F: (212) 226-3400.   **E:** nyartsmaga@aol.com
W: www.nyartsmagazine.com   **Open:** Tues.-Sat. 10-6.
Year established: 1997.   **Size:** 2,000 sq. ft.
Owner/Director: Abraham Lubelski, background as artist and collector.
Work shown: All styles and media. **Prices:** $500-10,000.
Artists represented: 12. All origins. 50% male/female.
Annual exhibitions: 8 solo/12 group.
Advertising: *NY SoHo Arts Magazine, NY SoHo Listing and Map.*
Focus/Mission: To offer an alternative and to be flexible and adaptive in working closely with artists as curators and organizers.
Selection process: We review artists' materials every Thurs., Fri., and Sat.
Response time: 1 week. **Requirement:** Artists should be highly self-motivated.
Fees: Artists should be prepared to pay exhibition and promotion expenses.

HERBERT LUST

61 Sullivan St., 10012.   **T:** (212) 925-5355.
Open: By appointment.   **Work shown:** Painting, drawing, sculpture.
Work by: Andre; Arakawa; Fish; Man Ray; Christo; Giacometti; Indiana; Hinman; Lewitt; Tanguey; and others.

MALCA FINE ART

580 Broadway, #603, 10012. **T:** (212) 966-8854.
F: (212) 966-0045. **E:** malcafineart@mindspring.com
Open: Mon.-Fri. 10-6. **Year established:** 1994.
Owner/Director: Leo Malca, formerly a private dealer.
Work shown: Contemporary art in all media.
Work by: Basquiat; Haring; Warhol; and Vik Muniz; in addition to younger artists.
Annual exhibitions: 4-5.
Selection process: We are currently not seeking new artists.

NANCY MARGOLIS

560 Broadway, #302, 10012. **T:** (212) 343-9523.
F: (212) 343-9524. **E:** MargolisNY@aol.com
Open: Tues.-Sat. 10-5:30. **Owner/Director:** Nancy Margolis.
Work shown: Ceramics and fiber work in a wide range of styles.
Artists represented: 30 plus. **Origins:** U.S., Canada, and Europe.
Work by: Jack Earl; Barbara Diduk; Lies Cosijn; Lissa Hunter; and Ferne Jacobs; among others.
Markets: Individual and museum. **Prices:** $100-25,000. Visa and MC accepted.
Annual exhibitions: 8-10 solo/ 3-4 group. **Advertising:** *American Craft Magazine, Art in America, Art and Auction,* and *American Ceramics.*
Focus/Mission: To specialize in European and American Contemporary Ceramics. To breakdown the belief that ceramics are solely a craft endeavor and present the public with a more sophisticated notion of ceramic arts, and to introduce ceramic artists into the realm of fine arts.
Selection process: 80% of the artists are selected from professional referrals, 20% from slides sent to the gallery. Artists should mail slides, photos, biography, resumé, and SASE. **Response time:** 2-3 weeks. **Requirements:** Artists must do clay or ceramic work. Artists are expected to share the costs of advertising.

LOUIS K. MEISEL

141 Prince St., 10012. **T:** (212) 677-1340.
F: (212) 533-7340. **W:** www.meiselgallery.com
Year established: 1968.
Open: Tues.-Sat. 10-6. Closed July 23-Labor Day.
Owners: Louis K. Meisel and Susan P. Meisel, backgrounds as private dealers and collectors. **Directors:** Diane Sena and Aaron J. Miller.
Work shown: Photo-Realist paintings and other technically skilled contemporary disciplines in all media. **Prices:** $5,000 and up.
Artists represented: 25. 80% of the artists are in museum collections.
Work by: Charles Bell: oil paintings; Audrey Flack: bronze sculpture; Gill Elvgren: oil paintings; Ron Kleemann: oil paintings; and Tony Brunelli: oil paintings; among others.
Collectors: MoMA, Metropolitan, Guggenheim, and Smithsonian.
Annual exhibitions: 12 solo/3 group.
Advertising: *ARTnews, Gallery Guide,* and *The New York Times.*
Focus/Mission: To exhibit fine art which is fun to look at and live with, which does not require lengthy explanations to understand and enjoy.

Selection process: Artists with appropriate work should send 10-20 slides or photographs by mail Sept.-June, with a cover letter, brief biography, and SASE.
Requirements: Artists are expected to be familiar with the gallery's concept; to be pleasant and professional; have technically advanced artistic abilities including drawing and painting; and have an understanding of materials and art history.

ARIEL MEYEROWITZ

580 Broadway, #1203, 10012.
T: (212) 625-3434.
E: arielmeyer@aol.com
W: www.arielmeyerowitz.com
Open: Wed.-Sat. 11-6.
Year established: 2000.
Owner/Director: Ariel Meyerowitz. **Artists represented:** 22.
Work shown: Contemporary and Vintage 20th and 21st Century photography.
Work by: Joel Meyerowitz; Thomas Roma; George Tise; Ezra Stoller; among others, and the estate of Dr. Harold Edgerton.
Annual exhibitions: 7.
Prices: $500-20,000.
Advertising: *Photography in New York, Gallery Guide* and *Art on Paper.*
Selection process: The gallery conducts a portfolio review the first Wed. of the month. Call to confirm.

MONTSERRAT

584 Broadway, 10012.
T: (212) 941-8899.
F: (212) 274-1717.
Open: Tues.-Sat. 12-6.
W: www.montserratgallery.com
Year established: 1987.
Director: Montserrat.
Work shown: Contemporary art by artists from all origins.
Additional information: Artists should be prepared to pay exhibition fees.

MULTIPLE IMPRESSIONS

128 Spring St., 10012.
T: (212) 925-1313.
F: (212) 431-7146.
W: www.multipleimpressions.com
Open: Tues. -Sat. 11-6:30, Sun 12-6:30, Mon. 11-5:30.
Year established: 1972.
Owner/President: Betty Feinman.
Size: 1,600 sq. ft.
Prices: $500-15,000.
Work shown: Contemporary originals, traditional pastels, Impressionistic paintings, and limited edition original graphics, mezzotints and monoprints.
Artists represented: 50. 50% male/female. **Ages:** 20's-70's. All origins. 75% of the artists are in museum collections.
Work by: Graciela Rodo-Boulanger: lithographs, oils and original etchings with music, play, and animal themes; Mikio Watanabe: female nudes in black and white mezzotints; Norman Laliberte: nature and man-inspired themes in original etchings, oil paintings, and sculpture; Eng Tay: family harmony themes in original etchings, oil paintings, and bronze sculpture; Harold Altman: original lithographs; among others.
Annual exhibitions: 5 solo. **Advertising:** *The New York Times.*
Markets: Individual, corporate and museum. Major credit cards are accepted.
Focus/Mission: To offer a wide spectrum of media by international artists of fine quality representing exceptional value. We offer service, and information on method and artist history. We are a user-friendly gallery.

continued

Selection process: 10% of the artists are selected from professional referrals, 5% from slides sent to the gallery, 10% from art seen in exhibitions or artists studios. Artists should mail slides, photos, biography, resumé, prices, SASE. **Response time:** 2-4 weeks. **Requirements:** Art must be outstanding examples of the media and aesthetically pleasing.

THE MUSEUM FOR AFRICAN ART

593 Broadway, 10012.   **T:** (212) 966-1313.
F: (212) 966-1432.   **W:** www.africanart.org
E: museum@africanart.org
Open: Tues.-Fri. 10:30-5:30; Thurs. 5:30-8:30; Sat.-Sun. 12-6.
Admission: Free for members. Free on Sun. $5 general; $2.50 students, senior citizens, and children.
Year established: 1984 as the Center for African Art. In 1992 it was renamed the Museum for African Art.   **Annual exhibitions:** 2-3.
Director of Exhibitions: Frank Herreman.
Work shown: African art, from traditional to Contemporary in all media.
Focus/Mission: To increase public understanding and appreciation of African art and culture. The museum is recognized worldwide as the preeminent organizer of exhibitions and publishers of books on African art, and is one of only two in the U.S. devoted to historical and contemporary African art.
Selection process: African Artists should submit proposals and slides to Frank Herreman.
Additional information: The museum offers ongoing educational programs, exhibition tours, and an annual African festival. On the third Thursday of the month the museum presents a special program or concert. The Museum Store offers an extensive array of distinctive and authentic African items. The Bookstore carries books on every aspect of African culture. Rental spaces within the museum are available for events of all kinds.

NEW MUSEUM OF CONTEMPORARY ART

583 Broadway, 10012.   **T:** (212) 219-1222.
F: (212) 431-5328.   **W:** www.newmuseum.org
Open: Tues. - Sun. 12-6, Thurs. 12-8.
Admission: $6 general; $3 students/seniors; free for 18 and under. $3 Thurs. 6-8.
Year established: 1977.   **Annual exhibitions:** 5.
Focus/Mission: To advance innovative art and artistic practice as a vital social force through its exhibitions, programs and organizational structure. Primary to the Museum's purpose are education and public outreach, original scholarship, and critical investigation of the Museum's role and function.
Selection process: Call for current policy.
Additional information: The Museum presents lectures, panels, visitor programs, seminars, films, and publications in addition to performances of art and music. The New Museum Store is open Tues.-Sun. 12-6:30, Thurs. 12-8.

THE NEWS, INC

495 Broadway, 5th floor, 10012.   **T:** (212) 925-9700 x117.
F: (212) 925-1550.   **E:** telliott@495news.com
Open: Tues.-Sat. 11-6.   **Year established:** 1997.
Owner: Stella Ishii.   **Director:** Tim Elliott.

Work shown: Contemporary art in all media. The NEWS is an internationally acclaimed fashion showroom. **Annual exhibitions:** 5.
Markets: Individual, corporate, and museum.
Exhibitons Have included: Robert Breer; Michael Elmgreen and Ingar Dragset; Gerald Kamitaki; Tomoko Takahashi; and "Shootback" Kids; among others.
Selection process: Artists should mail slides, biography, resumé, artist's statement and prices with SASE. **Response time:** Immediate.

NOLAN/ECKMAN

560 Broadway, 6th floor, 10012.   **T:** (212) 925-6190.
F: (212) 334-9139.   **E:** nolan.eckman@prodigy.net
Open: Tues.-Fri. 10-6, Sat. 11-6.   **Summer:** Call for hours.
Year established: 1987.   **Size:** 2,700 sq. ft.
Owners/Directors: Carol Eckman and David Nolan.
Work shown: Contemporary American and European work on paper.
Artists represented: 25 well-established, mid-career artists. All of the artists are in museum collections.
Work by: Carroll Dunham: drawing; William Copley: all media; Sigmar Polke: work on paper; Barry Le Va: work on paper; and Ian Hamilton Finlay: all media sculpture and prints; among others.
Collectors: Metropolitan, MoMA, Boston Museum of Fine Arts, and The Tate.
Annual exhibitions: 4 solo/4 group. **Advertising:** *Artforum* and *Gallery Guide.*

O.J. 121

121 Spring St., 10012.   **T:** (212) 343-2706.
F: (212) 343-9103.   **W:** www.ojart.com
Open: Daily, 10:30-6:30.   **Owner:** Jay Jalall.
Work shown: Lithographs and serigraphs.
Work by: Rizzi; Tarkay; Fazzino; McNight; Warhol; and Haring; among others.

OPERA

115 Spring St., 10012.   **T:** (212) 966-6675
W: www.operagallery.com   **Year established:** 1999.
Open: Daily 10-8   **Work shown:** Contemporary European art.
Annual exhibitions: 10.

THE PAINTING CENTER

52 Greene St., 10012.   **T:** (212) 343-1060.
W: www.thepaintingcenter.com **Open:** Tues.-Sat. 11-6.
Year established: 1993.   **Owner:** Non-profit, alternative space.
Size: 1,800 sq. ft.   **Director:** Christina Chow
Open: Tues.-Sat., 11-6; Closed mid June-mid Sept.
Work shown: Paintings by mature artists in all styles.
Artists represented: 12. 50% male/female. **Ages:** 30-60s.
Work by: Cecily Kahn; Mark O'Grady; and Lisa Lawley; among others.
Prices: $800-10,000. **Annual exhibitions:** 2 solo/5 two-person/4 group.
Focus/Mission: To reach the community with many artists' work.
Selection process: Artists should mail 10-15 slides with a letter and SASE.
Response time: 3 months. **Fees:** There are some exhibition fees.

PARKETT PUBLISHERS

155 Avenue of the Americas, 2nd floor, 10013.
T: (212) 673-2660.   F: (212) 271-0704.
W: www.parkettart.com   Open: By appointment Mon.-Fri.
Year established: 1997.   Owner: Dieter Von Graffenried.
Parkett Publishers are art book publishers and publishers of limited edition prints.
Work shown: Limited edition prints by contemporary artists in all styles and media.

PERRY

481 Washington St., 10013.   T: (212) 925-6796.
F: (212) 925-0849.   W: www.queenart publishers.com
Open: Mon.-Fri. 10-6.
Owner/Director: Israel Perry, PhD. in Polymer Science.
Work shown: Contemporary original paintings, serigraphs, lithographs and sculpture, in addition to antique posters.
Prices: $300-40,000.
Artists represented: Israeli and Brazillian artists.
Work by: Itzchak Tarkay: painting; David Schluss: painting; Arie Azene: painting; Ferjo: painting; and Galina Datloof: painting; among others.

MICHAEL PETRONKO

T: (917) 653-9818.   W: michaelpetronkogallery.com
E: michaelpetronko@michaelpetronkogallery.com
Open: By appointment   Year established: 1991.
Owner/Director: Michael Petronko.
Work shown: Post-War American including Pop, Abstract Expressionism, and Minimalism.
Markets: Individual, corporate, museum.   Prices: $2,000-100,000.
Artists represented: 15.   50% male/female. 90% are in museum collections.
Work by: Warhol; Francis; Lichtenstein; Basquiat; and Haring; among others.
Annual exhibitions: 6 solo/3 group.   Advertising: *Gallery Guide, ARTnews.*
Selection process: All artists are selected from professional referrals. Artists are not encouraged to send slides.

PHOENIX

568 Broadway, #607, 10012.   T: (212) 226-8711.
F: (212) 343-7303.   W: www.phoenixgallery.com
E: info@ phoenixgallery.com   Open: Tues.-Sat. 11-5:30;Closed in August.
Size: 2,000 sq. ft.   Year established: 1958. This is one of the
oldest artist-run, non-profit cooperative galleries in New York City.
Owner: Artist members.   Director: Linda Handler.
Work shown: All styles and media. Prices: $50-10,000.

Artist members: 7 male/26 female.   **Ages:** 30-78. All origins.
Work by: Cecily Barth Firestein; Pamela Bennett Ader; Margaret Pomfret; Beth Cartland; and David Raymond; among others.
Collectors: Westinghouse, CocaCola, Ernst & Young, Landmark Systems Corp.
Annual exhibitions: 14 solo/2 group.
Focus/Mission: To offer emerging and established artists a place to exhibit. The gallery is sensitive to artists' needs because it is operated by artists.
Selection process: Many artists are invited to join the gallery as a result of the annual National Juried Competition. Artists are also found through referrals and slides sent to gallery. Artists should call or write for an application.
Requirements: The gallery seeks professional artists with a record of shows.
Response time: 6 weeks.
Fees: Initiation fee: $300. Active members $480 per quarter; Inactive members: $615 per quarter.
Additional information: In addition to providing exposure for members the gallery conducts juried competitions, dance programs, poetry readings, book signings, plays and lectures. The Project Room presents guest artist exhibitions.

POP INTERNATIONAL
473 West Broadway, 10012.   **T:** (212) 533-4262.
F: (212) 533-6553.   **E:** art@popinternational.com
W: www.popinternational.com   **Year established**: 1997.
Owners/Directors: Jeff Jaffe and Rick Rounick, collectors and dealers in other locations in New York and throughout the U.S.
Work shown: Pop art and art that is derived from Pop culture. Painting, photography and sculpture.   **Artists represented:** 20.
Work by: Warhol; Lichtenstein; Haring; Britton; Morris; Leifer; among others.
Prices: $300-over 1,000,000.   **Annual exhibitions:** 5.
Selection process: Artists should mail slides and/or photographs with SASE. They are reviewed by a selection committee. **Response time:** 3 months.

PORTICO NEW YORK
139 Spring St., #2N, 10012.   **T:** (212) 941-1444.
F: (212) 941-8248.   **E:** steven@porticony.com
W: www.porticony.com and www.artnet.com/portico.html
Open: By appointment.
Director: Steven P. Lowy, artist, curator and art advisor.
Artists represented: Hilla Rebay (Founding Director of the Solomon Guggenheim Museum): Abstract paintings and watercolors; and Rolph Scarlett: Abstract paintings and watercolors; and Xanti Schawinsky. Portico Fine Art also handles the estate of Rudolf Bauer and "The Art of Tomorrow."

PORTRAITS AND PAINTING
203 Lafayette St., 10012.   **T:** (212) 334-9626.
F: (212) 334-4496.   **W:** www.portraitsandpainting.com
Open: Call for hours.   **Year established:** 1995.
Owner: Alan Hirsch, artist.   **Size:** 1,500 sq. ft.
Work shown: Portraits, self-portraits and NYC landscape oil paintings.
Work by: Alan Hirsch. **Prices:** $4,000-15,000.
Advertising: *The New York Times* and *Gallery Guide.*

P.P.O.W.

476 Broome St., 3rd floor, 10013. **T:** (212) 941-8642.
F: (212) 274-8339.   **E:** info@ppowgallery.com
W: www.artnet.com   **Open:** Tues.-Sat. 10-6.
Size: 5,000 sq. ft.
Year established: 1983.
Owners: Wendy Olsoff and Penny Pilkington.
Work shown: Figurative, Political and Conceptual art in all media.
Artists represented: 27. 50% male/female. **Ages:** 20-60s.
Origins: Primarily U.S. 90% of the artists are in museum collections.
Work by: David Wojnarowicz: social and political concerns in all media; Carrie May Weems: social and political concerns predominantly in photography; Carolee Schneeman: conceptual work in all media; Lynne Cohen: Conceptual photography; Bo Bartlett: large ealist paintings; among others.
Prices: $500-200,000.
Annual exhibitions: 8 solo/1 group.
Collectors: MoMA, Metropolitan, Getty, and Brooklyn Museum.
Focus/Mission: To show work by individuals rather than schools or trends.
Selection process: 80% of the artists are selected from referrals, 20% from exhibitions. Artists should mail slides, biography, and SASE. We review artists' materials in Jan. **Response time:** 3 months.

PRATT MANHATTAN

295 Lafayette St., 2nd floor, 10012. **T:** (718) 636-3517.
F: (718) 636-3785.   **W:** www.pratt.edu/exhibitions
Year established: 1985.
Director: Carl Rosenstein.
Open: Thurs.-Fri. 1-6, Sat.-Sun. 12-6.
Work shown: Group exhibitions with themes and issues in Contemporary fine art, design and architecture. Also exhibitions of students, faculty and alumni.
Annual exhibitions: 5-6.
Selection process: Artists should send materials and SASE to Schafler Gallery, Pratt Institute, Brooklyn, NY 11205. Exhibitions are scheduled 1 year ahead.

THE PUFFIN ROOM

435 Broome St., 10013.   **T:** (212) 343-2881.
W: www.home.earthlink.net\~puffinroom
Year established: 1995.
Open: Thur.-Fri. 1-6, Sat.-Sun.-12-6.
Owner: The Puffin Foundation, a non-profit organization that awards grants to artists of all disciplines including art, literature, dance, music, photography, theater, film, and video.
Work shown: Political and social related art.
Additional information: Applications for grants are issued October, November and December. Address all inquiries to: The Puffin Foundation Ltd., Dept. B., 20 East Oakdene Ave., Teaneck, NJ 07666-4198.

GEORGE A. RADA STUDIO

515 Greenwich St., #314, 10013.   **T:** (212) 741-1560.
E: georgerada00@yahoo.com   **W:** www.newyorkartworld.com and
www.artadvocate.com   **Open:** By appointment.

Work by: George A. Rada, painter of Contemporary figure, landscape, still life and portraiture of all ages, in Realist style reminiscent of 19th Century masters. Oil on canvas, pastel, charcoal, etching. All works are created from life.

MARGARETE ROEDER

545 Broadway, 4th floor, 10012.   **T:** (212) 925-6098.
F: (212) 431-7050.   **W:** www.roedergallery.com
Year established: 1978.   **Size:** 2,000 sq. ft.
Open: Wed.-Sat. 11-5:30 and by appointment.
Owner/Director: Margarete Roeder, art historian.
Work shown: Minimal and conceptual art, specializing in works on paper by American and European artists.
Markets: Individual, corporate, and museum. **Prices:** $700-1,000,000.
Artists represented: 25. 60% male/40% female. **Origins:** Europe and U.S. 80% of the artists are in museum collections.
Work by: Georg Baeselitz; John Cage; Eva Hesse; Bill Woodrow; and Gary Kuehn; among others.
Annual exhibitions: 3 solo/5 group. **Advertising:** *Gallery Guide.*
Focus/Mission: To expose the public to good contemporary art.
Selection process: The gallery is not accepting unsolicited materials at this time.

ROSENBERG + KAUFMAN

115 Wooster St., 10012.   **T:** (212) 431-4838.
F: (212) 431-1067.   **E:** rkart@earthlink.net
W: www.artnet.com   **Size:** 1,800 sq. ft.
Year established: 1983.
Open: Tues.-Sat. 11-6 and by appointment; August by appointment.
Owners/Directors: Stephen Rosenberg, attorney; Fran Kaufman, former TV executive.
Work shown: Contemporary American and European painting, drawing, work on paper, and 3-dimensional art.
Artists represented: 14. 90% of the artists are in museum collections.
Work by: Cheryll Goldsleger: painting, works on paper; Vadim Ketznelson: painting; Martha Keller: painting; Lex Braes: painting and drawing; David Stern: painting and drawing; among others. **Prices:** $750-70,000.
Annual exhibitions: 9.
Advertising: *Art in America, Gallery Guide, ARTnews* and *The Art Newspaper.*
Focus/Mission: To exhibit contemporary art by mid-career and emerging artists. The emphasis is on Abstraction and Abstract Figuration, from Minimal to Expressive, with a select group of artists who have a unique perspective on the landscape.
Selection process: Artists should visit the gallery and view several exhibitions to acquaint themselves with the work the gallery represents. At this time the gallery is not taking on any new artists.
Additional information: The gallery has another location in Midtown.

LUISE ROSS

568 Broadway, #402, 10012.
F: (212) 343-2468.
W: www.luiserossgallery.com
Size: 1,000 sq. ft.
Owner/Director: Luise Ross.

T: (212) 343-2161.
E: lrossgallery@earthlink.net
Open: Tues. - Sat. 10-5:30.
Year established: 1984.

Work shown: Contemporary art, Self-Taught art. Paintings, drawings, sculpture.
Annual exhibitions: 6-8 solo.   Markets: Individual, corporate, and museum.
Artists represented: 12-15.
Work by: Bill Traylor: self-taught artist, paintings and drawings on cardboard; Walter Anderson: watercolors; John R. Thompson: paintings and wood relief sculpture and paintings; Willie Birch: paper-maché sculpture, and paintings; and Minnie Evans: self-taught Visionary artist: paintings and drawings; among others.
Selection process: Artists should mail materials and SASE. Response: immediate.

JEFFREY RUESCH

134 Spring St., 10012.
F: (212) 226-8070.
Open: Mon.-Fri. 11-6.
Owner/Director: Jeffrey Ruesch.

T: (212) 925-1137.
E: Rueart@worldnet.att.net
Year established: 1980.

Work shown: Contemporary prints and work on paper.
Work by: Keith Haring; David Hockney; Roy Lichtenstein; Frank Stella; and Andy Warhol; among others.

RUSSECK

478 West Broadway, 10012.
F: (212) 475-5709.
Open: Daily 11-6.
Owner: Howard Russeck.

T: (212) 475-9939.
W: www.russeckgallery.com
Year established: 1970.
Director: Bernita Mirisola.

Work shown: Contemporary American sculpture and Modern art.
Work by: Boone Tyler; Peter Anton; Daniel Meyer; Sandy Scott; and Vladimir Kush. Also the work of Picasso; Chagall; Miro; Matisse; among others.
Additional information: The gallery's two other locations are in San Francisco, CA and Palm Beach, FL.

SARAJO

130 Greene St., 10012.
F: (212) 274-0462.
Owner: Yosi Barzilai.

T: (212) 966-6156.
Open: Daily 11-7.

Work shown: Indian miniatures, textiles, and ethnic art in a variety of media.
Markets: Individual, corporate and museum. Prices: $300-10,000.
Focus/Mission: Our purpose is to sell ethnographic material – cultures of the world all working together. We do not represent artists. We sell work that is unsigned from different cultures.

SCALO

560 Broadway, Room 301, 10012.
F: (212) 334-4290.
Year established: 1998.

T: (212) 334-9393.
Open: Tues.-Sat. 11-6.
Owner: Walter Keller, publisher, Scalo.

Associate Publisher: Ricky Lee. **Work shown:** Contemporary photography. **Work by:** Marianne Mueller; Wendy Ewald; Seydou Keita; and Malick Sidibe; among others.
Focus/Mission: We only show the works of the artists we publish.

JACQUELINE JOY SFERRA STUDIO

515 Greenwich St., #314, 10013.   **T:** (212) 741-1560
E: sferrajj@yahoo.com   **W:** www.newyorkartworld.com and
www.ArtAdvocate.com   **Year established:** 2000.
Open: By appointment.
Work by: Jacqueline Joy Sferra, Minimal Realist painter mainly informed by landscape and atmosphere. Work on paper, pastel, and watercolor.

TONY SHAFRAZI

119 Wooster St., 10012.   **T:** (212) 274-9300.
F: (212) 334-9499.   **E:** tsgallery@aol.com
Year established: 1981.
Owner/Director: Tony Shafrazi, artist and art consultant.
Open: Tues.-Sat. 10-6; Aug: by appointment.
Artists represented: 8.
Work shown: Contemporary paintings, sculpture, work on paper, prints and photography.
Work by: Keith Haring: all media; Kenny Scharf: all media; Michael Ray Charles: works on paper and canvas; Dennis Hopper: photographs; Brian Clarke: painting and stained glass; and Donald Baechler: paintings; Frances Bacon estate; among others. **Collectors:** All major museums.
Advertising: *Gallery Guide, Art in America*, and *Flash Art*.
Focus/Mission: To be committed to discovering, introducing and exhibiting important new developments in contemporary art. We also undertake large-scale, museum quality exhibitions to present historical perspectives.
Selection process: We are currently not looking for new artists.

SOHO PHOTO

15 White St., 10013.   **T:** (212) 226-8571.
W: www.sohophoto.com   **E:** sohophoto@aol.com
Year established: 1971.   **Size:** 4,000 sq. ft.
Open: Thurs. 6-8, Fri., Sat. and Sun. 1-6.
Owners: Artist members. Non-profit cooperative gallery.
President: Richard Zalk .
Work shown: All styles of photography. Exhibitions feature member artists in addition to visiting artists. They have featured such artists as Minor Whiter, Eric Renner, Jindrich Strieght, and Dan Burkholder.
Artists represented: 100 members. 50% male/female. **Ages:** 20-75.
Collectors: Metropolitan, Museum of the City of New York, Cravath Swan and Moore, and Dewey Ballentine.   **Prices:** $75-1,000.
Annual exhibitions: 40 solo/11 group. **Advertising:** *Photography in New York*.
Focus/Mission: To offer photographers a place to exhibit their own work and exchange ideas with others. The gallery provides a sounding board for new ideas, experimental work, and unorthodox techniques. It was formed as an alternative to commercial galleries that favor one style or technique. *continued*

Selection process: Prospective members' portfolios are reviewed the first Saturday of each month. Photographers should submit portfolios of 10-12 final, mounted prints. Drop them off by 11:00 the first Saturday of each month and pick them up around 2:00.

Fees: There is an annual membership fee and a one-time facility fee.

Additional information: Our annual national competitions are juried by leading members of the photographic community, such as Susan Kismaric, MoMA. Guest lecturers and a variety of workshops are also offered, and are open to the public. Opening receptions are held on the first Tues. of every month, 6-8 p.m.

SOHO TRIAD FINE ARTS

107 Grand St., 10013.
T: (212) 965-9500.
F: (212) 965-0537.
E: sohotriad@msn.com
W:www.artnet.com
Open: Mon-Fri. 10-6 and Sat and Sun. 11-6
Year established: 1996.
Size: 2,000 sq. ft.

Owners: Sidney S. Monroe, Barry S. Podgorsky, and Monica A. Pollock; They have over 40 years of collective experience in the fine arts.

Work shown: A wide range of fine art photography.

Artists represented: 20. 80% male/20% female. 75% are in museum collections.

Work by: Alfred Eisenstaedt: renowned father of photojournalism; Mick Rock: leading photographer of rock and roll; Margaret Bourke-White: *Life* magazine photographer; Howard Schatz: photographer of contemporary dance; and Richard Corman: portrait photographer of athletes.

Markets: 90% individual, 10% corporate. **Prices:** $500-20,000.

Advertising: *New York Times, Photo Guide,* and *Gallery Guide.*

Selection process: Artists should mail slides, photos, resumé, and SASE.

Response time: 1-2 months.

SPERONE WESTWATER

121 Greene St., 10012.
T: (212) 431-3685.
F: (212) 941-1030.
E: info@speronewestwater.com
W: www.speronewestwater.com
Year established: 1975.

Member of the Art Dealers Association of America.

Open: Tues.-Sat. 10-5; Summer: Call for hours.

Owners: Angela Westwater and Gian Enzo Sperone. **Director:** David Leiber.

Work shown: Contemporary European and American painting, sculpture and work on paper.

Work by: Malcolm Morley; Guillermo Kuitca; Jonathan Lasker; Richard Long; Bruce Nauman; Cy Twombly; and Mimmo Paladino; among others.

Markets: Individual, corporate, and museum.

SPRING STUDIO

64 Spring St., 10012.
T: (212) 226-7240.
Year established: 1992.
Owner/Director: Minerva Durham.

Open: Tues.-Fri. 11-5 and by appointment.

Work shown: Contemporary figurative art in all media. **Annual exhibitions:** 11.

Work by: Robert Haisley: gouache; Mariann Nowack: pastel; Robert Harding: charcoal and pencil; and Charles H. Connelly: oil painting; among others.

Prices: $200-2,000.

Focus/Mission: To promote figurative study with daily figure drawing workshops offered at reasonable prices. To encourage appreciation for the work of underexposed figurative artists.

Selection process: Artists who participate in the drawing workshops are shown in the group exhibitions. Artists should be prepared to pay some exhibition expenses.

SRAGOW

73 Spring St., 3rd floor, 10012.   **T:** (212) 219-1793.
Call for hours.   **Year established:** 1974.
Owner/Director: Ellen Sragow, previously worked in a museum.
Work shown: Representational and Abstract Art, and American Art from the 1930's and 1940's. Abstract Expressionist Prints, Mexican Prints, paintings, works on paper, sculpture, and works by African-American artists. 95% are in museum collections.
Work by: Elizabeth Catlett, prints; Louis Lozowick, prints; Alice Neel: prints; and Reginald Marsh: paintings and drawings; among others.
Collectors: Metropolitan Museum of Art, MoMA, Art Institute of Chicago, Whitney Museum of American Art, and National Portrait Gallery, Wash., D.C.
Advertising: *Gallery Guide, Journal of the Print World, Art and Auction,* and *Art in America.*
Selection process: We are currently not looking at artists' materials.

STALEY-WISE

560 Broadway, 3rd floor, 10012.   **T:** (212) 966-6223.
F: (212) 966-6293.   **W:** www.staleywise.com
Open: Tues.-Sat. 11-5.   **Year established:** 1981.
Owners/Directors: Etheleen Staley and Taki Wise.
Work shown: 20th Century Fine Photographic Prints.
Photography by: Louise Dahl-Wolfe; David LaChappelle; Horst; Herb Ritz; Bert Stern; and Cecil Beaton; among others.
Selection process: We are currently not looking at new artists' materials.

SWISS INSTITUTE

495 Broadway, 3rd floor, 10012.   **T:** (212) 925-2035.
F: (212) 925-2040.   **E:**info@swissinstitute.net
W: www.swissinstitute.net   **Open:** Tues.-Sat. 11-6.
Year established: 1986.   **Size:** 2,000 sq. ft.
Owners: Board of Trustees.   **Director:** Marc-Olivier Wahler.
Work shown: Contemporary art in all media by Swiss artists from NY and Switzerland.
Work by: Lori Hersberger; Ugoron Dinone; Urs Fischer; and Olaf Breuning; among others.
Annual exhibitions: 2 solo/4 group.   **Advertising:** *Artforum.*
Focus/Mission: The Swiss Institute is a non-profit cultural arts center, established to promote a cultural dialogue between Switzerland and the U.S.
Selection process: 70% of the artists are selected from referrals and slides, 15% from exhibitions, and 15% from publications.

JOHN SZOKE EDITIONS

591 Broadway, 2nd floor, 10012.   **T:** (212) 219-8300.
F: (212) 966-3064.   **W:** www.johnszokeeditions.com
Open: Mon.-Fri. 9-6.
Year established: 1974.
Size: 2 floors 4,000 sq. ft.
Owner/Director: John Szoke, collector.
Work shown: Contemporary Graphics, from Realism to Abstract, using traditional techniques as well as advanced technology: linocut, lithographs, silkscreen, etching, aquatint, mezzotint, collographs, and other forms. **Prices:** $100-35,000.
Artists represented: 30. 50% male/female. Ages 25-70. All origins. All of the artists are in museum collections.
Work by: James Rizzi; Berton Morris; Richard Haas; Janet Fish; Peter Milton.
Collectors: U.S. Dept. of State, Whitney, MoMA and The Brooklyn Museum.
Markets: Individual, corporate, and museum.
Annual exhibitions: Primarily group shows on a revolving basis.
Advertising: *ARTnews, Gallery Guide*, and *The New York Times*.
Selection process: Most artists are selected from referrals. Artists should mail slides, cover letter, biography and SASE. No calls, please.

TEAHOUSE

The New York Open Center, 83 Spring St., 10012.
T: (212) 219-2527 x 135.   **F:** (212) 219-1347.
E: nyocreg@aol.com   **W:** www.opencenter.org
Open: Mon.-Fri. 9:30-4, Sat. and Sun. by appointment.
Year established: 1992.
Gallery Director: Maria Rodriguez.
Owner: The Open Center, a not-for-profit holistic learning center.
Size: Downstairs: 900 sq. ft. Upstairs: 900 sq. ft.
Work shown: Paintings and photography that reflect the mission of the Open Center. The emphasis is on many diverse cultures, with a focus on humanity by artists from all origins.
Annual exhibitions: 6.
Selection process: Artists should mail slides, biography, artist statement and cover letter to Maria Rodriguez. **Response time:** 3 months.

SUSAN TELLER

568 Broadway, #103 A, 10012.   **T:** (212) 941-7335.
Open: Tues.-Sat. 11-6; Summer by appointment.
Year established: 1988.
Director: Susan Teller.
Work shown: Drawings, paintings and prints of the 1930's and 1940's by American artists.
Work by: Hananian Harari; Fannie Hillsmith; Dorothy Dehner; and Will Barnet; among others.

TERRAIN

Aesthetic Realism Foundation, 141 Greene St., 10012.   **TEL:** (212) 777-4490.
FAX: (212) 777-4426.
WEB SITE: www.AestheticRealism.org; www.TerrainGallery.org
Open: Wed.-Sat. 2-5 and by appointment.
Owner: Aesthetic Realism Foundation, an educational, not-for-profit foundation.
Coordinators: Carrie Wilson, et. al.   **Work shown:** All styles and media.
Work by: Chaim Koppelman; Dorothy Koppelman: prints; Marcia Rackow:
paintings; Louis Dienes: Len Bernstein: photographs; among others.
Focus/Mission: Exhibitions with commentary are based on this historic principle
stated by Eli Siegel, founder of Aesthetic Realism: "All beauty is a making one of
opposites, and the making one of opposites is what we are going after in
ourselves." The Foundation's public seminars, dramatic presentations, classes in
the visual arts, poetry, music, acting, education, marriage, anthropology, and
individual consultations, show how the questions of life are answered in the
technique of art.
Selection process: Artists may submit work on loan or as a contribution for the
Gallery's exhibitions. Call or write for details.
Additional information: The Foundation presents art talks, free to the public, the
first Sat. of every month at 2:30, and by appointment for organizations and schools.

JACK TILTON

49 Greene St., 10013.   **T:** (212) 941-1775.
F: (212) 941-1812.   **W:** www.jacktiltongallery.com
Open: Tues.-Sat. 10-6.   **Year established:** 1983.
Owners: Jack Tilton and Susan Hort.   **Director:** Susan Maruska.
Size: 2,500 sq. ft.
Work shown: Abstract painting, figurative drawing, conceptual sculptures and
installation art; performance art.
Artists represented: 12. 70% male/30% female. All ages.
Origins: U.S. and Europe. All of the artists are in museum collections.
Work by: Nicole Eisenman: installation, painting, drawing, collages and
assemblages, whose subjects and their treatment is at once serious and hilarious;
David Scher: paintings, drawings, photos, ceramics, and films; and Huang Wong
Ping: Contemporary Chinese installation; among others.
Collectors: All major museums.   **Prices:** $1,000-25,000.
Annual exhibitions: 11.   **Advertising:** *Gallery Guide.*
Focus/Mission: To promote emerging artists from around the world.
Selection process: 98% of the artists are selected from professional referrals,
2% are selected from art seen in exhibitions or artists' studios. We are currently
not looking for new artists.

THE TIME IS ALWAYS NOW

476 Broome St., 10013.   **T:** (212) 343-2424.
F: (212) 966-2408.   **W:** www.ttian.com
Open: Tues.- Sun. 11-7.
Year established: 1994.   **Size:** 16,000 sq. ft.
Director/Owner: Peter T. Tunny, investment banking.
Associate Director: Janique Svedberg.

continued

Work shown: Contemporary work on canvas, paper, and wood, in addition to photography.
Artists represented: 15. **Ages:** 25-90. All origins. 50% of the artists are in museum collections.
Work by: Victor Hayden and Peter Tunney.
Collectors: Metropolitan, Guggenheim, Stedelijk Museum, Louisiana Museum.
Markets: 90% individual, 10% corporate. **Prices:** $200-100,000.
Advertising: *Gallery Guide* and *The New York Times*.
Focus/Mission: To show artists with an intense passion for the expression of life. The work here is alive. We feel the creative process is as important as the end product; the wetter the paint the better. The art in this gallery is honest with messages and images people can mentally access and really feel.
Selection process: Artists should mail slides, resumé, and SASE.
Response time: 2 months.

VISUAL ARTS

137 Wooster St., 10012.   **T:** (212) 598-0221.
F: (212) 529-9149.   **W:** www.schoolofvisualarts.edu
Open: Tues.-Sat. 11-6. Closed Aug. 23-Sept. 1.
Year established: 1978.   **Size:** 1,700 sq. ft.
Director: Francis di Tommaso. **Assistant Director:** Mura Smith.
Work shown: Contemporary art by current School of Visual Arts students. All traditional media in addition to video, computer art, and site-specific installations.
Collectors: Princeton University Museum and Prudential. **Prices:** $5-5,000.
Annual exhibitions: 16 group.
Advertising: *Gallery Guide*, *Village Voice*, and *New York Review of Books*.
Focus/Mission: As a division of the School of Visual Arts we present the work of advanced students of SVA in a professional gallery context and provide an opportunity for the NY community to view the work of our most talented students.
Selection process: Artists are selected by prominent faculty curators. Applications are not accepted. Exhibitors are currently enrolled students only.
Additional information: We show the work of the up-and-coming. Previous artists have included Keith Haring, Kenny Scharf and Rodney Alan Greenblat.

VORPAL

459 West Broadway, 5th floor, 10012.   **T:** (212) 777-3939.
F: (212) 777-5030.   **E:** vorpalsoho@msn.com
W: www.vorpalgallery.com   **Open:** Tues.-Sat. 11-6.
Year established: 1962.   **Owner:** Muldoon Elder.
Associate Director: Gabriella G. Herrera.   **Work shown:** All styles and media.
Artists represented: 50+. 50% male/female. All ages. **Origins:** 30 countries.

Work by: Hamaguchi: mezzotints; James Ensor: paintings, watercolors and etchings; M.C. Escher: drawings, lithographs, woodcuts, and mezzotints; Picasso: paintings, drawings and prints; and Sabastian Matta: paintings and work on paper; among others.
Collectors: Metropolitan, MoMA, Art Institute of Chicago, and Syntex.
Focus/Mission: A wide cross section of Contemporary and Master artists.
Selection process: The gallery is always interested in looking at new artists' work. Artists may send slides, photographs, resumé, and SASE. **Response time:** 1-4 months. Artists may call 3 weeks after sending materials for a response.

IN THE SPIRIT OF COOPERATION

There are many artist-owned, artist-operated, non-profit cooperative galleries in NYC. Some examples are Amos Eno, Bowery, Ceres, Phoenix, Pleiades, NoHo, SoHo 20, and Ward-Nasse.

WARD-NASSE

178 Prince St., 10012.
F: (212) 334-2095.
W: www.wardnasse.org
Year established: 1970.
Executive Director: Harry Nasse.
Work shown: All styles and media.
Annual exhibitions: 10 group.

T: (212) 925-6951.
E: markherd@www.wardnasse.org
Open: Tues.-Sat. 11-6, Sun. 1-6.
Owner: Non-profit cooperative gallery.
Artists represented: 360.
Prices: $50-9,000.
Advertising: *Gallery Guide* and *ARTnews*.

Focus/Mission: To give all artists a chance to exhibit and develop their work, regardless of age, gender, race or beliefs. We offer a free referral consultant service, providing curators, collectors and other art professionals direct contact with artists.

Selection process: 95% of artists are selected from slides and other materials sent to gallery, 5% of the artists are selected from art seen in exhibitions or artists studios. Artists may mail slides, photos, biography, prices, SASE.

Response time: 2 weeks.

Fees: Artists are expected to pay for their framing. 15% commission. U.S. members: $40 annual membership fee, $50 outside U.S., $10 additional website or $50/ft. monthly rental fee. We offer group advertising opportunities.

WESTWOOD

578 Broadway, First Floor, 10012.
F: (212) 226-5442.
E: info@westwoodgallery.com
Year established: 1995.

T: (212) 925-5700.
W: www.westwoodgallery.com
Open: Tues.-Sat. 11-6.
Size: 5,000 sq. ft.

Owners: James Cavello, President, owner of Corporate Art Associates, Ltd., art consultant, appraiser and collector for over 20 years; and Margarite Almeida, Executive Director, international art consultant.

Assistant Directors: Dana Altman and Karen Mulqueen.

Work shown: All media. Contemporary to traditional painting and sculpture. Vintage and Contemporary photography. Multi-media and installation. Estate and corporate collections. **Markets:** Individual, corporate, and museum.

Prices: $1,500-1,000,000. **Artists represented:** 12. 60% are in museum collections. **Origins:** Europe, U.S., Asia, Russia, South America.

Work by: Ben Freeman: mixed media; Igor Gorsky: painting; Chet Kempczynski: monotype and painting; Jeff Maron: sculpture; and Karen Mulqueen: painting; among others.

Annual exhibitions: 7 solo/1 group/3 international art projects.

Advertising: *Art in America, Gallery Guide, ARTnews,* among others.

Focus/Mission: To exhibit outstanding artwork and establish ongoing relationships with collectors, corporations, museums and institutions. To provide art and educational services.

continued

Selection process: 60% of the artists are selected from referrals, 20% from slides, 20% from art in exhibitions and artists studios. Artists should mail slides or photographs of new work in a theme format, include biography, resumé, prices, SASE. **Response time:** 4-6 weeks.

Additional information: We also exhibit estate and corporate collections.

WALTER WICKISER

568 Broadway, #104B, 10012.   **T:** (212) 941-1817.
F: (212) 625-0601.   **Open:** Tues.-Sat. 11-6.
Year established: 1992.   **Owner:** Walter Wickiser.
Work shown: Contemporary paintings. **Size:** 1,100 sq. ft.
Artists represented: 18 artists. 40% male/60% female.
Work by: Yuran Lee: paintings; Sei Arimori: paintings; Yumi Yohyama: paintings; Stephen Pace: paintings; March Avery: paintings; among others.
Focus/Mission: To intermingle American and Asian-American painters in order to create a dialectic between the Expressionist aesthetics of these cultures.
Selection process: Artists should approach the gallery only if they have an established following. The gallery sometimes exhibits the work of emerging artists during the Summer.

WOODWARD

476 Broome St., 5th floor, 10013.   **T:** (212) 966-3411.
F: (212) 966-3491.   **E:** wdwrdgllry@aol.com
W: www.artnet.com   **Size:** 1,800 sq. ft.
Open: Tues.- Sat. 11-6, and by appointment; Aug. by appointment.
Year established: 1994.
Owners: John Woodward and Kristine Woodward, background in art and public relations for over 17 years.
Director: John Woodward.
Work shown: Contemporary painting and sculpture by emerging, mid-career and established artists. Also secondary market, from Old Masters to Contemporary.
Artists represented: 15, from U.S., Italy and Sweden.
Work by: Margaret Morrison: Surreal, Figurative, still life and portrait painter; Cristina Vergano: Contemporary painter who combines art historical background to create neo icon, modern paintings; Drew Roth: Self-taught, Neo-Expressionist, Neo-Primitive painter/sculptor; Susan Breen: Surrealist; and Mark Mastroianni: Abstract Expressionist sculptor who works in bronze and stone; among others.
Markets: Individual, corporate, and museum.
Prices: $450 and above.
Annual exhibitions: 6 solo/ 2-3 group.
Advertising: *Gallery Guide, Art in America*, and *ARTnews*.
Selection process: 8% of the artists are selected from professional referrals, 2% from slides sent to the gallery, 90% from art seen in exhibitions or artists studios. Artists should mail slides, photos, resumé, prices, and SASE. We review artists' materials in Jan., Feb. and March. We charge a $20 processing fee.
Requirements: Artists must maintain professional behavior and discipline.

THE WORK SPACE

96 Spring St., 8th floor, 10012.   **T:** (212) 219-2790.
F: (212) 925-0690.   **W:** www.dnclaw.com
Open: Mon.-Fri. 10-5, Sat. 1-5; Summer: Tues.-Fri. 12-5.
Year established: 1994.   **Size:** 1,200 sq. ft.
Owners: Dologenos, Newman and Cronin law firm.
Director: Lesley Heller.
Work shown: Contemporary art.   **Prices:** $500-10,000.
Annual exhibitions: 6 group.   **Advertising:** *Gallery Guide.*
Focus/Mission: To present exhibitions by emerging as well as established artists that cannot easily be mounted at a regular gallery. The exhibitions are frequently curated by artists.
Selection process: Artists should mail slides, resumé, and SASE.

YORK'S SHONA

99 Spring St., 10012.   **T:** (212) 431-7444.
F: (212) 431-6644.   **E:** mail@yorksshona.com
Open: Mon.-Sun. 11-7.
Owner: York's International, an art and antique company.
Director: Michael Ahuja, owner of York's International.
Year established: 1991.   **Size:** 1,500 sq. ft., two levels.
Annual exhibitions: 5.   **Advertising:** *Gallery Guide.*
Work shown: Contemporary and Primitive African art.
Work by: Henri Munyaradzi: stone sculpture; Nicholas Mukomberanwa: stone sculpture; Moses Masaya: stone sculpture; and Joseph Muzoando: stone sculpture; among others.
Selection process: We are currently not seeking new artists.

DAVID ZWIRNER

43 Greene St., 10013.   **T:** (212) 966-9074.
F: (212) 966-4952.   **W:** www.davidzwirner.com
Open: Tues.-Sat. 10-6.
Year established: 1993.   **Size:** 3,600 sq. ft.
Owner: David Zwirner, previously worked at Brooke Alexander gallery.
Director: Angela Choon.
Work shown: All ranges of Contemporary art.
Prices: $1,000-100,000.
Artists represented: 11. Ages: 20-50's.
Origins: Predominantly from U.S., Canada and Europe. All of the artists are in museum collections.
Work by: Franz West: sculpture; Jason Rhodes: installation; Stan Douglas: video installation, multi-media; Diana Thater: video installation; and On Kawara: painting; among others.
Focus/Mission: We show good artists, keeping an eye open for new talent.
Selection process: Most of the gallery's artists come through referrals. Artists should not submit slides at this time.

WHAT IS THEIR FOCUS OR MISSION STATEMENT?

We asked owners of galleries and directors of alternative exhibition spaces for the motivation behind the art they select.

ABC NO RIO
"To connect socially engaged artists with political activists."

RICHARD ANDERSON FINE ARTS
"To present art work that deals with the question of beauty."

ART IN GENERAL
"To focus on the development of contemporary art that is often under-represented in larger museum and commercial gallery structures."

AXIS
"This is the only gallery in the U.S. specializing in South African art, providing an "axis" between South Africa and other points on the globe."

CHRISTINEROSE
"To exhibit art that reflects quality, enthusiasm, advance thinking, and unique, contemporary vision."

EXIT ART
"To be dedicated to transcultural, multi-disciplinary explorations of contemporary art issues."

SHERRY FRENCH
"The gallery exhibits Contemporary American Realism where the emotional or psychological element is heightened."

This kind of diversity is what we love about New York City!

LOWER EAST SIDE
EAST VILLAGE
GREENWICH VILLAGE
WEST VILLAGE
UNION SQUARE
GRAMERCY PARK

AMERICAN INDIAN COMMUNITY HOUSE

"As a Native American art organization we feel it is important to educate the non-Native public about our issues and culture. It is also important to nurture upcoming talent as well as established artists."

A + A COMPANY (ART IS SUPERIOR)

13 Stanton St., 10002.
T: (212) 226-1716.
F: (212) 473-9395.
E: info@antantics.com
W: www.antantics.com
Open: Tues.-Sat. 12-6.
Year established: 1995.
Size: 750 sq. ft.
Work shown: All styles of two- and three-dimensional media.
Artists represented: 5.
Prices: $20-5,000.
Work by: Nzomo: photography, installation and word art, and sculpture; Maria Chen: photography and fashion design; among others.
Annual exhibitions: 9.
Selection process: We are currently not looking for new artists.

ABC NO RIO

156 Rivington St., 10002.
T: (212) 254-3697.
W: www.abcnorio.org
Open: Check web site for hours.
Year established: 1980
Owner: Non-profit organization.
Work shown: All media.
Director: Steven Englander, Associate Editor of *Autonomedia*.

Focus/Mission: To connect socially engaged artists with political activists. This is an art center that includes 4 stories of fine art exhibition space and performance space that presents the musical and spoken word. **Annual exhibitions:** 10-12. **Selection process:** Artists should submit proposals for group shows that match the organization's philosophy. **Response time:** Up to 3 months.

A CLEAN, WELL-LIGHTED PLACE

363 Bleecker St., 10014.   **T:** (212) 255-3656.
F: (212) 691-0245.   **E:** acwlp@msn.com
Open: Tues.-Sun. 12-5.   **Size:** 700 sq. ft.
Directors: Thomas and Marjorie Martinelli Printer; Artist.
Work shown: Contemporary original prints including intaglio, lithography, woodcut, mezzotint, and relief prints.
Artists represented: 32 male/20 female. **Ages:** 30-70. Predominantly American. 90% of the artists are in museum collections.
Work by: David Hockney: lithographs; Robert Motherwell: lithographs, intaglio; Susan Rothenberg: intaglio, woodcut; Sean Scull: woodcuts; and Brice Marden: etchings; among others.
Annual exhibitions: 3 group.
Collectors: MoMA, Metropolitan, Whitney, and The Walker Museum.
Prices: $65-30,000.
Focus/Mission: To educate people about contemporary prints by exhibiting graphics of the highest quality and the broadest range that appeal to us.
Selection process: 90% of the artists approach us directly, 5% from exhibitions, 5% from publications. Artists are advised to visit the gallery first, then call for an appointment for a portfolio review.
Requirements: Technical expertise and artistic excellence.

A GALLERY @ WARES FOR ART

421 Hudson St., #220, 10014.
T: (212) 989-7845.   **F:** (212) 627-1797.
E: info@waresfor art.com   **W:** www.waresforart.com
Open: By appointment.   **Year established:** 1994.
Owners/Directors: Bitty O'Sullivan-Smith: Jewelry designer, and Phil Demise Smith: Artist and poet.
Work shown: European and American Folk, Outsider, Self-taught, and Contemporary art in stone, wood, canvas, works on paper, ceramic and metal; also jewelry and glass art.   **Artists represented:** 20.
Work by: Phil Demise Smith: works on paper, canvas, metal and wood; Gerard Sendrey: works on paper; Charles Keeling Lassiter: early works on paper and canvas; Ross Broder: mixed media on canvas and wood; and Ody Saban: painting on canvas and paper.
Prices: $15-2,000.
Annual exhibitions: There is an ever-changing permanent collection. The owners also curate exhibitions in other venues in N.Y. and throughout the U.S.
Advertising: *Raw Vision* and *Folk Art* magazine.
Focus/Mission: We are dedicated to keeping art and all the expressions of our delicate civilization in its proper perspective, placing spiritual value above monetary value.
Selection process: The gallery is currently not accepting unsolicited materials.

PHILIP ALAN

30 Avenue B,10009. **T:** (212) 529-6160.
E: gjw171@aol.com **Year established:** 1990.
Open: Thurs.-Sat. 1-6, Sun. 12-5, and by appointment.
Owner/Director: Gail Stein Weinstein, landlord. This is a tenant-landlord collaboration.
Work by: Calmix; Valerie Constantino; James Romberger; Takuami Fukanaga; and Jill Waterman; among others.
Focus/Mission: To have good relationships between tenants and the landlord.
Additional information: The gallery also presents performances.

AMERICAN INDIAN COMMUNITY HOUSE GALLERY & MUSEUM

708 Broadway, 2nd floor, 10003. **T:** (212) 598-0100 ext. 241.
Open: Tues.-Sat. 12-6. **Mailing address:** 404 Lafayette St., 10003.
F: (212) 598-4909. **W:** www.aich.org
Year established: 1980. **Size:** 3,000 sq. ft.
Director: Rosemary Richmond. **Owner:** American Indian Community House.
Work shown: Native American contemporary painting, sculpture, photography, installation, printmaking and video.
Work by: Joanna Osburn-Big Feather: sculpture; Susan Steward: painting; and Duane Slick: Installation; among others.
Collectors: Smithsonian, Brooklyn Museum, Heard Museum, and Whitney.
Prices: $300-30,000.
Annual exhibitions: 5 group. **Advertising:** *Gallery Guide.*
Focus/Mission: As a Native American art organization we feel it is important to educate the non-Native public about our issues and culture. It is also important to nurture upcoming talent as well as established artists. There are only 10 galleries owned and operated by Native Americans that exhibit Native American contemporary art in the U.S. This is the only Native-owned and operated gallery in the NY area. Slide lectures and artists' talks are presented on a monthly basis.
Selection process: Artists should mail 20 slides, letter and SASE and follow up by phone. We require the avant-garde in Native American art, and artists who follow through on commitments. **Fees:** There are some exhibition expenses.

ANSONIA WINDOW SHOW

442 Sixth Ave., corner of Sixth Ave. and West 10 St., 10011. **T:**(212) 942-6218.
Owner: Ansonia Pharmacy. **Curator:** Dan Scher.
Open: 24-hour viewing: Front window and side window.
Work shown: Painting, sculpture and photography.
Focus/Mission: To exhibit the best work I can find for sidewalk viewing by the general public. The work is immediately accessible to anyone.
Selection process: Artists should send slides or color prints that best represent their work with SASE. A resumé is not mandatory, but may be included. Mail to Dan Scher, 97 Arden St, #6D, New York, NY 10040. **Response Time:** 1-2 weeks.

APPLE RESTAURANT

17 Waverly Pl., 10003. **T:** (212) 473-8888.
Open: Daily Mon-Thurs. 12-11, Sat. 12-12, Sun. 12-10.
Year established: 1992. **Size:** 3,500 sq. ft.
Owner: Cheuong Nghiem. **Curator:** Jennifer Mulhearn.

continued

Work shown: All styles of painting and photography. **Prices:** $300-15,000.
Artists represented: all origins.   **Annual exhibitions:** 15.
Advertising: *New York Observer* and *New York* magazine.
Selection process: Artists should call Jennifer Mulhearn for an appointment.
Fees: Expenses vary depending on the show, but usually artists pay only a commission on sales.
Additional information: Apple Restaurant has two kitchens: Asian and Vegetarian. There is a private room available for other exhibitions and parties.

ARONSON

66 Fifth Ave., 10003.
T: (212) 229-8987.
F: (212) 229-8975.
Open: Mon.-Fri. 9-9, Sat. 10-6 during school session; Summer: Mon.-Fri. 9-6.
Owner: Parsons School of Design.
Director: Clinton Kuopus.
Work shown: Design and fine arts with an emphasis on international design. Parsons is the largest school of Design in U.S.
Annual exhibitions: 26 installations. Student exhibitions are held in the Spring.
Focus/Mission: The first part of the year focuses on work from the National and International Design and Fine Arts Community in an effort to bring ideas from them to our students. The second half of each season is focused upon our students and graduating seniors as they enter the same community of Artists and Designers.
Selection process: An Exhibition Committee, composed of Parsons faculty and staff members, establishes and reviews policy matters affecting the Exhibition Program. Proposals for exhibitions are submitted to the Director of Exhibitions. Artists should write to Director's office for guidelines.

LUDMILLA BACZYNSKY

12 East 11 St., 10003.
T/F: (212) 260-0924.
W: www.baczynsky.com
Open: By appointment.
Year established: 1995.
Owner/Director: Ludmilla Baczynsky.
Work shown: Contemporary jewelry, functional art in silver and paintings.
Work by: Ludmilla Baczynsky: sculptural silver *objets d'art* and 18k gold jewelry designs.
Prices: $200-10,000.

BARUCH COLLEGE/SIDNEY MISHKIN

135 East 22 St., 10010.
T: (212) 802-2690.
W: www.baruch.cuny.edu/mishkin
Open: Mon.-Fri. 12-5, Thurs. 12-7.
Director: Sandra Kraskin.
Annual exhibitions: 5.
Work shown: 20th Century art in a wide range of media. Historical as well as Contemporary art. This is primarily a teaching gallery as well as a community gallery.
Focus/Mission: To present exhibitions that reflect original scholarship. To also present interdisciplinary and multi-cultural exhibitions.
process: We arrange exhibitions through curators and museum professionals. We do not accept proposals from individual artists.

JAYNE H. BAUM

26 Grove St., 10014.
T: (212) 255-9286.
F: (212) 229-8998.
E: jhbgal@bellatlantic.net
Open: By appointment.
Year established: 1982.

Director: Jayne H. Baum.
Work shown: Contemporary art in all media, focusing on photography.
Work by: Nigel Rolfe; Ellen Carey; Alain Fleischer; Marco Breuer; and Don Freeman; among others.

BLUE HERON ART CENTER

123 East 24 St., 10010.   **T:** (212) 979-5000.
F: (212) 979-8144.   **Open:** Tues.-Sun. 1-5.
Year established: 1999.   **Curator:** Patrick Christiano.
Owner: Blue Heron Art Center, a non-profit theater. The Center meets a critical need for performance, rehearsal and office space used by a variety of cultural and artistic organizations. Exhibitions are held in the theater lobby.
Work shown: Contemporary art in all media by established and emerging artists.
Annual exhibitions: There is an ever-changing display of art work.
Focus/Mission: To challenge the mind, stir the emotions and focus on provocative issues and ideas – the universal qualities of the human experience relevant to today's world: freedom and oppression, politics, racism, and the individual and society.
Selection process: Artists should mail slides resumé and SASE or call (212) 979-5000 extension 13.
Additional information: The Blue Heron Arts Center is the first new arts complex dedicated to theater, arts education and live performance to be built under one roof in New York in over 20 years. Heron Theatre is known for its issue-oriented, award-winning productions and education programs.

BRAINARD

279 East 10 St., 10009.   **T:** (212) 533-3143.
E: bookmonk@earthlink.net   **W:** www.colophon.com/gallery/b.carey
Open: By appointment   **Year established:** 1997.
Owner/Director: Brainard Carey.
Work shown: This is a space in which long-term endurance projects are performed and documented. This is Carey's studio and gallery in which he shows current work as well as long-term projects, including his lavishly illustrated *Book of Job*, a 70 lb., handwritten manuscript, 27" x 21" x 6" which contains 100 paintings.

BROADWAY WINDOWS

Broadway at 10 St., 10003.   **T:** (212) 998-5751.
Administrative offices: 80 Washington Square East, 10003.
F: (212) 998-5752.   **W:** www.nyu.edu/pages/gallery
Contact: Ruth D. Newman.   **Open:** 24 hour viewing.
Work shown: Site-specific work in 5 window spaces.
Annual exhibitions: 10.
Selection process: Artists should call and request a detailed prospectus. They should be prepared to submit slides and/or photographs, resumé, and a site-specific proposal.

WHAT'S IN A NAME?

In recent years many gallery owners have broken from tradition and becoming more imaginative in naming their venues...
A Taste of Art, Ch'i, Fresh Art, Fuse, Goliath, Eye Beam,
Eye Storm, Eye Wash, Fish Tank, and Pierogi, to name a few.

BRONFMAN CENTER GALLERY AT NEW YORK UNIVERSITY

7 East 10 St., 10003 **T:** (212) 998-4121.
F: 212.995.4774. **W:** www.nyu.edu/bronfman/gallery
Open: Mon- Fri 9-5, Sun 12-8. **Year established:** 1997
Size: 224 sq. ft. **Owner:** New York University.
Director/ExhibitionCoordinator: Undergraduate Fellows.
Annual exhibitions: 5, at least one student group show.
Artists exhibited: Students and professionals – including but not limited to NYU students, faculty, and alumni.
Work shown: Contemporary art, usually with Jewish themes.
Focus/Mission: Exhibitions explore the influence of Judaism and other religions or cultures in the field of visual art. The gallery also offers a venue for students to gain experience as curators in a non-traditional exhibition space. Here, the visual arts become a lens through which we focus on the cultural, intellectual, and spiritual implications of Judaism in a contemporary context.
Selection process: Artists should contact the gallery by fax, email or phone. Exhibitions are planned on a year-to-year basis but submissions are accepted anytime.
Additional information: The Gallery is a working space in NYU's Hillel house, providing a unique synthesis of art and Judaism. The gallery and the community are not separate entities, and related events represent the interests of both. Additional events include workshops, slide presentations, and artist lectures.

BURDEN

Aperture Foundation, 20 East 23 St., 10010. **T:** (212) 505-5555.
F: (212) 979-7759. **W:** www.aperture.org
Open: Mon-Fri. 9:30-5:30. **Director:** Sara Wolfe
Year established: 1982. The Aperture Foundation was established in 1956.
Owner: Aperture Foundation, a non-profit publisher of books and periodicals relating to photography. It is involved in the direct sale of limited editions and select prints.
Work shown: Photography by Classic and Contemporary masters, as well as younger, emerging photographers. The gallery also directs an extensive program of traveling exhibitions, collaborating with major museums around the world.

COMMON GROUND

113 West 10 St., 10011. **T:** (212) 989-4178
F: (212) 989-0573. **Open:** Mon.-Fri. 12-7:30, Sat. 11:30-6:30
Year established: 1979. **E:** thecommonground@att.net
Owner/Director: Rolando Reyes. **Background:** Artist and collector.

Markets: Individual, corporate, museum. **Annual exhibitions:** 2-3.
Advertising: *American Indian Art Magazine, Tribal Art Magazine* and *Gallery Guide.*
Selection process: Artists are selected from professional referrals, from slides and other materials sent to the gallery, and from art seen in exhibitions, publications and artists' studios. Artists should mail slides, photographs, biography, resumé, artist's statement, prices and SASE. Artists should call for an appointment. **Response time:** 1 month.
Fees: Artists are expected to pay for framing and advertising.

COOPER CLASSICS COLLECTIONS

137 Perry St., 10014.
E: info@cooperclassiccars.com
Open: Mon.-Fri. 9-6, Sat. 10-6.
Year established: 2001.

T: (212) 929-3909.
W: www.cooperclassiccars.com
Size: 1,500 upstairs; 2,500 downstairs.
Owner/Director: Elliot Cuker.

Cooper Classics specializes in classic and exotic automobiles.
Work shown: Contemporary art. Painting and photography, and classic cars that are presented as sculpture.
Work by: Irene Neal: painting; Roy Lerner: painting; Randy Bloom: painting; Robert Welsh: photography; and Mick Rock: photography; among others.

THE COOPER UNION GALLERIES:

HEWITT, 41 Cooper Square

ARTHUR A. HOUGHTON JR., 7 East 7 St.

HERB LUBALIN STUDY CENTER OF DESIGN & TYPOGRAPHY, 7 East 7 St.

GREAT HALL, 7 East 7 St.

HUMANITIES, 51 Astor Place, Cooper Square, 10003.
T: Business Office, (212) 353-4140, School of Art: (212) 353-4200.
W: www.cooper.edu   **Open:** Mon.-Fri. 12-7, Sat. 12-5.
Director: Robert Rindler, Dean.
Work shown: Painting, drawing, lithography, and graphic design.
Annual exhibitions: 2-6 solo/2-6 group.
Advertising: *The New York Times, New York,* and *The New Yorker.*
Focus/Mission: The exhibitions are arranged in relationship to the work of the educational program.

CORNELIA STREET CAFE

29 Cornelia St., 10014.   **T:** (212) 989-9319.
W: www.corneliastreetcafe.com
Open: Sun.-Thurs. 10-midnight, Fri.-Sat. 10-1:30 am.
Year established: 1977.
Owner/Director: Bob Siegler.
Work shown: Paintings.
Annual exhibitions: 10-12.
Selection process: Artists should call Bob Siegler for an appointment.

CORPORATE ART PLANNING

27 Union Square West, Suite 407, 10003. **T:** (212) 242-8995.
F: (212) 242-9198. **E:** corporateartplanning@e-architect.com
W: www.corporateartplanning.com **Open:** Mon.-Fri. 9-5.
Director: Maureen McGovern. **Work shown:** Contemporary art.
Work by: Alberto Allegri; Suzanne Brookens; Caroline Corey; Beatrice Coron; and Bonnie Dobson; among others.
Focus/Mission: To provide full-service exhibition planning, art acquisition, corporate identity, and digital media programs.

CRICKET HILL

900 Broadway, 10003. **T:** (212) 529-5615.
Open: Tues.-Fri. 11-5 and by appointment.
Year established: 1993. **Size:** 1,500 sq. ft.
Owners/Directors: Stephanie Perell, former museum educator and corporate art consultant; and Nan Perell.
Work shown: Contemporary British painting.
Artists represented: 35. **Annual Exhibitions:** 4-5.
Work by: Alan Parker; Helen Flockhart; Peter Thomson; Alexander Gardner; and Alexander Guy; among others.
Prices: $300-30,000. **Advertising:** *Art in America* and *Art News*.
Focus/Mission: To introduce American collectors to Contemporary British painting.
Selection process: British artists should send materials. The gallery prefers to receive information by email. Slides and photographs, resumé and SASE are also accepted by mail.
Additional information: The gallery hosts events with British cultural groups.

EROTICS

41 Union Square West, #1011, 10003. **T:** (212) 633-2241.
F: (212) 633-6406. **E:** eroticrarites@erogems.com
W: www.eroticrarities.com **Open:** By appointment.
Year established: 1975. **Size:** 300 sq. ft.
Owner/Director: Edie Solow. **Background:** Buyer, merchandising.
Work shown: Contemporary Realism and Antique Erotica in a broad spectrum.
Prices: $20-20,000.
Artists represented: 19th century artists; some contemporary artists. All origins.
Work by: Doug Johns: sculpture in many materials; Olivia: silkscreen and paintings; Betty Dodson: painting and drawing; among others.
Focus/Mission: The objective of the gallery is to establish a forum for promising contemporary artists as well as to exhibit erotica of historical significance.
Selection process: We are currently not accepting new artists.

14 SCULPTORS

332 Bleecker St., Ste. K35, 10014. **T:** (212) 966-5790.
E: 14sculptors@14sculptors.com **W:** www.14 sculptors.com
Open: By appointment. **Owner:** Non-profit membership organization.
Work shown: Sculpture. **Origin:** Members include sculptors from Europe, Asia and diverse regions of the U.S.
Work by: Allan Cyprys; Esther A. Grillo; Caroline Hallas; Donald Kapela; and Bernice Sokol Kramer; among others.

Focus/Mission: To provide the opportunity to members and invited artists to exhibit original sculpture on a regular basis; to meet regularly with other professionals for discussion and artistic exchange; and to actively stimulate dialogue between the community, the artists and critical review.

FRESH ART

135 West 4 St., 10012.
F: (212) 254-0791.
W: www.freshartnyc.org
Year established: 2001.
T: (212) 254-9156.
E: wendy@freshartnyc.org
Open: Wed.-Sat. 1-7.
Size: 350 sq. ft.
Owner: New York City non-profit organization that represents and promotes NYC artists with special needs. **Director:** Wendy Werlick.
Work shown: All styles, media and handcrafted items.
Work by: Mary Johnson; Bill Oleksa; Paul Stehle; Charles Dudley and Barbara Simon; among others.
Selection process: Artists should respond to call for entries throughout the year. Artists are found through social services. Artists with special needs may call for information.

FUSE

93 Second Ave., 10003.
W: www.fusegallery.com
Year established: 2002.
Open: Tues.-Sat. 12-5:30.
T: (212) 777-7988.

Size: 550 sq. ft.
Director: Michael McGrane.
Work shown: New-Brow-Wacky-Surreal-Innovative sculpture, painting, drawings, mixed media.

GALLERY AT THE ASIAN / PACIFIC /AMERICAN STUDIES PROGRAM & INSTITUTE

269 Mercer St., Suite 609, 10003. **T:** (212) 992-9653.
E: apa.studies@nyu.edu **W:** www.apa.nyu.edu/gallery
Open: Mon.-Fri. 10-5, Sat. by appointment.
Year established: 1996. **Annual exhibitions:** 2-3.
Work shown: Work by emerging and established artists of Asian / Pacific descent.
Focus/Mission: Founded in response to student interest, combined with NYU's commitment to global excellence, the Institute is focused on community and intercultural studies within a broad, rigorous international and comparative framework.
Selection process: Exhibitions are often organized in collaboration with A/P/A Artist-in-Residence program.

GALLERY B AKA ATM

170 Avenue B, 10009.
E: william@gallery-b.com
Open: Thurs.-Sun. 12-6.
T: (212) 375-0349.
W: www.gallery-b.com
Director: William Brady. MFA, School of Visual Arts. He has been involved with the JPMorgan Chase Corporate Art Collection since 1995.

continued

Work shown: Contemporary art. Painting, photography, and work on paper.
Work by: Peter Gourfain; Mary Beth Edelson; Michael Ferris; Chris Gaston; and Tom Behrens; among others.
Focus/Mission: Based on the knowledge that art can make a difference in one's life.

GALLERY E 3

47 East 3 St., 10003. **T:** (212) 982-0882.
E: art@e3gallery.com **W:** www.e3gallery.com
Open: Thurs. and Fri. 3-7, Sat. 2-6; Summer: Sat. 2-6.
Owner/Director: Mary Ann Fahey, former photographer and real estate broker.
Work shown: Primarily Contemporary fine art photography (predominantly black and white print), some Contemporary painting and mixed media.
Prices: $250-600. **Artists represented:** 50% male/female.
Ages: 24-45. All origins. **Size:** 300 sq. ft
Work by: John Morse: collage; Jean Loughton: photography; Patricia O'Maille: illustration; and Rita Rivera: photography; among others.
Annual exhibitions: 6 solo/3 group. **Advertising:** *Photography in New York*.
Focus/Mission: We are committed to exhibiting the work of professional fine art photographers and visual artists.
Selection process: 75% of the artists are selected from referrals, 25% from slides it receives. Artists should call or check our web site for submission guidelines. They may also mail slides/photographs with resumé and SASE.

GALLERY ONETWENTYEIGHT

128 Rivington St., 10002. **T:** (212) 674-0244.
F: (212) 673-3664. **Open:** Wed-Sat. 1-7
Year established: 1986. **Director:** Kazuko.
Work shown: Contemporary art in all media by artists from all origins.
Annual exhibitions: 10-11.
Work by: Fran Kornfeld: drawing, painting; and Angela Valeria: film, painting.
Focus/Mission: To exhibit unknown artists.

GREENWICH HOUSE POTTERY

16 Jones St., 10014. **T:** (212) 242-4106.
F: (212) 645-548 **W:** www.greenwhichhousepottery
Open: Mon., Thurs., Fri. 10-1:30, 2:30-5:30; Tues. 10-1:30, 2:30-8; Wed. 3-8; and Sat. 10-11, 3-6. **Year established:** 1970.
Size: 425 sq. ft. **Owner:** Non-profit gallery.
Director: Elizabeth Zawada.
Work shown: Contemporary ceramics, functional art, and sculpture.
Annual exhibitions: 6.
Work by: Exhibitions have featured: Peter Gourfain; Annabeth Rosen; Greg Pitts; and Malcolm Davis; among others.
Advertising: *Gallery Guide* and *Ceramics Monthly*
Focus/Mission: This is the only non-profit gallery for ceramics in NYC and is among the handful of galleries that show clay work in NYC.
Additional information: Our exhibitions, like "Artists On Their Own", are especially significant in supporting new artists and in exposing the New York community to the wealth of undiscovered talent in the ceramic field.

THE CHAIM GROSS STUDIO MUSEUM
*"To foster an understanding of how
working artists live and create.
Gross' studio is still the way he left it."*

GREY ART / NYU
100 Washington Square East, 10003. **T:** (212) 998-6780.
F: (212) 995-4024.   **E:** greygallery@nyu.edu
W: www.nyu.edu/greyart   **Open:** Tues., Thurs., Fri. 11-6, Wed 11-8,
Sat.11-5; Summer: Call for hours. **Year established:** 1975.
Owner: New York University.
Director: Lynn Gumpert.
Deputy Director: Frank Poueymirou.
Assistant to Director: Gwen Stolyarov
Work shown: Photography, painting, sculpture, film, video, installation, and
performance art.
Annual exhibitions: 4-5 group. One of the exhibitions is usually a traveling
exhibition. Other exhibitions often come from other institutions.
Selection process: Proposals from institutions and individual artists should be
submitted in writing, accompanied by slides, biographies and SASE to the
attention of the Director. Mail to Grey Art, 100 Washington Square East.
Response time: 1-6 months.

THE CHAIM GROSS STUDIO MUSEUM,
526 LaGuardia Pl., 10012.   **T:** (212) 529-4906.
F: (212) 529-1966.   **E:** grossmuseum@earthlink.net
Open: Tues.-Fri. 12-5 and by appointment.
Size: 2,500 sq. ft.   **Year established:** 1989.
Owner: Renée and Chaim Gross Foundation, Inc.
Director: Renée Gross.
President: Irwin Hersey.
Curator of Collections: April Paul.
Work shown: Permanent collection of 70 years of work by Chaim Gross (1904-
1991), noted for his direct wood carvings of acrobats and other circus performers,
dancers, and women and children. Stone carvings in marble, alabaster and
bronze castings constitute major part of oeuvre, as well. Watercolors and
drawings of fantastic subject matter and suites of prints (lithographs).
Collectors: Metropolitan, National Museum of American Art, Smithsonian,
Whitney, and Hirshhorn.
Focus/Mission: To display, collect, preserve, and interpret the works of art
created by Chaim Gross, to promote in the general public an appreciation of his
art in its historical context, and to foster an understanding of how working artists
live and create. Gross' studio is still the way he left it.
Additional information: The Chaim Gross Archive and Library loans exhibitions
and we mount temporary exhibitions of Gross's work in context of permanent
collections. Historian-guided group tours are available by appointment.

GULF & WESTERN

721 Broadway, Lobby of the Tisch School of the Arts, 10003. **T:** (212) 998-1930.
F: (212) 995-4068.
W: www.nyu.edu/tisch/photo and August.
E: photo.tsoa@nyu.edu
Open: Mon.-Fri., 10-6, Sat 12-5; Closed July and August.
Year established: 1981.
Owner: New York University. administrator/adjunct professor.
Director: Karl Peterson,
Annual exhibitions: 6-7.
Work shown: Photo-based artwork.
Advertising: *Photography in New York.*
Focus/Mission: The gallery exists as part of the University's B.F.A. Photography and Imaging Program. Outside professionals are exhibited as well as graduating seniors' work and annual faculty exhibitions.
Selection process: The artists are selected by a committee. Proposals from artists are reviewed twice a year. **Response time:** months. **Requirements:** Early to mid-career artists. Artists should have their work framed. There is no gallery commission.

HEBREW UNION COLLEGE – JEWISH INSTITUTE OF RELIGION

1 West 4 St., 10012.
W: www.huc.edu
Director: Jean Bloch Rosensaft.
Curator: Laura Kruger.
T: (212) 824-2209.
Year established: 1983.
Open: Mon.-Thurs. 9-5, Fri. 9-3.
Size: 4,500 sq. ft., includes 3 interconnected gallery rooms as well as exhibition space in the general lobby.
Focus/Mission: Exhibitions are the visual extension of the spiritual, cultural and educational life of the College-Institute. They illuminate the 4,000 year-long span of Jewish experience and include fine arts, contemporary craft, folk art, photography and book arts, theater, journalism, archeology, and historical artifacts. The regular presentation of works by contemporary artists expressing Jewish identity and Jewish themes is a priority in exhibition planning.
Selection process: An exhibition committee convenes to review and vote on proposals. Proposals should come from artists whose work contain content that is related to Jewish or Israeli culture, history or concerns. Artists should submit proposal, CV, or artist's statement, and slides, facsimiles, or photographs to Laura Kruger: Curator and Exhibition Committee Chair. **Response time:** Varies. Materials will be returned only by request; the committee prefers to retain proposals for future consideration.
Additional information: Exhibitions usually have an opening reception. There are also opportunities for related lectures, panel discussions, musical or dance programs, depending on the content of the show and the cooperation of the artist.

HERE ART

145 Sixth Ave., 10013.
F: (212) 647-0257.
W: www.here.org
Year established: 1993.
T: (212) 647-0202.
Open: Tues.-Sat. 2-10 pm.
E: hereart@hotmail.com
Size: Main Gallery: 1,200 sq. ft.; Down Under Gallery: 500 sq. ft.
Work shown: Curator driven collaborations between artists, large-scale initiatives by artists; experiments in approach, perspective or new-media, hybrids of media, cultures or professional disciplines; site specific installations and solo projects in development.

Annual exhibitions: 8-10 in each gallery.
Focus/Mission: HereArt is the visual component of HERE, which supports unique viewpoints, brave initiatives, autonomy and collaboration. HEREArt grows opportunities for emerging visual artists.
Selection process: The review panel reviews applications. Artists should visit the web site for details.

AKIRA IKEDA NEW YORK

17 Cornelia St., #1C, 10014.　　**T:** (212) 366-5449.
F: (212) 366-5778.　　　　　　**Open:** By appointment.
W: www.akiraikedagallery.com　**Year established:** 1992.
Owner: Akira Ikeda, background in business.
Chief Liason: Takuma Kanaiwa.
Work shown: Contemporary sculpture, paintings and drawings by American, European and Asian artists.
Artists represented: 45. All of the artists are in museum collections.
Work by: Noriyuki Haraguchi: sculpture; Tomiaki Yamamoto, paintings; and Frank Stella: originals and limited editions; Sandro Chia: paintings; and the Estate of David Smith; among others.
Advertising: *Artforum.*
Selection process: We prefer that artists visit the website and submit a jpeg. Otherwise, artists should mail materials with SASE.

THE JACKLIGHT

208 East 7 St., 10009.　　　　　　**T:** (212) 477-7159.
Open: Wed.-Sat. 12-7, and by appointment.
Year established: 1994.　　　　**Size:** 2,500 sq. ft.
Owner/Director: Walter Fields, painter and film critic.
Work shown: Symbolist and Metaphysical.
Prices: $400-3,000.　　　　　　**Artists represented:** 6-8.
Markets: 80% private, 15% corporate, 5% museum.
Origins: U.S. and Europe. 60% male/40% female.
Work by: Maura Sullivan: photography; Susan Shatter: watercolor; Claire Sabastiani: pen and ink; among others.
Collectors: James Krell, Steven Ettridge, Brooke Adams, and Jon Vorhees.
Annual exhibitions: 5 solo.
Focus/Mission: To show quality painters from New York.
Selection process: Artists should call for an appointment. We want to see the work, not slides. **Requirements:** No mixed media. Size limit: 600 sq. in.
Response time: 2 weeks.

WILMER JENNINGS

219 East 2 St., 10009.　　　　　　**T:** (212) 674-3939.
F: (212) 505-5080.　　　　　　　**Open:** Wed.-Sat. 11-6.
Year established: 1973.　　　　　**Size:** 4,000 sq. ft.
Owners/Directors: Joe Overstreet and Corrine Jennings.
Work shown: African-American Contemporary Art. Ethnic Minority. All media.
Selection process: We review art anytime throughout the year. Artists should mail slides, photographs, artist's statement, resumé and SASE.

KELLY GLASS STUDIO & GALLERY

122 Ave. C., 10009.
Open: Tues.-Sat. 11-7.
Size: 1,800 sq. ft.

T: (212) 677-9480.
Year established: 1995.

Owner/Director: Patti Kelly, stained glass artist and teacher.
Work shown: Stained glass.
Work by: Kathleen Collins: photography; Patti Kelly: stained glass and sculptural lamps; among others.   **Prices:** $25-15,000.
Focus/Mission: To give talented unknown artists the opportunity for exposure in a professional atmosphere.
Selection process: All of the artists are selected from materials sent to gallery. Artists should mail photos, biography, resumé, and SASE, and call for an appointment.
Fees: Artists are expected to pay for framing, advertising, and opening fees. The artists and staff work together as a team, gearing towards a cooperative experience.

KENKELEBA

214 East 2 St., 10009.
F: (212) 505-5080.
Year established: 1973.

T: (212) 674-3939.
Open: Wed.-Sat. 11-6.
Size: 4,000 sq. ft.

Owners/Directors: Joe Overstreet and Corrine Jennings.
Work shown: African-American Contemporary Art. Ethnic Minority. All media.
Selection process: We review art anytime throughout the year. Artists should mail slides, photographs, artist's statement, resumé and SASE.

LA MAMA LA GALLERIA

6 East 1 St., 10003.
Open: Thurs.-Sun. 1-6.

T: (212) 505-2476.
Size: 2,500 sq. ft.

Owner: Non-profit organization.
Directors/Curators: Merry Geng and Cesar Llamas.
Work shown: All styles and media.
Annual exhibitions: 14.   **Advertising:** *Gallery Guide*.
Selection process: Artists should mail slides, resumé and SASE anytime from September-January. Shows are scheduled 18 months in advance.

LOWENHERZ

The Camera Club of New York, 853 Broadway, 2nd floor, 10003.
T: (212) 260-7077.   **W:** www.cameraclubofnewyork.org
Year established: The Organization was established in 1884.
Owner: Not-for-profit visual arts organization.
Annual exhibitions: 5-6.
Focus/Mission: Dedicated to the art and science of photography.
Artists represented: There are 200 members.
Selection process: Membership is limited. Applicants may meet with members of the Admissions Committee for an interview.
Additional information: The Camera Club has seven fully equipped darkrooms for members' use 24 hours a day, 365 days of the year. It also has a conference area and a fully equipped professional studio, and conducts seminars, lectures, and field trips.

MALLET FINE ART LTD

220 Park Ave. South, Suite 9-B, 10003. **T:** (212) 477-8291.
F: (212) 673-1051.   **E:** JMallet@ixpres.com
Size: 2,000 sq. ft.   **W:** www.artregister.com/malletfineart
Open: By appointment. Closed in August.
Year established: 1982.   **Owner:** Jacques R. Mallet, MBA.
Work shown: 20th Century master works in oils, drawings, watercolors and sculpture.
Work by: Gerd Sonntag: painting; Ouattara: pastel and mixed media; Calder: mobiles; Johns, lithographs; and Lipchitz: drawing; among others.
Collectors: MoMA, Whitney, and Guggenheim.
Markets: Individual and museum.   **Prices:** $1,000-5 million.
Focus/Mission: The preservation of cultural heritage through the promotion and sale of 20th century master works.
Selection process: 50% of the artists are selected from referrals, 50% from slides sent to the gallery. Artists should mail letter, 20 slides, and SASE.
Response time: 1 month.

CURT MARCUS

2 Fifth Ave., Suite 17N, 10011.   **T:** (212) 226-3200.   **F:** (212) 941-6365.
Open: Mon.-Fri. 10-6; Summer: Call for hours.
Year established: 1986.   **Owner:** Curt Marcus.
Size: 5,000 sq. ft.   **Annual exhibitions:** 7.
Work shown: Contemporary American and European painting, sculpture, photography and installation in all media.
Artists represented: 14. All of the artists are in museum collections.
Work by: Richard Misrach: photography; Barbara Ess: photography; Richard Pettibone: painting and sculpture; and Bruce Conner: varied media; among others.
Prices: $600-175,000.   **Collectors:** Metropolitan, Whitney, Walker Art Center, and Modern Art Museum of Fort Worth.
Advertising: *Artforum* and *Gallery Guide*.

NATIONAL ARTS CLUB

15 Gramercy Park South, 10003.   **T:** (212) 475-3424.
F: (212) 475-3692.   **Open:** Daily 10-5.
Year established: 1898.   **Owner:** Non-profit organization/private club.
Director: Janice Fremolaro.   **Work shown:** Varied.
Size: Four gallery spaces.   **Annual exhibitions:** Approximately 40.
Focus/Mission: To support and embrace all of the arts disciplines.

continued

Selection process: Artists should contact Janice Fremolaro for an application. Submit slides for jury and pending acceptance dates for shows are scheduled. The committee meets two times a year to judge new members. Call to inquire about deadlines. **Fees:** There are space rental fees.

NEW YORK STUDIO SCHOOL

8 West 8 St., 10011.　　　　　　**T:** (212) 673-6466.
F: (212) 777-0996.　　　　　　**W:** www.nyss.org
Open: Mon.-Sat. 10-6; closed in August.
Year established: 1967.　　　　**Size:** 2 rooms, each 350 sq. ft.
Work shown: Painting, drawing and sculpture.
Annual exhibitions: 2-3 solo/4 group. October Benefit Exhibition features historical masterworks. Other exhibitions are organized by guest curators, or feature artworks of faculty and alumni.
Advertising: *Gallery Guide* and *New York Observer*.
Focus/Mission: To serve its students and the serious community with shows of historical and contemporary interest.
Selection process: Artists should mail slides and a written proposal. Curated and group shows are welcome. There are some exhibition expenses.
Additional information: The building is the original site of the Whitney Museum and the former home of Gloria Vanderbilt Whitney.

THE OLD PRINT SHOP

150 Lexington Avenue, 10016.　　**T:** (212) 683-3950.
F: (212) 779-8040.　　　　　　**E:** info@oldprintshop.com
W: www.oldprintshop.com　　　**Open:** Tues.-Fri. 9-5, Sat. 9-4. Summer:
Mon-Thurs. 9-5, Fri. 9-4.　　　　**Year established:** 1898.
President: Robert Newman.
Work shown: American fine prints and antiquarian maps through 1950.
Work by: Isabel Bishop; Stuart Davis; Joe Jones; Diego Rivera; and Levon West; among others.
Prices: $50-190,000.　　　　　**Annual exhibitions:** 8-9.
Advertising: *Antiques Magazine* and *New York Observer*.
Additional information: The bookstore has an inventory of reference books, illustrated books, color plate books and artist books.

ONE GREAT JONES

1 Great Jones St., 10012.　　　　**T:** (212) 460-8456.
F: (212) 460-8644.　　　　　　**W:** www.onegreatjones.com
E: galleries@onegreatjones.com　**Open:** By appointment.
Year established: 1996.　　　　**Director:** John Campione.
Work shown: Primarily Minimal prints and drawings. **Annual exhibitions:** 9.
Selection process: The gallery is not accepting unsolicited materials at this time.

ANGEL ORENSANZ FOUNDATION CENTER FOR THE ARTS

172 Norfolk St., 10002.　　　　　**T:** (212) 529-7194.
F: (212) 529-1864.　　　　　　**E:** orenfound@aol.com
W: www.orensanz.org　　　　　**Open:** Tues.-Sun. 1-6.
Size: 4,000 sq. ft. and 750 sq. ft.　**Year established:** 1992.
Owner: Arbol 172 Corporation.　**Director:** Al Orensanz, Ph. D.

Background: Sociology Professor and art writer.
Assistant Director: Michael Coltman.
Work shown: All styles of contemporary art, mostly experimental, in all media.
Artists represented: All origins.   **Prices:** $300-6,000.
Annual exhibitions: 5 solo/7 group.
Advertising: *Village Voice, Time Out,* and *The New York Times.*
Focus/Mission: To present art work that is exploratory in nature – mixed media, visual arts combined with performing arts.
Selection process: Artists are selected by an exhibition committee. Artists should send 20 slides and materials with SASE anytime. **Requirements:** Art work that has a difficult market or venue.
Fees: The galleries are rented for exhibitions. The 4,000 sq. ft. gallery may be rented for $2,200-2,500 per day, which includes lights and sound, mailing list, and opening reception. The 750 sq. ft. gallery may be rented for $700 per day. There is no gallery commission.

PACIFICO FINE ART
The gallery plans to relocate to Chelsea. Call for new location.
T: (212) 462-2709.   **F:** (212) 462-2646.
W: www.pacificoart.com   **Open:** Tues.-Sat. 11-6 and by appointment.
Year established: 1999.   **Size:** 2,000 sq. ft.
Owner: Vincent Pacifico.   **Background:** Art collector and entrepreneur.
Director: James Pernotto.
Work shown: A very eclectic range of Contemporary art in all media.
Work by: David Opdyke; Vincent Pomilio; Jim Conti; Jessica Miller; and Kaoritlaruki; among others.
Annual exhibitions: 10-12.
Prices: $400-20,000.
Focus/Mission: To show the best in contemporary art of young and mid-career artists in addition to rediscovering deceased artists.
Selection process: The Director looks at materials on Thurs. 11-1. Artists should call Wed. to confirm.

PARSONS SCHOOL OF DESIGN EXHIBITIONS
2 West 13 St., 10011.   **T:** (212) 229-8987.
F: (212) 229-8975.   **Open:** Mon.-Fri. 9-9, Sat. 10-6.
Director: Clinton Kuopus.
Work shown: Exhibitions are related to design and fine arts.
Annual exhibitions: 26. Student exhibitions are held in the spring.
Focus/Mission: Parsons is the largest school of design in the U.S. The first part of the year focuses on work from the National and International Design and Fine Arts Community in an effort to bring ideas from them to our students. The second half of each season is focused upon our students and graduating seniors as they enter the same community of Artists and Designers.
Selection process: An Exhibition Committee, composed of Parsons' faculty and staff members, establishes and reviews policy matters affecting the Exhibition Program. Proposals for exhibitions are submitted to the Director of Exhibitions. Artists should write to the Director's office for guidelines.

PEN & BRUSH CLUB, INC.

16 East 10 St., 10003.　　　　**T:** (212) 475-3669.
F: (212) 475-6018.　　　　**W:** www.penandbrush.org
Open: Tues.-Sun. 2-6.　　　**Size:** 3 rooms totaling 1,000 sq. ft.
Year established: 1892.　　　**Owner:** The Pen & Brush Club, the oldest
organization of professional women in the arts in the U.S.
Members have included: Eleanor Roosevelt; Faith Baldwin; and Pearl S. Buck.
President: Liz Cenedella.　　　**Work shown:** Contemporary paintings,
graphics, mixed media, sculpture, collage, and crafts.
Prices: $275-20,000.
Artists represented: 200 female artist members. Ages 20-80. All origins.
Annual exhibitions: 7 solo/9 group.　**Advertising:** *Gallery Guide*.
Focus/Mission: The purpose is educational: To establish high standards in the
various arts and to stimulate and develop the professional activities of its
members and to enrich cultural diversity of the neighborhood.
Selection process: 95% of the artists are selected from referrals; 5% from slides
it receives. Artists must be professional, and recommended by 2 members, juried
by 5 members, then approved by the governing board. Artists should submit a
proposal, slides and resumé to the attention of the Pen and Brush Chair.
Fees: Initiation fee: $15. Annual fees: $150. Non-member solo shows: $950/wk.
Additional information: Activities also include prose, poetry, and play writing
workshops, lectures, films, slide presentations, art demonstrations, and vocal and
instrumental concerts. A monthly bulletin is published.

SCOTT PFAFFMAN

35 East 1 St., 10003.　　　　**T/F:** (212) 353-8415.
E: pfaffman@interport.net　　**Open:** By appointment.
Year established: 1996.　　　**Size:** 650 sq. ft.
Owner/Director: Scott Pfaffman, sculptor and curator.
Work shown: New Media – photography, film, and video.
Work by: John Buchanan: video; Charles Burns: photography; Molly Romero:
photography; Richard Mock: printmaker; and Mitch Corber: mixed media; among
others.　　　　　　　　　　**Prices:** $200-2,000.
Selection process: Artists should call and arrange for an appointment.
Additional information: Scott Pfaffman is curating exhibitions throughout the
U.S. in universities and alternative spaces outside the gallery.

PHOTO CENTER,

721 Broadway, 8th floor, Tisch School of the Arts, 10003.
T: (212) 998-1930.　　　　**F:** (212) 995-4068.
Open: Mon.-Fri. 10-5, Sat 12-5. Closed July and August.
Year established: 1981.　　　**Owner:** New York University.
Director: Karl Peterson.　　　**Work shown:** Photo-based work.
Annual exhibitions: 6.　　　**Advertising:** *Photography in New York*.
Focus/Mission: As part of the University's B.F.A. Photography and Imaging
Program, to offer exhibitions to professionals, graduating seniors and faculty.
Selection process: The artists are selected by a committee. Proposals from
artists are reviewed twice a year.　**Response time:** months.
Requirements: Early to mid-career artists.　**Fees:** Artists are expected to pay for
framing their work. There is no gallery commission taken on work sold.

PROGRESSIVE ART GALLERY AT THE WELL

85 Fifth Ave., 5th floor, 10003.　　．**T:** (212) 620-0220.　**F:** (212) 352-1881.
Open: By appointment.　　　**Year established:** 2002.
Owner/Director: Lucy Stylianou, studied art in Russia and owned a software business.
Work shown: Contemporary art, all styles and media.
Origins: International.　　**Annual exhibitions:** 10.
Selection process: Artists should send slides, photographs, resumé and SASE.

P.S. 122

150 First Ave. (Entrance is 409 East 9 St.), 10009. **T:** (212) 228-4249.
Open: Thurs.-Sun. 12-6; Closed in Aug.
Year established: 1978.　　　**Size:** 700 sq. ft.
Owner: Painting Space 122 Association, a not-for-profit alternative space.
Director: Susan Schreiber, previously owner of a gallery in SoHo, and curator.
Work shown: Contemporary art by under-recognized artists in all media.
Work by: Exhibitions have featured Leslie Bostrom: paintings; Michael Ashkin: installations; Steven Brower: small scale installations; Wendy Small: small sculptures in mixed media; among others.
Annual exhibitions: 8 two-person/2 group.　**Advertising:** *Gallery Guide.*
Focus/Mission: To showcase the work of emerging artists.
Selection process: 80% of the artists are selected by jury, 20% by the gallery director. For an application artists should send SASE to "Exhibitions" or "Studio." Individual and group proposals are accepted. A jury makes selections during April-May.
Additional information: P.S. 122 maintains 4 studio spaces that rotate on a yearly basis. Artists wishing to apply for the project spaces may send SASE to "Project Spaces." Applications are available in February.

ROBIN RICE

325 West 11 St., 10014.　　　　**T:** (212) 366-6660.
F: (212) 366-6664.
Open: Mon.-Wed. by appointment, Thurs.-Sat. 1-7, and Sun. 1-6.
Year established: 1990.
Owner/Director: Robin Rice, 20 years experience as commercial and fine art photographer.
Artists represented: 20.
Work shown: Photography – ethereal, surreal, dark but beautiful – to evoke emotions. Many of the photographers use a lot of turn-of-the-century processes such as platinum, cyanotypes and sepia toned images.
Work by: Andrea Gentl: 8x10" contact prints; Craig Barber: 8x20" platinum/pinhole camera; Mark Sink: black and white Diana camera; Jose Picayo: Cuban work; among others.
Collectors: The Brooklyn Museum, New York Public Library, Allen and Co., and Flemming, Zulack and Williamson.　**Prices:** $450-2,000.
Focus/Mission: I promote and believe in artists who are alive, doing extremely high-quality work. Collectors, you be the judge: Be smart and buy it before it costs a million dollars.
Selection process: Artists should submit slides, photographs, resumé and SASE. Robin Rice will respond if interested.

RIVINGTON ARMS

102 Rivington St., 10002. **T:** (646) 654-3213.
Open: Tues.-Fri.11-6; Sat.- Sun., 12-6.
Year established: 2002. **Size:** 1,000 sq. ft.
Owners/Directors: Melissa Bent and Mirabelle Marden, both have BA from Sarah Lawrence College.
Work shown: Contemporary art in all media. The gallery primarily exhibits the work of artists who are still in school or recent graduates.
Prices: $10 - $4,000. **Annual exhibitions:** 10.
Selection process: Artists should send slides, photographs, resumé and SASE.

ROSENBERG

NYU Dept. of Art and Art Professions, 34 Stuyvesant St., Barney Building, 10003.
T: (212) 998-5700. **F:** (212) 995-4320.
W: www.nyu.edu./education/art/rosen.html
Open: Mon.-Fri. 9-6, Sat.& Sun. 12-6. **Size:** 200 sq. ft.
Director: Mary Anne Santos. **Work shown:** All styles and a broad spectrum of media. **Annual exhibitions:** 10.
Focus/Mission: This is a student gallery within the department of Art and Arts Professions, NYU School of Education. The gallery presents the work of undergraduate and graduate students.

ERNST RUBENSTEIN

The Educational Alliance, 197 East Broadway, 10002. **T:** (212) 780-2300 / 378.
F: (212) 533-2654. **W:** www.edalliance.org
Owner: Non-profit organization and community center.
Year established: 1985. **Size:** 900 sq. ft.
Director of Art School and Gallery: Walter O'Neill.
Work shown: Contemporary art and historical exhibitions related to the Educational Alliance and the Lower Eastside. All media.
Annual exhibitions: 12. Exhibitions have included: Professional Women Photographers; and Figurative Alliance; among others.
Selection process: Artists are selected from referrals or slide submissions. Artists should send photographs, color copies or one sheet of slides, with resumé and SASE, to Walter O'Neil.
Additional information: Classes are offered in photography, ceramics, welding, mold making, oil painting, clay or stone sculpture and other subjects.

RX ART, INC.

1 Astor Pl, #4K, 10003. **T:** (212) 260-8797.
Founder/Executive Director: Diane Brown, former owner of Diane Brown Gallery in Washington, DC and New York, NY.
Focus/Mission: RxArt, Inc. is a not-for-profit organization selects and installs original works of contemporary art in patient rooms, treatment rooms, and public areas of healthcare facilities to enhance the healing environment.

SABA

902 Broadway, 4th Floor, 10010. **T:** (212) 477-7722.
F: (212) 477-8750. **E:** Saba@Sabapress.com
W: www.sabapress.com **Open:** Mon.-Fri. 10-6, Sat. by appointment.
Year established: 1996. **Size:** 1,500 sq. ft.

Owner: Marcel Saba, photographer and photojournalist.
Director: Don Standing.
Work shown: Photojournalism with a fine-art slant.
Prices: $400-1,200.
Work by: Antonin Kratochvil; Claudio Edinger; Fabio Sgroi; Chris Buck; and Chris Ranier; among others.
Annual exhibitions: 5 solo/1 group.   **Advertising:** *Photography in New York.*
Focus/Mission: To show the best in contemporary photography from photojournalism to fine art and conceptual.
Selection process: Mail slides, photographs, biography, resumé and SASE. Call for appointment. **Response time:** 2 weeks.

THE SALMAGUNDI CLUB

A Center For American Art, 47 Fifth Ave., 10003.   **T:** (212) 255-7740.
F: (212) 229-0172.   **Open:** Daily 1-5.
Year established: 1871.   **President:** Richard Pionk.
Work shown: All styles, but predominantly representational, in all media.
Artists represented: Over 500 members from all origins. **Ages:** 21 and up.
Annual exhibitions: 15-20. The Club presents 2 non-members shows, 1 non-juried members' show, several juried members' shows, and 8 annual auctions.
Focus/Mission: To advance art in all media, to aid artists in exhibiting their work, and to help emerging artists present their work in a professional gallery.
Selection process: Artists seeking membership should request a member's sponsorship application. Artists need sponsorship and exceptional talent.
Additional information: The Scholarship Program is available to artists ages 21-30. The Junior Program is available to artists and non-artists, ages 30-35

SAVACOU

240 East 13 St., 10003.   **T:** (212) 473-6904.
E: savacou@webspan.net   **W:** www.savacougallery.com
Open: Tues.-Sat. 10-6.   **Year established:** 1985.
Owner/Director: Loris Crawford.
Work shown: African-American art, and art from the Caribbean and Latin America.   **Artists represented:** 15-20.
Work by: James Denmark: collage; Frank Morrison: collage and painting; George Wilson: painting; Carl Davis: fresco on board; and Leroy Campbell: collage; among others.   **Prices:** $500-5,000.
Annual exhibitions: 6.   **Advertising:** *Amsterdam News.*
Focus/Mission: To show emerging and mid-career artists who are traditionally locked out of the mainstream.
Selection process: Artists should send slides, photographs, resumé and SASE.
Response time: 2 weeks.

KENNY SCHACHTER CONTEMPORARY

14 Charles La., 10014.   **T:** (212) 807-6669.
W: www.rovetv.net.   **Open:** Tues.-Sat. 10-6.
Owner/Director: Kenny Schachter, lawyer, and writer for *Tema Celeste* and *Art Investor.*
Work shown: Contemporary paintings, sculpture, installation and video by international artists.   *continued*

Work by: Lisa Ruyter; Sanford Biggers; Graham Gillmore; Susan Smith-Pinelo; and Rachel Harrison; among others.

Prices: $1,000-21,000.   **Annual exhibitions:** 10.

Focus/Mission: To present art in an entirely new architectural context which is the first departure from the white cube in 60 years.

Selection process: Artists should send slides, photographs, resumé and SASE

Additional information: The gallery was designed by Vito Acconci.

SCHOOL OF VISUAL ARTS EAST SIDE

214 East 21 St., 2nd floor, 10010.   **T:** (212) 592-2145.

F: (212) 592-2095.   **W:** www.sva.edu.

Open: Mon.-Thurs. 9-8, Fri. and Sat. 9-5.

Director: Francis DiTommaso.

Associate Director: Rachel Gugelberger.

Work shown: All styles and media.

Prices: $100-1,000.

Artists represented: Full-time students of SVA, from all origins.

Annual exhibitions: 60.

Advertising: *Gallery Guide* and *Time Out.*

Selection process: Exhibitions are juried by student committees. Artists should submit 10-15 slides according to the deadlines which are posted by the gallery.

Response time: 6 weeks. There is no gallery commission.

Requirements: Artists must be full time students at SVA.

SENIOR & SHOPMAKER

21 East 26 St., 2nd floor, 10010.   **T:** (212) 213-6767.

F: (212) 213-4801.   **E:** gallery@seniorandshopmaker.com

W: www.seniorandshopmaker.com

Year established: 1988.

Open: Tues.-Sat. 10-6; Summer: Mon.-Fri. 10-5:30.

Owners: Betsy Senior and Laurence Shopmaker.

Work shown: American and European Contemporary paintings, sculpture and photography. Contemporary prints and works on paper.

Artists represented: Siah Armajani; John Hilliard; Robert Lobe; Georgia Marsh; Tim Maul; and Ellen Phelan; among others.

Collectors: MoMA, Whitney, Walker Art Center, and Minneapolis Institute.

Annual exhibitions: 3 solo/3 group.

Advertising: *Art in America, On Paper* and *Artforum.*

SWANN

104 East 25 St., Suite 635, 10010. **T:** (212) 254-4710.

F: (212) 970-1017.   **E:** swann@swanngalleries.com

W: www.swanngalleries.com

President: George S. Lowry.

Open: Mon.-Fri. 10-6. Call for Sat. hours.

Work shown (in auction): Rare and antiquarian books; photographs; prints; drawings; watercolors; decorative posters; autographs; manuscripts; maps and atlases.

Additional information: Call to obtain their newsletter, brochure and to order catalogues for auctions.

TALWAR

108 East 16St., 10003 T: (212) 673-3096.   F: (212) 673-3097.
E: mail@talwargallery.com W: www.talwargallery.com
Open: Tues.-Sat. 11-6. Year established: 1995.
Owner: Depak Talwar.
Work shown: Contemporary art in all media.
Work by: Zarina Bhimji; and Allan DeSouza; among others.
Annual exhibitions: 7.
Selection process: The gallery is not currently looking for new artists.

TATTOO SEEN

163 W. 4 St., 10014. T: (212) 691-3852
Open: Mon.-Sat., 12-10. Year established: 2000.
This is a graffiti tattoo parlor. Size: 600 sq. ft.
Owners/Directors: Michael Hong and Seen, known as The Godfather of Graffiti.
Work shown: Graffiti, paintings.
Annual exhibitions: 3-4.
Selection process: Graffiti artists can contact Michael Hong.

TOMPKINS SQUARE

New York Public Library, 331 East 10 St., 10009. T: (212) 228-4747.
Open: Library hours are Mon. 10-6, Tues. and Wed. 12-8, Thurs. 10-6, Fri. 12-6 and Sat. 1-5. Call for gallery hours.
Size: 900 sq. ft.
Branch Librarian/Exhibition Contact: Hara Seltzer.
Work shown: All styles of painting and photography.
Selection process: Artists should send color xerox prints and/or slides, resumé, and SASE to Hara Seltzer.
Requirements: Preference is given to artists from the downtown Manhattan area.

TRIBES

285 East 3 St., 10009. T: (212) 674-3778.
F: (212) 388-9813. E: info@tribes.org
W: www.tribes.org Open: Daily 7am-6 pm.
Year established:1992. Size: 700 sq. ft.
Owner: Steve Annon
Director of Photography: Dora Espinosa.
Director of Painting/Sculpture: Mary S. Chen.
Work shown: Contemporary paintings, drawings, art installation, photography, video and computer art.
Work by: David Hammons; Julio Gonzales; Alice Ziness; Lorenzo Pace; and Susan Yung; among others.
Prices: $150-15,000.
Focus/Mission: To show artists who don't have the opportunity to show in the mainstream. To provide opportunities for all artists.
Annual exhibitions: 12.
Advertising: *Gallery Guide.*
Selection process: Artists should contact the gallery by phone. An appointment will be made and the work will be reviewed.

HEALTHY COMPETITION

*Washington Square East Gallery, at New York University,
hosts an annual "Small Works Competition" in January.
It is open to all artists and is juried by leading art professionals.
Juried competitions are also presented by Pleiades Gallery,
SoHo 20 Gallery, A.I.R Gallery, the Camera Club, and
National Academy Museum, among others.*

UNION SPACE STUDIO

32 Union Square East, #1018, 10003.   **T:** (212) 979-2809.
F: (212) 777-0607.   **E:** unionspace@aol
Open: By appointment.   **Year established:** 1996.
Owner: Gene Wisniewiski, artist.
Work by: Gene Wisniewiski: Surrealist paintings, collages, and drawings. The artist also does portraiture and illustrations by commission. Occasionally the artist invites other artists to exhibit their work in the studio.

VERLAINE

10 Riving ton St., 10002.
T: (212) 614-2494.   **F:** (212) 777-0607.
Open: Mon.-Sat. 5 pm-closing.   **Year established:** 2001.
Owner: Gary Weingarten.
Verlaine is a Vietnamese cocktail lounge with changing exhibitions.
Work shown: Contemporary art in all media.
Selection process: Artists should call and arrange an appointment.

DIANE VILLANI EDITIONS

271 Mulberry St., 10012.   **T:** (212) 925-1075.
E: staff@villanieditions.com   **W:** www.villanieditions.com
Open: By appointment.
Year established: 1992.
Owner: Diane Villani.   **Director:** Amy Wilson.
Work shown: Prints: etchings, silk screen prints, and lithographs.
Prices: $300-10,000.
Work by: Michelle Stuart; Christo; Alison Saar; Lesley Dill; and Suzanne McClelland; among others.
Collectors: MoMA, Philadelphia Museum, and Chicago Art Institute.
Focus/Mission: We are the publishers of American Contemporary Prints.
Selection process: We are currently not seeking any new artists.

VISUAL ARTS MUSEUM

209 East 23 St., 10010.   **T:** (212) 592-2144.
F: (212) 592-2095.   **W:** www.sva.edu.
Open: Mon., Tues., Wed., Fri., 9-6:30,Thurs. 9-8, and Sat. 10-5.
Owner: School of Visual Arts.
Director: Francis DiTommaso.   **Associate Director:** Rachel Gugelberger.

Work shown: All styles and media by artists from all origins.
Prices: $100-1,000.
Annual exhibitions: 8.
Advertising: *Gallery Guide* and *Time Out.*
Selection process: Exhibitions are selected by invitation by the Board of Directors.

WALDEN

9 Clinton St., 10002.   **T/F:** (212) 533-4121.
E: postpost@usa.net   **W:** www.postpost.net
Year established:1999.   **Size:** 300 sq. ft.
Open: Fri., Sat., Sun. 12-6. Closed in July and August.
Owner/Director: Robert Walden.
Background: BFA Painting. Former Assistant Director in Atlanta, GA gallery.
Work shown: Everything from video to painting and drawing to multi-media installation.
Work by: Elizabeth Zawada; Robert Lansden; James Cullinane; and Dennis Bellone; among others.
Prices: $200-10,000.
Focus/Mission: I seek to explore issues and ideas, both social and artistic, that impact contemporary society by exhibiting the work of provocative local, national, and international artists.
Annual exhibitions: 6.
Selection process: Artists should send slides or photographs or CD-ROM, resumé, prices, and artist's statement with SASE.
Response time: 3-6 months.
Requirements: Artists who pay particular attention to both the visual and conceptual in their work. Artists who display a high level of craftsmanship and professionalism. The owner looks for beauty, humor, subtly and the sublime. Most of all, he looks for provocative, interesting ideas.

WASHINGTON SQUARE EAST

80 Washington Square East, 10003. **T:** (212) 998-5747.
F: (212) 998-5752.
W: www.nyu.edu/pages/gallery
Open: Tues. 10-7, Wed. and Thurs. 10-6, Fri. and Sat. 10-5.
Owner: New York University.
Director: Dr. Marilyn Karp.   **Associate Director:** Ruth D. Newman.
Work shown: All styles and media.
Size: 8 galleries.
Annual exhibitions: 8-10 solo/1-2 group.
Advertising: *Gallery Guide* and *Photography in New York.*
Focus/Mission: To serve primarily as a teacher gallery, as part of NYU's Art Dept., Art and Arts Professions. To exhibit thesis work of Art Dept. graduate students.
Additional information: We host an annual "Small Works Competition" in January, open to all artists in any medium and juried by leading art professionals.

WASHINGTON SQUARE WINDOWS
"Site-specific art in 3 windows that offer 24-hour viewing."

WASHINGTON SQUARE WINDOWS
80 Washington Square East, 10003.　**T:** (212) 998-5748.
F: (212) 998-5752.　**W:** www.nyu.edu/pages/gallery
Work shown: Site-specific art in 3 windows that offer 24-hour viewing.
Selection process: Artists should call and request a prospectus. Artists will be required to submit slides and/or photographs, resumé, and a site-specific proposal.

WESTBETH
55 Bethune St., 10014.　**T:** (212) 989-4650.
W: www.westbeth.org　**Year established:** 1967.
Open: Sat. and Sun. 2-6. Call to confirm and for weekday hours.
Owners: Westbeth Artists Residence Council. This is an artist-run gallery.
Size: 5,000 sq. ft.　**Work shown:** Contemporary paintings, works on paper, sculpture, computer-generated and mixed media. Curated exhibitions of resident and non-resident artists.
Ages: 25-70 multi-ethnic, multi-cultural artists. 35% of the artists are in museum collections.
Work by: Marion Lane: painting and sculpture; Tom Shooter: painting; Anita Steckel: mixed media; Beverly Brodsky: painting; and Athos Zacharias: painting; among others.
Collectors: Metropolitan, MoMA, Whitney, and Guggenheim.
Prices: $175-10,000.
Annual exhibitions: 6 solo/6 group.
Advertising: *Gallery Guide.*
Focus/Mission: To exhibit art by our artist residents and invited guests. The gallery is run for, by and about artists, and is community-based. All curatorial and planning decisions are made by artists.

ZORA
37 East 1 St., 10003.　**T:** (212) 254-6575
W: www.zoraonline.com　**E:** zora@rcn.com
Open: Tues.-Sun. 12-7.　**Year established:** 1999.
Owner: Bushra Gill.　**Background:** Artist and fashion designer.
Work shown: This is a fashion boutique where occasionally art exhibitions are presented.
Selection process: If artists are interested in showing their work they may email or call Bushra Gill.

CHELSEA
SOUTH CHELSEA
MEAT PACKING DISTRICT

13-29 Street – West of Fifth Avenue

CENTER FOR BOOK ARTS
"The Center ensures that the ancient craft of the book, that containter which preserves the knowledge and ideas of our culture, remains a viable and vital part of our civilization."

ACA

529 West 20 St., 5th floor, 10011.   T: (212) 644-8300.
F: (212) 644-8306.   E: info@acagalleries.com
W: www.acagalleries.com
Open: Tues.-Sat. 10-5:30. Summer: Tues.-Fri. 10-5:30.
Year established: 1932.   **Owner/Director:** Jeffrey Bergen.
Member of the Art Dealers Association of America.
Work shown: American Contemporary art, 19th and 20th Century American and European painting, drawings and sculpture.
Work by: Benny Andrews; Joseph Cornell (The Family Collection); George McNeil (estate); Sidney Goodman; Grace Hartigen; and Faith Ringgold; among others.
Annual exhibitions: 10.   **Advertising:** *The New York Times.*
Focus/Mission: The gallery specializes in American Art from 1875 to the present.
Selection process: Artists are selected as a result of referrals, publications, and gallery or museum exhibitions. The President makes the selections.
Requirements: A major museum show, and a published monograph.

RACHEL ADLER FINE ART

1200 Broadway, 10001.   T: (212) 308-0511.
F: (212) 308-0516.   W: www.racheladler.com
Open: By appointment.   **Year established:** 1978.
Owner: Rachel Adler.
Work shown: Original early 20th century European Modernist works.
Work by: Archipenko; S. Dulaunay; Leger; and Lipchitz; among others.

ALEXANDER AND BONIN

132 Tenth Ave., 10011.   **T:** (212) 367-7474.
E: gallery@alexanderandbonin.com
W: www.alexanderandbonin.com
Year established: 1995.   **Open:** Tues.-Sat. 10-6
Work shown: Contemporary art.   **Annual exhibitions:** 2 group/5 solo.
Artists represented: 14.   **Work by:** John Ahearn; Robert Bordo;
Eugenio Dittborn; Mona Hatoun; and Paul Thek; among others.
Selection process: We are currently not accepting artists' slides.

ALP

291 Seventh Ave., 10001.   **T:** (212) 206-9108.
E: alp.gal@verizon.net   **Year established:** 2000.
Owner/Director: Maria Anna Alp.   **Annual exhibitions:** 4.
Work shown: Sepcializing in German contemporary painting and sculpture.
Artists represented: 10.
Work by: Willi Bucher; Bruno Griesel; Thomas Moller; Cabriele Von Lutzau; and
Caro Jost; among others.
Selection process: German and German-American artists should send
photographs, resumé, and SASE.

AMERICAN FINE ARTS AT PHAG, INC.

530 West 22 St., 10011.   **T:** (212) 727-7366.   **F:** (212) 727-7467.
Open: Tues.-Sat. 11-6; Summer: Mon.-Fri. 11-6.
Year established: 1983.   **Size:** 2,500 sq. ft.
Owner: Colin de Land, background as an artist.
Work shown: Contemporary art and art by emerging artists in U.S. and Europe.
Artists represented: 15-20.   All origins.
Work by: Monique Prieto: painting; Jeff Elrod: painting; Mary Heilmann: painting;
Renée Green: video installation. Also the estate of Mark Morrisroe: photography;
and the estate of Jimmy Desana; among others.
Collectors: Whitney, MoMA, MoCA (Los Angeles), and Corcoran.
Prices: Varied. Visa and MC are accepted.
Annual exhibitions: 7-10.
Advertising: *Artforum, Flash Art*, and *Frieze*.
Focus/Mission: To exhibit the work and develop careers of emerging artists.
Selection process: Artists are selected from referrals. We do not accept
unsolicited submissions.

ART FIELD

114 West 14 St., 4W, 10011.   **T:** (212) 627-9893.
E: fourteen@thing.net   **W:** www.14thstreetpainters.org
Open: By appointment. Call Mon.-Sat. 11-7.
Director: Craig Killy.
Work by: Rosetta Bentz; Valerie Chirigos; Rupert Stechman; Richard Combes.
Focus/Mission: This is an atelier with exhibition space offering artists exhibitions
and the opportunity with growth in NYC while interfacing in a professional setting
including an international art community and patrons. In its educational capacity
artists learn about diverse materials and approaches to creating art. We offer
figure drawing workshops and have an art slide bank.

ART MACHINE

421 West 14 St., #2 W/R, 10011. **T:** (212) 627-9893.
E: fourteen@thing.net **W:** www.14thstreetpainters.org
Open: By appointment. Call Mon.-Sat. 11-7.
Year established: 1995. **Director:** Craig Killy.
Annual exhibitions: 2.
Work by: Barbara Sansone; Gregg Smith; Mark Brenner; and Thomas Garner.
Focus/Mission: This is an atelier with exhibition space offering artists exhibitions and the opportunity with growth in NYC while interfacing in a professional setting including an international art community and patrons. In its educational capacity artists learn about diverse materials and approaches to creating art. We offer figure drawing workshops and have an art slide bank.

A.R.T. INC. AKA ART RESOURCES TRANSFER

210 Eleventh Ave. #403, 10001. **T:** (212) 691-5956.
F: (212) 741-1356. **E:** artretran@earthlink.net
W: www.artretran.com **Open:** Tues.-Sat. 11-6.
Year established: 1986. **Size:** 3,000 sq. ft.
Owner: Non-profit organization. Publisher of books and limited edition prints.
Director: William Bartman, book publisher.
Work shown: Contemporary art in all media.
Prices: $100-5,000.
Annual exhibitions: 72 in 6 exhibition spaces.
Work by: Bija Celmins; Mike Kelley; Andy Spence; and Laurie Simmons; among others.
Selection process: Artists should bring in a portfolio containing color xeroxes of their work in an easy to read format. No slides, please.
Additional information: ART has a complete art and culture bookstore. Artists, art students, and art professionals receive 25% discount on all books.

ATELIER A/E

323 West 22 St., 3nd floor, 10011. **T:** (212) 620-8103.
F: (212) 620-8106. **E:** peckham@atelierae.com
Owner: Anson Peckham, artist. **Open:** By appointment.
Year established: 1993. **Size:** 1,380 sq. ft.
Work shown: Contemporary art by mature artists in printmaking, watercolor, oil, and sculpture.
Prices: $1,000 and above.
Artists represented: 8. 45% male/55% female. 62% are in museum collections.
Work by: Roberto de Lamonica: printmaker, mostly surreal images in glazed monoprints; Dan Welden: prints and mixed media, also collaborative works; Ellen Peckham: prints and constructions; Ellen Crowley: watercolors; and Mohammed Kahlill: etchings; among others.
Advertising: *Gallery Guide.*
Focus/Mission: To provide an opportunity for experienced and under represented painters, sculptors and printmakers who have created and continue to develop a lifelong *oeuvre* of innovative, beautiful, and masterfully realized works of art.

PAMELA AUCHINCLOSS PROJECT SPACE

601 West 26 St., 12th floor, 10011. **T:** (212) 727-2845.
F: (212) 727-9509. **E:** us@artsms.com.
W: www.artsms.com **Open:** Mon.-Fri. 10-6,
Year established: 1980. **Size:** 1,600 sq. ft.
Owner/Director: Pamela Auchincloss.
Work shown: Abstract, Figurative, and Conceptual painting, photography, and sculpture.
Artists represented: 4. **Annual exhibitions:** 3 solo/3 group.
Origins: U.S. and Europe. All of the artists are in museum collections.
Prices: $3,000-150,000. **Markets:** Individual and corporate.
Focus/Mission: To represent or promote mid-career artists who are seriously committed to an aesthetic style. We coordinate traveling exhibitions world-wide.
Selection process: We are currently not looking for new artists.

AUDIELLO

526 West 26 St., #519, 10001. **T:** (212) 675-9082.
F: (212) 675-8680. **E:** audiello@msn.com
Open: Tues.-Sat. 11-6. **Owner/Director:** Massimo Audiello.
Year established: 1998. **Size:** 600 sq. ft.
Work shown: Contemporary painting, sculpture, photography, installation, and other media.
Prices: $1,000-200,000. **Markets:** Individual, corporate, and museum.
Work by: Ann Sew Hoy: Conceptual photography, murals and sculpture; Luis Tispert: Multi-media, sculpture, photography; Cynthia Sisson: painting; and Warren Isensee: painting; among others.
Annual exhibitions: 7solo/3 group.
Advertising: *Gallery Guide* and *Artforum*.
Focus/Mission: Contemporary/Experimental. Search for the new, guided from the knowledge of the past.
Selection process: 50% of the artists are selected from professional referrals, 50% from art seen in exhibitions, publications and artists' studios. Artists should send materials with SASE. **Response time:** 2 weeks.

AXEL RABEN

526 West 26 St., # 304, 10001. **T:** (212) 691-5958.
F: (212) 691-5850. **E:** info@axelraben.com
W: www.axelraben.com **Open:** Tues.-Sat. 11-6,
Year established: 1996.
Owners/Directors: Catherine Weinstock and Hubertus Raben, both have a background in art history; and Hubertus Raben is a cultural journalist.
Work shown: Contemporary abstract painting and sculpture, work on paper.
Annual exhibitions: 10 solo and 1 group.
Selection process: Artists should call to make an appointment. The owners prefer to meet the artist in person, however, out of town Artists should also mail slides and/or photographs, resumé and SASE.

AXIS

453 West 17 St., 4th floor, 10011. **T:** (212) 741-2582.
F: (212) 924-2522. **W:** www.axisgallery.com
E: axisgallery@aol.com **Open:** Tues.-Sat. 11-6.
Year established: 1997. **Size:** 1,200 sq. ft.
Directors: Lisa Brittan, filmmaker and artist; and Gary Van Wyk, Phd., African Art History, author and scholar.
Work shown: Specializing in art of South Africa.
Work by: Berni Searle: digital multi-media; Rudzani Nemasetoni: mixed media and work on paper; Thabiso Phokompe: mixed media painting; Brett Murray: sculpture and digital media; and Sue Williamson: multi-media.
Annual exhibitions: 8.
Focus/Mission: This is the only gallery in the U.S. specializing in South African art, providing an "axis" between South Africa and other points on the globe.
Selection process: Artists from South Africa should send slides and/or photographs, resumé, and SASE.
Additional information: We sell books related to South African art. There is a library attached to the gallery. We also have an online store.

B & B INTERNATIONAL

601 West 26 St., 14th floor, 10001. **T:** (212) 243-0840.
F: (212) 645-5029. **E:** Bbgallery@aol.com
W: www.bbintl.net
Open: Mon.-Fri. 10-6. Appointments are recommended.
Owners: Nuala and Anne Boylan. **Director:** Tracey Harrison.
Year established: 1997. **Size:** 5,000 sq. ft.
Work shown: Varied styles and media by international artists.
Markets: Individual; corporate; museum.
Prices: $9-100,000.
Work by: Juan Carlos Pallarols: silversmith from Argentina; Carolyn Roumeguerse: ethnic African jewelry; and Marsia Trinder-Holzer: designer of whimsical lamps from North America; among others.
Annual exhibitions: 2. **Advertising:** *Gallery Guide.*
Focus/Mission: To introduce artists and treasures from around the world. We return a percentage of the sales from the objects to charities in their country of origin.
Selection process: All artists are selected from professional referrals. Artists should mail slides or photographs, biography, resumé, artist's statement, prices and SASE. **Response time:** 1 month.
Fees: Artists are expected to pay for framing, advertising, and exhibition fees.

BARBARA BACHNER STUDIO

526 West 26 St., Studio 815, 10001.
T: (212) 675-4323. **E:** blbachner@earthlink.net
W: www.barbara.bachner.com **Open:** By appointment.
Year established: 1995.
Work by: Barbara Bachner: Mixed media painting, sculpture, installation, video, artist's books and some prints. Abstract Expressionism with Realistic photo transfers.

WHERE TO FIND IT

Master Prints at Jim Kempner, New Media at White Box,
Contemporary American Realism at Sherry French, and
Glass Art and Works in Wood at Heller Gallery.

BARNES & NOBLE BOOKSTORE

675 Sixth Ave., 10011. **T:** (212) 727-1227.
Open: Mon-Sat. 9 am-11 pm. Sun. 10 am-10 pm.
Community Relations Manager: Jennifer Stark.
Work shown: Painting, photography and drawings.
Annual exhibitions: 12.
Focus/Mission: To encourage students, as well as emerging and mid-career artists, by showcasing their work.
Selection process: Artists should mail slides, photographs, resumé and SASE to Jennifer Stark. **Response time:** 1-6 months.

BAUMGARTNER

418 West 15 St., 10011. **T:** (212) 633-2276.
F: (212) 633-2695. **E:** baumgartnr@aol.com
W: www.baumgartnergallery.com **Size:** 3,600 sq. ft.
Open: Tues.-Sat. 10-6; Summer: Mon.-Fri. 10-6.
Year established: 1999. Original location: Washington, DC.
Owner/Director: Manfred Baumgartner.
Work shown: Contemporary art in all media.
Work by: Fernanda Gomes: sculpture/installation; and Tim Rollins & K.O.S: painting; Rainer Ganahl, Bruna Esposito, and Walter Obholzer among others.
Annual exhibitions: 8. **Advertising:** *Gallery Guide.*
Selection process: Artists should mail slides, photographs, resumé with SASE.
Response time: 1 week.

DENISE BIBRO FINE ARTS

529 West 20 St., 4th floor, 10011. **T:** (212) 647-7030. **F:** (212) 647-7031
E: bibroart@aol.com **W:** www.dbibrofineart.citysearch.com
Open: Tues.-Sat. 11-5 and by appointment.
Year established: 1992. **Size:** 2,800 sq. ft.
Owner/Director: Denise Bibro: curator, artist representative, arts writer, advisor, and art appraiser.
Assistant Director: Joanne Isaac.
Work shown: All styles of painting, sculpture, work on paper, and some photography.
Artists represented: 25. 30% male/70% female. **Ages:** 35-70. All origins. 30% of the artists are in museum collections.
Work by: Audrey Ushenko: narrative realistic oil painting; Carol Goebel: metal sculpture; Don Perlis: figurative and landscape painting; Jan Wunderman: abstract painting and work on paper; Tom Sime: encaustic and mixed media painting.

Markets: Individual, corporate, and museum. **Collectors:** Guggenheim, Carnegie Institute, First National Bank, and General Electric Corp.
Annual exhibitions: 12 solo/3 group.
Advertising: *The New York Observer, Art in America* and *ARTnews.*
Focus/Mission: To provide a venue for emerging and established artists, to promote their work and facilitate their careers.
Selection process: 75% of the artists are selected from professional referrals, 20% from slides sent to the gallery, and 5% from art seen in exhibitions or artists studios. Artists should mail slides, photos, biography, resumé, prices, and SASE.
Response time: 3-4 months.
Additional information: Denise Bibro offers advisory services for artists and collectors in addition to art appraising.

GEORGE BILLIS

526 West 26 St., Suite 9F, 10011.   **T:** (212) 645-2621.
F: (212) 645-2397.   **W:** www.georgebillis.com
Open: Tues.-Sat. 11-6.   **Year established:** 1997.
Owner/Director: George Billis: curator, and former owner of another gallery.
Assistant Director: Colleen Theis.
Artists represented: 12.
Work shown: Painting, prints and drawings by emerging artists.
Prices: $1,000-12,000.
Size: 1,000 sq. ft.
Work by: Ron Milewicz: painting; Alejandro Mazon: painting; Richard Orient: painting; Brian Novatny: Figurative painting and Surrealistic painting and drawings; and Christine Blair: work on paper, organic intuitive art using printmaking and papercasting; among others.
Annual exhibitions: 8 solo/2 group.   **Advertising:** *Gallery Guide.*
Focus/Mission: To specialize in emerging artists.
Selection process: All artists are selected from professional referrals. We are currently not looking for new artists.

MICHELLE BIRNBAUM FINE ART

510 West 21 St., 10011.   Mailing address: P.O. Box 286232, NY, NY 10128.
T/F: (212) 427-8250.   **E:** mbfany@nyc.rr.com
Open: By appointment.   **Size:** 1,000 sq. ft.
Year established: 1981.   **Owner/Director:** Michelle Birnbaum.
Work shown: Modern and contemporary art. All media. Inquiries welcome for specific works of art or for specific artists.
Work by: Motherwell; Rauschneberg; Diebenkorn; Miró; Moore; among others.
Markets: Individual, corporations and museums.
Collectors: Museum of the City of New York, Vatican, Hirshhorn Collection and Absolut Vodka.
Advertising: *Gallery Guide.*
Selection process: Artists are selected from referrals, slides sent to gallery, gallery or museum exhibitions, and publications. We are currently not looking at new artists' materials.

MIGRATION TO CHELSEA

Since the 4th *Edition of New York Contemporary Art Galleries dozens of galleries moved to Chelsea from other areas of the city including Blue Mountain, Bowery, CJG Projects, First Street, Fischbach, Galerie Le Long, New Century Artists, NoHo, Prince Street, SoHo 20, Stricoff, and Tatischeff, among others.*

BIT FORMS

529 West 20 St., 2nd floor, 10011.   **T:** (212) 366-6939.
F: (212) 366-6959.   **E:** info@bitforms.com
W: www.bitforms.com   **Open:** Tues.-Sat. 11-6.
Year established: 2001.
Owner/Director: Steve Sachs, Creative Director and co-founder of Digital Pulp.
Work shown: Digitally oriented art. Artists represented: 10.
Work by: Casey Reas; Golen Levin; Kelly Heaton; Danny Rozin; and Mark Mapier; among others.
Annual exhibitions: 10.
Advertising: *Gallery Guide* and *Art in America.*
Focus/Mission: We focus solely on digital and digitally influenced art work.
Selection process: Artists should send jpeg, pdf files or CD.

BLUE MOUNTAIN

530 West 25th, 4th Floor, 10001.   **T:** (646) 486-4730.
F: (646) 486-4345   **Open:** Tues.-Sat 11-6. Closed July 20-Sept 1.
W: www.artincontext.org/new_york/blue_mountain_gallery
Year established: 1974.   **Size:** 700 sq. ft.
Owners: Artist members. Non-profit cooperative gallery.
Director: Marcia Clark.
Work shown: Mostly landscape, Figurative, and some Abstract. Painting and sculpture.
Markets: Individual, corporate, and museum.
Artists represented: 28 members.   50% male/50% female.   Ages: 30-70s. Most artists are based in New York.   20% are in museum collections.
Work by: Matthew Feinman: painting; Marcia Clark: painting; Owen Gray: painting; Morgan Taylor: painting; and Anne Diggory: painting; among others.
Collectors: Hunter College, Metropolitan, Boston University, and the Connecticut Insurance Group of North America. **Prices:** $200-10,000.
Annual exhibitions: 11solo/1 group/3 guest exhibitions.
Advertising: *Gallery Guide, The New York Times* and *Art in America.*
Selection process: Artists should send slides, resumé and SASE and contact the gallery for additional information.
Fees: Initial membership: $450. Monthly fee for NY members: $100; out-of-town members: $160. Members receive a 3-week, one-person show, once every 2-½ years, and a 3-week group show every year. Artists pay for their own framing and publicity.

MARIANE BOESKY

535 West 22 St., 2nd floor, 10011.   **T:** (212) 680-9889.
F: (212) 680-9897.   **E:** info@marianeboesky.com
W: www.marianeboeskygallery.com
Open: Tues.- Sat. 10-6.   **Size:** 2,500 sq. ft
Year established: 1996.   **Owner:** Marianne Boesky
Work shown: Contemporary art.
Artists represented: 7, from U.S., Europe and Japan. Most of the artists shown are in museum collections.
Work by: Lisa Yuskavage: painting; Sarah Cze: installation; Steve Doughton: video; and Diti Almog: painting; among others.
Annual exhibitions: 6-8.   **Advertising:** *Artforum* and *Gallery Guide.*
Market: Private individuals.
Selection process: Artists are generally selected from art seen in exhibitions or artists' studios. Artists should send materials to the gallery with SASE. No calls please. **Response time:** 1 month.

TANYA BONAKDAR

521 West 21 St., 2nd floor, 10011.   **T:** (212) 414-4144.
F: (212) 414-1535.
E: mail@tanyabonakdargallery.com   **W:** www.tanyabonakdargallery.com
Open: Tues.-Sat. 10-6. Mon.by appointment; Summer: Mon.-Fri. 10-6.
Year established: 1994.   **Size:** 4,000 sq. ft.
Owners/Directors: Tanya Bonakdar and Marc Jancou.
Work shown: Conceptual painting, sculpture, photography and video.
Artists represented: 19. **Ages:** 25-34.
Origins: Primarily U.S. and U.K. 30% of the artists are in museum collections.
Work by: Charles Long: sculpture; Uta Barth, photography; Ernesto Neto: installation sculpture; Olafur Elliasson: installation and photography; among others.
Markets: 80% individual, 10% corporate, and 10% museum.
Collectors: Hirshhorn, Israel Museum, The Tate, MOCA Los Angeles, Walker Art Center, and Whitney.
Prices: $2,000and above.   **Annual exhibitions:** 8 solo/2 group.
Advertising: *Artforum, Art Diary International* and *Art and Text.*
Focus/Mission: To promote young contemporary artists.
Selection process: Artists should approach the gallery after spending at least a year looking at the gallery's program. Materials are reviewed in July and January.

BOSE PACIA MODERN

508 West 26 St., 11th floor, 10011.   **T:** (212) 989-7074.
F: (212) 989-6982.   **E:** mail@bosepaciamodern.com
W: www.bosepaciamodern.com
Open: Tues.- Sat. 12-6 and by appointment.
Work shown: 20th Century Masters and Contemporary fine art of India.
Work by: Manjit Bawa; Arun Bose; Madhvi Parekh; and F.N. Souza; among others.
Selection process: Artists should call or email the gallery. They may also send materials with SASE. **Response time:** 1 month.

BOUND & UNBOUND

601 West 26 St., 12th floor, 10011. **T:** (212) 463-7348.
F: (212) 463-8948. **Open:** By appointment or by chance.
Year established: 1996.
Owner: Barbara Moore, a private rare book dealer for 20 years.
Work shown: This is a bookstore and exhibition space with theme shows and group shows. We present frequently changing unannounced exhibitions of books, objects and ephemera related to happenings, Fluxus, Conceptual art, artists' books, performance, concrete and visual poetry, audio art and mail art.

BOWERY

530 West 25 St., 4th Floor, 10001. **T/F:** (646) 230-6655.
W: www.bowerygallery.org
Open: Tues.-Sat. 11-6. Closed Aug. 17-Sept. 2.
Year established: 1969.
Owner: Artist members. Non-profit, cooperative gallery.
Director: Lynda Caspe.
Work shown: Contemporary American painting, drawings and some sculpture.
Work by: Barbara Grossman: painting; Rita Baragona: nature-inspired watercolor painting; Maria Roberts: painting; Deborah Rosenthal: painting; and Esti Dunow: rhythmic oil painting of landscapes; among others.
Annual exhibitions: 9 solo/1 group/2 invitational/1 juried.
Advertising: *Gallery Guide.*
Focus/Mission: To provide an exhibition space for quality, independent work, always selected and presented by the artists themselves.
Selection process: Artists should call to obtain the date of the new members meeting and bring works.
Requirements: Members must live within 100 miles from the gallery.
Fees: There are initiation and monthly fees. Artists pay for their own exhibition expenses. Members have solo shows about every 2-3 years.
Additional information: The gallery also sponsors free talks and panel discussions.

CYNTHIA BROAN

423 West 14 St., 10014. **T:** (212) 633-6525.
F: (212) 633-2855. **E:** contact@cynthiabroan.com
W: www.cynthiabroan.com **Open:** Tues.-Sat. 12-6
Year established: 1998. **Owner/Director:** Cynthia Broan.
Work shown: Contemporary art in all media.
Prices: $500-25,000. **Artists represented:** 12, from all origins.
Work by: Clarina Bezzola: sculpture; Jeff Reese: photography; and Adrian Ting: painting; among others. **Annual exhibitions:** 8.
Selection process: Artists should be familiar with the gallery before submitting materials. Send slides or photographs, resumé and SASE.

GAVIN BROWN'S ENTERPRISE

436 West 15 St., 10013. **T:** (212) 627-5258.
F: (212) 627-5261. **E:** passerby@bway.net
Open: Tues.-Sat. 10-6. **Year established:** 1994.
Owner: Gavin Brown **Director:** Corinna Durland

Work shown: Contemporary art in all media.
Annual exhibitions: 6 solo/2 group.
Work by: WoddyGwyn: large scale egg tempra landscape; Tim Thyzel: sculpture; Steven Pippin: photography and sculpture; Peter Doig: painting; Laura Owens: paining; Rirkrit Tiravanija: sculpture installation; Udomask Krisanamis: painting; and Elizabeth Peyton: painting; among others.
Selection process: Artists should mail slides, photographs, resumé and other materials with SASE. **Response time:** 1 month.

CHRISTINE BURGIN

243 West 18 St.,10011.   **T:** (212) 462-2668.
F: (212) 462-2564.   **E:** gallery@christineburgin.com
W: www.christineburgin.com   **Open:** Tues.-Sat. 10-6.
Owner/Director: Christine Burgin. **Work shown:** Contemporary art in all media.
Annual exhibitions: 8-10.
Work by: Stanley Brouwn; Victor Burgin; Anne Chu; Allen Ruppersberg; and Victoria Sambunaris, among others.
Selection process: The gallery is currently not looking for artists.

J. CACCIOLA

501 West 23 St., 10011.   **T:** (212) 462-4646.
F: (212) 462-4556.   **W:** www.jcacciolagallery.com
Open: Tues.-Sat. 10:30-6; Summer: Call for hours.
Year established: 1982.
Managing Director: Theresa Reeves.
Size: 3,000 sq. ft and outdoor sculpture garden.
Owner/Director: John Cacciola.
Artists represented: 14.
Work shown: Realistic/Figurative art in all media.
Work by: Jesus Bautista Moroles, granite sculptures which evoke a range of moods; Dan Naningha, a Native American painter and sculptor who uses symbolic imagery and iconography of Mother Earth; and R.B. Sprague, whose painting of fruits, balls, buildings, and other objects are depicted in deceptive simplicity; and George Fischer: Figurative oil painting; among others.
Prices: $1,500-40,000.
Annual exhibitions: 4 solo/10 group.
Advertising: *Southwest Art, Art & Antiques* and *The New York Times.*
Focus/Mission: To exhibit artists whose work is Realistic/Figurative in style.
Selection process: Artists should mail 10 slides with SASE. Artists must be established with work that complements the other artists represented by the gallery.

CAELUM

526 West 26 St., #315, 10011.   **T/F:** (212) 924-4161.
E: capacity@msn.com   **W:** www.caelumgallery.com
Open: Tues.-Sat 11-6.   **Year established:** 1996.
Owner: Nicholas Bergman, former artist.
Director: Misuzu Takemoto.
Work shown: Contemporary Abstract and Realism. Painting, constructions, and work on paper by national and international artists.
Artists represented: 3, from Europe & U.S.   *continued*

Work by: Shin Miyazaki: mixed media; Lawrence Berzon: painted constructions; Wojciech Ulrich: installation work; Gerd Kanz: synthesis of painting and sculpture; among others.

Markets: Individual, corporate, and museum. **Collectors:** Patricia Phelps; De Cisneros; Museo de Bellas Artes; Microsoft; and the Estate of Henry Geldzahler. **Prices:** $300-15,000.

Annual exhibitions: 15. **Advertising:** *ARTnews, Review* and *Gallery Guide.*

Focus/Mission: To champion excellence in art, originality, good technique and a balance between a personal and a universal expression.

Selection process: Artists are selected from professional referrals, from slides sent to the gallery, and from art seen in exhibitions or artists studios. Artists should call for an appointment and should mail slides, photos, biography, resumé, prices, SASE. **Response time:** 2 weeks.

Fees: Artists should be prepared to pay exhibition fees and other expenses.

CAFÉ BIONDI

7 West 20 St. 10011.
W: www.bondi-ny.com
Year established: 1990.

T: (212) 691-8136.
Open: Daily 11:30-11.
Contact: Salvatore Anzalone.

Focus/Mission: This is a restaurant that shows varied photography exhibitions, fitting its location in the heart of New York's photography district.

Annual exhibitions: 12 solo.

Work by: Woody Gwyn: large scale egg tempera landscape; Tim Thyzel: sculpture; among others.

Selection process: Artists should come to the restaurant with their portfolios and ask for Salvatore Anzalone, anytime except between the hours of 12-3.

CAMHY STUDIO

526 West 26 St., 10001.
E: sherrycamhy@aol.com
Owner: Sherry Camhy, artist.
Annual exhibitions: 6.

T: (212) 741-9183.
Year established: 1997
Work shown: Figurative work in all media.

Selection process: Artists should mail slides, resumé and SASE.

CENTER FOR BOOK ARTS

28 West 27 St., 3rd floor, 10001.
T: (212) 481-0295.
E: info@centerforbookarts.org
Open: Mon.-Fri. 10-6, Sat. 10-4.
Owner: Non-profit organization.

F: (212) 481-9853.
W: www.centerforbookarts.org
Year established: 1974.
Director: Rory Golden.

Work shown: Traditional and Contemporary, one-of-a-kind and limited edition, artists books, in all media.

Prices: $10 and above.   **Markets:** Individual and museum.

Artists represented: Approximately 300, but exhibitions include general call-to-artists. All origins. 40% male/60% female.

Annual exhibitions: 1-2 solo/4-5 group.   **Advertising:** *NY Press, Village Voice, Time Out New York, Gallery Guide,* and *Museums New York.*

Focus/Mission: To preserve the traditional crafts of bookmaking, and letterpress printing as well as contemporary interpretations of the book as an art object. The Center ensures that the ancient craft of the book, that container which preserves the knowledge and ideas of a culture, remains a viable and vital part of our civilization.

Selection process: 20% of the artists are selected from professional referrals, 60% from slides sent to the gallery, and 20% from art seen in exhibitions or studios. Artists should mail slides, biography, resumé, and SASE. Artists represented are members of the Center. Call for information and application. **Response time:** 2-3 weeks.

CHAMBERS FINE ART

210 Eleventh Ave., 2nd floor, 10001. **T:** (212) 414-1169.
F: (212) 414-1192. **E:** cfa@chambersfineart.com.
W: www.chambersfineart.com. **Open:** Tues.-Sat. 10-6.
Year established: 2000. **Director:** Christoph W. Mao.
Work shown: Chinese Contemporary art and classicial Ming Ching Dynasty furniture.
Artists represented: 12. **Annual exhibitions:** 8.
Advertising: *Gallery Guide.*

DOMINIQUE HAIM CHANIN FINE ARTS

210 Eleventh Ave. Ste. 201, 10011. **T:** (646) 230-7200.
F: (646) 230-7989. **E:** art@haimchanin.com
 W: www.haimchanin.com **Open:** Tues.-Sat. 10-6.
Year established: 1995.
Owner/Director: Dominique Haim Chanin, background with family business in Paris since 1958.
Work shown: Primarily paintings and public art by modern masters, with occasional contemporary artists.
Markets: Individual, corporate, and museum.
Prices: $3,000-2,000,000.
Artists represented: 12, from Europe, Japan, and U.S.
Work by: Federica Matta: public art sculpture; Fernand Leger: mosaics, bronze reliefs, ceramics; and Miró: sculpture; among others.
Selection process: Artists should mail materials and SASE.

CHAPPELL

526 West 26 St., #904, 10001. **T:** (212) 414-2673.
F: (212) 414-2678. **E:** amchappell@aol.com.
W: www.chappellgallery.com. **Open:** Tues.-Fri. 11-6, Sat. 11-5:30.
Year established: 2000. **Owner:** Alice Chappell.
Manager: Miriam Kienle. **Work shown:** Glass art.
Artists represented: 30. **Annual exhibitions:** 10.
Work by: Toshio Iezumi; Preston Singletary; Naomi Shioya; Nicole Chesney; and Jamie Harris; among others.
Selection process: Artists should send slides, photographs, resumé and SASE.

CHEIM & REID

547 West 25 St., 10001. **T:** (212) 242-7727.
F: (212) 242-7737. **E:** gallery@cheimread.com.
W: www.artnet.com/cheim-reid.html
Open: Tues.-Sat. 10-6. **Year established:** 1996.
Owners: John Cheim and Howard Read, art dealers since 1977.
Work shown: Contemporary painting, sculpture, and photography.
Artists represented: 11. All are in museum collections. *continued*

Work by: Louise Bourgeois; Adam Fuss; Juan Uslé; Louise Fishman; Richmond Burton; Diane Arbus; Jean-Michel Basquiat; Lynda Benglis; among others.
Annual exhibitions: 7-8.
Advertising: *Artforum* and *Photography NY.*

CHELSEA CERAMIC GUILD (CCG)

233 West 19 St., 10011.   **T:** (212) 243-2430.
F: (212) 277-2778.   **E:** chelseaceramic@aol.com
Open: Mon.-Fri. 11-9.
Year established: 1988.
Director: Fred Rose.
Work shown: Primarily Raku. This is a gallery that shows ceramic art as well as a studio space that conducts classes.
Prices: $30 and above.
Artists represented: 12, primarily U.S., yet receptive to artists from all origins.
Annual exhibitions: 4.
Selection process: Artists should send slides, photographs, resumé, and SASE.

CJG PROJECTS – CORTLAND JESSUP

135 West 29 St., #500, 1001.   **T/F:** (212) 695-8338.
E: cjgfineart@aol.com
Open: Wed. 12-5, Thurs.-Sat. 12-5:30 and by appointment.
Owner/Director: Cortland Jessup.
Work shown: Contemporary American and Japanese painting, photography with an emphasis on mixed media and photography.
Additional information: Cortland Jessup presents projects in Japan. Her organization Lamia Ink! Is an instigator of dialogue across, between and amongst cultures, genders, generations and media in alternative formats/forums in both urban and remote areas.

CLEMENTINE

526 West 26 St., 2nd floor, 10001.   **T:** (212) 243-5937.
F: (212) 243-3927.   **W:** www.clementine-gallery.com
Open: Tues.-Sat. 11-6.   **Size:** 750 sq. ft.
Year established: 1996.
Owners: Abby Messitte, BA in Art History from Amhurst College and MA in Art History from Columbia University; and Elizabeth Burke, BFA, Gulford College.
Work shown: Work by contemporary emerging artists.
Prices: $150-5,000.   **Markets:** Individual, corporate, and museum.
Artists represented: 4. 50% are in museum collections.
Work by: David Rathman: work on paper; Nina Borasso: Abstract compositions in water-based media in work on paper, and painting; Steve DeFrank: wall sculpture; and Rob de Mar: sculpture; among others.
Annual exhibitions: 7 solo/1 group.
Focus/Mission: To make art more accessible to younger and first-time buyers while providing a venue for under-recognized artists.
Selection process: 20% of the artists are selected from professional referrals, 5% from slides sent to the gallery, 75% from art seen in exhibitions, publications and artists' studios. Artists should mail slides, biography, and SASE. Work will not be considered without a SASE. **Response time:** 6 weeks.

COHAN LESLIE AND BROWNE

138 10th Ave., 10011.   T: (212) 206-8710.
F: (212) 206-8711.   E: info@clbgallery.com
Open: Tues.-Sat 10-6.
Year established: 2001.
Owners/Directors: Leslie Cohan, Andrew Leslie and Martin Browne.
Work shown: Contemporary art in all media by U.S. and international artists.
Work by: Axel Hutte; and Elisa Sighicelli; among others.

COMMON GROUND

55 West 16 St., 10011.   T: (212) 620-3122.
F: (212) 989-0573.   E: thecommonground@att.net
Open: Wed.-Sat. 1-6:30 and by appointment.
Year established: 1995.
Owner/Director: Rolando Reyes, artist and collector.
Work shown: Primarily antique with some Contemporary art of the North American Indian. Sterling silver with turquoise jewelry, cedar, argillite, beads, buffalo skin, deer skin, paper, canvas, oil, pastel, Navajo textiles.
Markets: Individual, corporate, and museum.
Annual exhibitions: 2-3.
Advertising: *American Indian Art Magazine, Tribal Art* and *Gallery Guide.*
Selection process: Artists are selected from professional referrals, from slides and other materials sent to the gallery, and from art seen in exhibitions, publications and artists' studios. Artists should mail slides, photographs, biography, resumé, artist's statement, prices and SASE. Artists may call for appointment. Response time: 1 month.
Fees: Artists are expected to pay for framing and advertising.

PAULA COOPER

534 West 21 St., 10011.   T: (212) 255-1105.
F: (212) 255-5156.   Open: Tues.-Sat. 10-6.
Year established: 1969.   Size: 2 spaces: 4,000 sq. ft.
Owner: Paula Cooper.
Director: Steve Henry.
Work shown: Contemporary painting, sculpture, drawings, prints, photographs, and video.
Artists represented: 14. Ages: 35-60.
Annual exhibitions: 10.
Selection process: We are currently not looking for new artists.

PAULA COOPER

521 West 21 St., 10011.   T: (212) 255-1105.
Open: Tues.-Sat. 11-6.   Year established: 1999.
Owner: Paula Cooper.
Director: Steve Henry.
Work shown: Contemporary painting, sculpture, drawings, prints, photographs, and video.
Selection process: We are currently not looking for new artists.

JEFFREY COPLOFF FINE ART

508 West 26 St., #318, 10011.

T: (212) 741-1149
E: jcoploff@aol.com
Year established: 1996.

F: (212) 741-1189.
Open: Tues.-Sat. 11-6.
Size: 1,200 sq. ft.

Owner/Director: Jeffrey Coploff, background in commercial law.
Work shown: Primarily abstract painting; all media.
Prices: $200-20,000.
Artists represented: 8 male/12 female, from U.S., Europe, and Asia. 50% of the artists are in museum collections.
Annual exhibitions: 7 solo/1 group.
Advertising: *Gallery Guide* and *Artforum.*
Selection process: 50% of the artists are selected from professional referrals, 10% from slides and other materials sent to the gallery, and 40% from art seen in exhibitions or artists' studios. Artists should mail slides, resumé, and SASE.
Response time: 3 weeks.
Additional information: We also offer fine art appraisal services.

CRISTINEROSE

529 West 20 St., 10011.

F: (212) 206-8494.
W: www.cristinerose.com
Year established: 1994.
Size: 4,000 sq. ft.

T: (212) 206-0297.
E: crgallery@aol.com
Open: Tues.-Sat. 11-6.

Owner: Maria Cristina Parravicini, BS and Master of Arts.
Work shown: Painting, photography, sculpture, video, installation and drawing.
Artists represented: 12.
Work by: Jason Young: 3-D painting in acrylic and resin on wood; Nancy Dwyer: sculpture; Janieta Eyre: black and white and color photographs using dual images of herself with props; Laurent Badessi: black and white photography; and Michelle Handelman: video installation and sculpture; among others.
Prices: $1,000-20,000.
Annual exhibitions: 5 solo/2 group.
Advertising: *Artforum, Art in America, Flash Art, Frieze,* and *Tema Celeste.*
Focus/Mission: To exhibit art that reflects quality, enthusiasm, advance thinking, and unique, contemporary vision.
Selection process: Artists should mail slides or photos, biography, resumé and artist's statement. **Response time:** 1 month.
Requirements: Artists must have quality, craftsmanship and a unique vision.

CRG ART

535 West 22 St., 10011.

F: (212) 966-4099.
W: www.crggallery.com

T: (212) 229-2766
E: mail@crggallery.com

Open: Tues.-Sat. 11-6; July and August by appointment.
Year established: 1990. **Size:** 2,400 sq. ft.
Owners: Carla Chammas, Richard Desroche and Glenn McMillan.
Work shown: Contemporary painting, sculpture, photography, video, installation by emerging and established American and European contemporary artists.
Artists represented: 12. **Ages:** 30-50.

Work by: Siobhan Liddell: installation; Melissa McGill: installation; Sandra Scolnik: painting; Sam Reveles: painting; Jim Hodges: installation; and Jeffrey Saldinger: painting; among others.
Collectors: Whitney Museum, Centres George Pompidou, and Tate.
Annual exhibitions: 6-8 solo.
Selection process: Artists should submit slides, resumé, and SASE for consideration in the Fall. Response time: 1 month.

D'AMELIO TERRAS

525 West 22 St., 10011.   T: (212) 352-9460.
F: (212) 352-9464.
Open: Tues.-Sat. 10-6; Summer: Mon.-Fri. 10-6.
Year established: 1996.
Size: 3,000 sq. ft.
Owners: Christopher D'Amelio and Lucien Terras.
Work shown: Contemporary sculpture, painting, drawings, photography and installations.
Artists represented: 11 international artists.
Annual exhibitions: 5 solo/2 group.
Advertising: Artforum.
Work by: Polly Apfelbaum: sculpture; Tony Feher: sculpture; Glenn Ligon: painting.

DANCE THEATER WORKSHOP (D.T.W.)

219 West 19 St., 10011.   T: (212) 691-6500.
W: www.dtw.org
Year established: 1965.
Size: 272 sq. ft.
Owner: Non-profit organization.
Assistant Producer/Curator: Lili Mollet-Vieville.
Work shown: 2-D Contemporary art in all media by artists from all origins.
Annual exhibitions: 8.
Focus/Mission: Dance Theater Workshop serves to support and advance the work of artists. It is constantly evolving to sustain them at every stage of their development.
Selection process: Artists should mail slides, resumé and SASE.
Response time: 3 months.

DCA

525 West 22 St. 10011.   T: (212) 255-5511.
F: (212) 255-8005.   W: www.dcagallery.com
Open: Tues.-Sat. 10-6.
Year established: 1994.   Size: 5,000 sq. ft.
Owner: Seven Danish Galleries.   Director: Miles Manning.
Work shown: Danish Contemporary painting, sculpture, and installation.
Work by: Balder Olrik: oil on computer-manipulated photographs; Jesper Christiansen: painting; Maya Lisa Engelhardt: painting; and Jes Fomsgaard: drawings; among others.
Annual exhibitions: 7 solo.
Advertising: Artforum, Art in America and Cover.
Selection process: We are currently not looking at new artists' materials.

DEBS & CO.

525 West 26 St., 2nd floor, 10001.   T: (212) 643-2070
F: (212) 643-0026.   E: NDebs@aol.com
W: www.debsandco.com   Open: Tues.-Sat. 11-6.
Year established: 1997.   Size: 1,200 sq. ft.
Owner: Nick Debs.   Director: Choire Sicha.
Work shown: Art by contemporary and emerging artists from North America, Asia and Europe. All media with an emphasis on painting and drawing.
Prices: $100-20,000.
Annual exhibitions: 7solo/2-3 group.
Selection process: 34% of the artists are selected from professional referrals, 1% from slides sent to the gallery, and 65% from art seen in exhibitions, publications, and artists' studios. We review artists' materials only by referral.
Response time: 1 month.

DE CHIARA

521 West 26 St., 10001.   T: (212) 967-6007.
E: office@dechiara.com   W: www.artnet.com/dechirat-stewart.html
Open: Tues.-Sat. 11-6; July closed Sat.; closed in Aug.
Year established: 1998.
Size: 1,500 sq. ft.
Owner: Laurie DeChiara: background as an independent curator.
Work shown: Contemporary and Conceptual art by international artists. Photography, painting, sculpture, and installation.
Work by: Monica Bravo; Suzanne Wright; Thomas Eller and Mick O'Shea.
Annual exhibitions: 6 solo/2 group.
Prices: $300-17,000.
Advertising: *Artforum, Gallery Guide, Art in America* and *Frieze*.
Selection process: 50% of the artists are selected from professional referrals, 5% from materials sent to the gallery, 45% from art seen in exhibitions, publications and artists' studios. We review artists' materials on an on-going basis. Artists should mail slides, biography, resumé, artist's statement, prices, and SASE. Response time: 2-3 months.

DEE/GLASOE

545 West 20 St., 10001.   T: (212) 924-7545.
F: (212) 924-7671.   E: deeglasoe@aol.com
W: www.deeglasoe.com   Open: Tues.-Sat 11-6
Year established: 1998.   Size: 1,500 sq. ft.
Owners: Elizabeth Dee, former private dealer and owner of Elizabeth Dee Gallery; and Carolyn Glasoe, former private dealer and owner of Montgomery Glasoe.
Director: Pearl Albino.
Work shown: Contemporary art in all media, emphasis on emerging artists.
Prices: $1,000-20,000.   Annual exhibitions: 9.
Work by: Doug Wada: painting; Shannon Kennedy: video, Yardley Leonard: painting; Charlotta Westergren: painting, sculpture, installation and video; Charles Avery: painting and work on paper; among others.
Selection process: Artists should send cover letter, slides, biography and SASE.
Response time: 1 month.

CORNELL DE WITT

547 West 27 St., 2nd floor, 10001.　T: (212) 695-6845.
E: cornell@dewittgallery.com　W: www.dewittgallery.com
Open: Tues.-Sat., 11-6 and by appointment.
Year established: 2000.
Owner: Cornell De Witt, former private dealer and co-owner of Joseph Raj Gallery, Austin, TX.
Work shown: Emerging and established artists.
Work by: Linda Girvin; Terry Maker; Eric Ringsby; The Art Guys and Jenny Laden; among others.
Focus/Mission: Many of the artists shown are people who choose, or even need, to work outside the New York art scene, and are thus often completely overlooked. The gallery shows how the work of these artists is great precisely because they are less influenced by the sometimes myopic New York scene.

DIA CENTER FOR THE ARTS

548 West 22 St., 10011.　T: (212) 989-5566.
F: (212) 989-4055.　W: www.diacenter.org.
Open: Wed.-Sun. 12-6, September-June.
Admission: $6 general admission; $3 students, seniors; members and children under 10 years are free.
Year established: 1977.　Size: 5,000 sq. ft. (5 floors)
Director: Michael Govan.
Assistant Director: Stephen Dewhurst.
Work shown: Contemporary art in all media.
Focus/Mission: The exhibition program in this four-story renovated warehouse building is principally dedicated to large-scale, single-artist projects, produced on a substantial scale and with a commitment to site specificity. Exhibitions are long-term, usually with a minimum duration of one year, to allow for repeated visits and the opportunity to view work over an extended period of time.
Selection process: Artists are selected from art seen in curated exhibitions or artists' studios.

DJT FINE ART/DOMINC J. TAGLIALATELLA

511 West 25 St., 2nd Floor, 10001.　T: (917) 305-1885.
F: (917) 305-1886.　Open: Tues.-Sat. 10:30-5:30.
E: Dom@cobraart.com　W: www.DJTFineArt.com
Owner: Dominic J. Taglialatella, an appraiser and curator for more than 20 years. Member of Appraisers Association of America.
Work shown: CoBrA, New Realists, Modern and Contemporary and Impressionst European and American art including painting, drawing, sculpture, prints and photography. Work by contemporary masters and emerging artists.
Work by: Arman; Chia; Christo; Warhol; Wesselman; among others.

DORFMAN PROJECTS

529 West 20 St., 7th Floor, 10011.　T: (212) 352-2272.
F: (212) 352-2273.　Open: Tues.-Sat. 12-6 and by appointment.
E: fred@dorfmanprojects.com　W: www.dorfmanprojects.com
Year established: 1978.
Owner/Director: Fred Dorfman, background in fine art publishing.
Work shown: Contemporary multi-media art.　*continued*

Artists represented: 20.
Origins: International. All of the artists are in museum collections.
Work by: Alex Katz: all media; Lynda Benglis: sculpture, hand blown colored glass; Laurie Simmons: sculpture and graphics; Andy Warhol: screen prints: Pop uniques and graphics; and Roy Lichtenstein: prints; among others.
Annual exhibitions: 6.
Advertising: *Gallery Guide.*
Markets: Individual, corporate, and museum.   **Prices:** $500-1,000,000.
Focus/Mission: To introduce multi-media projects by leading contemporary artists.
Selection process: All artists are selected from referrals. We are currently not looking at unsolicited artists' materials.

DRAGON FLY'S ELECTRIC TATTOO

158 West 15 St., 10011.   **T:** (212) 255-1490.
F: (212) 691-6643.   **W:** www.dragonflytattoo.com.
Open: Tues.-Sat. 12-8 and by appointment.
Year established: 1995.   **Size:** 1,000 sq. ft.
Owner: Dragon Fly, painter.
Work shown: Fantasy, Surreal, non-traditional, Tattoo Art/Flash in all media.
Artists represented: 10, from all origins. **Ages:** 19-59.
Work by: Andre Lassen: sculpture; Spider Webb: painting; Dragon Fly: painting; and Charles Gatewood: photography; among others.
Annual exhibitions: 3 solo/3 group.
Advertising: Tattoo magazines.
Markets: Individual and museum.   **Prices:** $175-6,000.
Focus/Mission: To break with stale tradition. To support the work of friends. To promote Tattoo art as a fine art medium.
Selection process: Artists should contact the gallery.
Requirements: We seek artists who create out of the mainstream, revolutionary, surreal or fantasy, non-traditional, outlaw, totally unique and radical art.
Fees: Artists incur some costs for exhibitions.

EDITION SCHELLMANN

210 Eleventh Ave., Suite 1104.   **T:** (212) 219-1821.
F: (212) 941-9206.   **W:** www.editionschellmann.com
Open: Tues.-Sat. 12-6 and by appointment.
Year established: 1983 in New York, 1969 in Munich.   **Size:** 2,200 sq. ft.
Owner: Jorg Schellmann, background as an art publisher.
Director: Lara Burakowski.
Work shown: Contemporary art, focusing on Minimal and Conceptual. Prints and multiples in a wide variety of media.
Artists represented: 20.
Work by: Bernd and Hiller Becher: portfolio of duotone offset prints; Cindy Sherman: lightbox; Robert Longo: lithographs; and Joseph Beuys: mixed media; among others.
Collectors: MoMA, Guggenheim, and Walker Art Museum.
Prices: $300-80,000.
Annual exhibitions: 4-6.   **Advertising:** *Artforum* and *Flash Art.*
Focus/Mission: To publish prints and multiples by challenging, established artists.
Selection process: We are currently not looking at new artists' materials.

JOHN ELDER

529 West 20 St., 7th floor, 10011.   **T:** (212) 462-2600.
F: (212) 462-2510.   **W:** www.johnelder.com
Open: Tues.-Sat. 11-6.   **Size:** 3,500 sq. ft.
Year established: 1997.
Owner: John Elder, former Associate Director, Peter Joseph Gallery.
Director: Don Thomas.
Work shown: Art furniture/sculpture in wood, ceramic, metal, glass, and mixed media.
Prices: $500-25,000.   **Artists represented:** 30, from the U.S.
Work by: Judy Moonelis: ceramic and mixed media sculpture; Michael Hurwitz: wood furniture and sculptural lighting; Steven Whittelsey: furniture from reclaimed wood and mixed media; Robert Brady: wood carved sculpture and ceramic sculpture; and Andy Buck: furniture and objects in painted wood; among others.
Annual exhibitions: 7 solo/7 group. **Advertising:** *American Craft.*
Focus/Mission: A showcase for media-based work in furniture, ceramics, metal and glass. Works shown range from functional to pure sculpture but are always involved in process and media.
Selection process: 90% of the artists are selected from professional referrals, 10% from slides and other materials sent to the gallery. Artists should mail slides, resumé and an artist's statement with SASE. **Response time:** 2 months.

DEREK ELLER

526-30 West 25 St., 2nd floor, 10001.   **T:** (212) 206-6411.
F: (212) 206-6977.   **E:** derekeller@aol.com
Open: Tues.-Sat. 11-6.   **Size:** 1,100 sq. ft.
Year established: 1997.   **Owner/Director:** Derek Eller.
Work shown: Contemporary art in all media.
Markets: Individual, corporate, museum.   **Prices:** $100-20,000.
Work by: D.L. Alvarez; David Dupuis; Chris Hammerlein and Calvin Seibert among others.
Annual exhibitions: 8-12 solo/1 group.
Advertising: *Artforum* and *Gallery Guide.*
Selection process: 25% of the artists are selected from professional referrals; 25% from slides and other materials sent to the gallery; and 50% from art seen in exhibitions, publications and artists' studios. Artists should mail slides, photographs, biography, resumé, and SASE. **Response time:** 1-3 months.

THOMAS ERBEN

516 West 20 St., 10011.   **T:** (212) 645-8701.
F: (212) 645-9630.   **E:** info@thomaserben.com
W: www.thomaserben.com   **Open:** Tues.-Sat. 10-6.
Year established: 1989.   **Size:** 1,400 sq. ft.
Owner: Thomas Erben, background studies in fine art, art history, philosophy and education.
Work shown: Contemporary art by international artists in all media.
Markets: Individual and museum.   **Prices:** $600-200,000.
Artists represented: 6, from North America and Europe.
Work by: Adrian Piper: Conceptual work; Oladele Bamgboye: New Media; Tom Wood: photography; Sarah Rossiter: photography; Preston Scott Cohen: architecture; and Jutta Koether: painting; among others.
Annual exhibitions: 5 solo/1 group.   *continued*

Focus/Mission: The gallery is interested in work that explores and widens our concepts of existence, employing various media in a formally innovative manner.
Selection process: 50% of the artists are selected from professional referrals; 50% from art seen in exhibitions, publications, and artists' studios. Artists should mail slides, photographs, biography, resumé, and SASE.
Response time: 2-3 weeks.

ESSO

211 West 28 St., 10001.   **T:** (212) 560-9728
F: (212) 560-9729.   **E:** esso@spacelab.net
W: www.essogallery.com   **Open:** Tues.-Sat. 10-6.
Year established: 1996.   **Directors:** Jennifer Bacon and Filippo Fossati.
Work shown: Mostly Conceptual art from the 60's to current in all media by well-known European and contemporary international artists.
Work by: Alighiero Boetti; Carol Rama; Jeanette Louie; and Giovanni Rizzoli; among others.   **Prices:** $200-100,000.
Annual exhibitions: 8.   **Advertising:** *Gallery Guide* and *Artforum*.
Selection process: Artists should mail slides and resumé with SASE.

EYEBEAM

540 W 21 St., 10011.   **T:** (212) 937-6581.
E: info@eyebeam.org   **W:** www.eyebeam.org
Open: Wed.-Sat. 12-6.   **Year established:** 2001.
Founder/Director: John S. Johnson.
Work shown: Artworks created with computers and other digital equipment.
Focus/Mission: To expand the public's appreciation of new media. To expand and improve artists' and the public's access to electronic, graphic, network and moving image arts. To research and develop new technologies that will catalyze the creation of these artworks.
Additional information: Founding memberships are available. There is also an artist-in-residence program.

FEATURE

530 West 25 St., 10001.   **T:** (212) 675-7772.
E: featureinc@featureinc.com   **W:** www.featureinc.com
Open: Tues.-Sat. 11-6.   **Year established:** 1984.
Size: 2,800 sq. ft.
Owner/Director: Hudson, background as an artist, dancer, and President of the National Association of Artists Organizations.
Assistant Director: Jim Pedersen. **Work shown:** All media and all styles.
Work by: Tom Friedman: all media; Judy Linn: photography; Lucky DeBellebue: sculpture; and Jason Fox: painting; among others.

FEIGEN CONTEMPORARY

535 West 20 St., 10011.   **T:** (212) 929-0500.
F: (212) 929-0065.   **Open:** Tues.-Sat. 11-6.
E: gallery@feigencontemporary.com
Year established: 1989. The parent company was formed in 1957.
Owners/Directors: Lance Kinz and Susan Reynolds.
Size: 2 floors: 7,500 sq. ft.   **Work shown:** Contemporary art in all media.
Annual exhibitions: 7.
Work by: Gregory Green; Jeanne Dunning; Jeremy Blake; and Shirley Kaneda; among others.

Selection process: Artists should hand deliver slides and resumé for review.
Response time: 2 weeks. When artists pick up their materials they should ask for Lance or Susan and if available, they will discuss their materials with them.

FIRST STREET

526 West 26 St., #915, 10001.　**T:** (646) 336-8053.
F: (646) 336-8054.　**W:** www.firststreetgallery.net
Open: Tues.-Sat. 11-6.
Year established: 1968.　**Size:** 2,100 sq. ft.
Owner: Artist members. Non-profit cooperative gallery.
Work shown: Representational painting, drawings and prints. A wide range of Realistic styles. **Prices:** $300-50,000.
Artists represented: 26, from all origins; primarily US artists from the NY area. 60% male/40% female. **Ages:** 25-60.
Annual exhibitions: 12 solo/2 group.
Selection process: Artists should bring original work for viewing during monthly gallery member meetings. Call for information.
Fees: $350 initiation fee; $110 per month for local, participating artists; $160 for non-participating artists. Artists receive one-person show every 2 years and 2 group shows.

FISCHBACH

210 Eleventh Ave., 10001.　**T:** (212) 759-2345.
FAX: (212) 757-0202.　**E:** fischbachgallery@msn.com
W: www.artnet.com/fischbach.html
Open: Tues.-Sat. 10-5:30, Summer: Mon.-Fri. 10-5.
Year established: 1960.　**Size:** 3,000 sq. ft.
Member of Art Dealers Association of America.
Director: Lawrence L. DiCarlo.　**Associate Director:** Matt Kirsch.
Work shown: Contemporary American Representational Realism. Painting and drawing. **Artists represented:** 15 male/18 female from the U.S.. **Ages:** 31-85.
Work by: Alice Dalton Brown: painting and pastel; Lois Dodd: painting; Nancy Hagin: painting and watercolor; David Jermann: painting; and Denise Mickilowski: oils on panel; among others. **Prices:** $1,000-100,000.
Collectors: Metropolitan, Whitney, MoMA, Hirshhorn Sculpture Garden.
Annual exhibitions: 15 solo/2 group.
Advertising: *The New York Times, ARTnews* and *Gallery Guide.*
Focus/Mission: To present serious and engaging works of art by established and emerging American artists.
Selection process: Artists are selected from referrals, slides sent to the gallery, exhibitions, and publications. Artists should submit 10-20 slides, biography and SASE. No walk-ins, please. **Response time:** Immediate.
Requirements: Artists must have a focus and consistency.

KIM FOSTER

529 West 20 St., 10011.　**T:** (212) 229-0044.
W: www.artnet.com/kfoster.html　**Open:** Tues.-Sat. 11-6.
Year established: 1994.　**Size:** 3,000 sq. ft.
Owner/Director: Kim Foster.
Work shown: Representational, Conceptual, and Abstract painting, sculpture, and photography.　　　　　　　　　　　*continued*

Artists represented: 12, from Korea, Europe and U.S. **Ages:** 28-50's. 90% of the artists are in museum collections.
Work by: Antonio Petracca: oil on wood constructions; Diane Samuels: photo narrative; John Kirchner: Conceptual; Kwang Yung Chun: painting; Sarah Leahy: painting; and Mike Cockrill: painting; among others.
Markets: Individual, corporate and museum. **Prices:** $6,000-25,000.
Annual exhibitions: 9 solo/1 group.
Advertising: *Artforum, ARTnews, Art in America, New York Times.*
Focus/Mission: To exhibit Contemporary art by mid-career artists.
Selection process: We are not looking for new artists.

14TH STREET PAINTERS

114 West 14 St., 2nd floor W, 10011. **T:** (212) 627-9893.
W: www.14thstreetpainters.com **Open:** By appointment. Call Mon.-Sat. 2-8.
Director: Craig Killy. **Artists represented:** 37 active; 300 affiliated.
Annual exhibitions/events: 4.
Work by: Deborah Greek: painting; Craig Killy: painting; Gregg Smith: painting; and Rupert Stechman: painting; among others.
Focus/Mission: This is an atelier with exhibition space offering artists annual exhibitions and the opportunity with growth in NYC while interfacing in a professional setting including an international art community and patrons. In its educational capacity artists learn about diverse materials and approaches to creating art. Figure drawing workshops are offered in addition to an art slide bank.

FREDERICKS FREISER

504 West 22 St., 10011. **T:** (212) 633-6555.
F: (212) 367-9502. **Open:** Tues.-Sat. 11-6.
Year established: 1996.
Owners/Directors: Jessica Fredericks and Andrew Freiser.
Work shown: Contemporary painting, photography, installation and sculpture.
Artists represented: 9. 50% are in museum collections.
Work by: John Wesley: painter; Robert Overby: sculpture and painting; Michael Bevilacqua: painting; Julie Moos: photography; and Steve Gianakos: painting; among others.
Annual exhibitions: 7 solo/1 group.
Selection process: Artists should mail slides, biography, and SASE. Materials must include a cover letter explaining why the artist's work fits in our gallery.

SHERRY FRENCH

601 West 26 St., 13th floor, 10001. **T:** (212) 647-8867.
F: (212) 647-8899.
E: sherryfrench@earthlink.net **W:** www.sherryfrenchgallery.com
Open: Tues.- Sat. 10-6; Summer: Mon.-Fri. 10-6.
Year established: 1983. **Size:** 2,000 sq. ft.
Owner/Director: Sherry French.
Work shown: Contemporary American Realism. Painting.
Artists represented: 20 male/10 female. Predominantly American.
Work by: Stephen Tanis: painting; Bill Patterson: painting; William Dunlap: mixed media; Michael Zigmoud: painting; and John Briggs: painting; among others.
Collectors: Metropolitan Museum and NYNEX. **Prices:** $1,000-40,000.
Annual exhibitions: 5 solo/5 group. **Advertising:** *Gallery Guide.*
Focus/Mission: The gallery exhibits Contemporary American Realism where the emotional or psychological element is heightened.

Selection process: 30% of the artists are selected from referrals, 30% from slides sent to the gallery, 30% from exhibitions, and 10% from publications. Artists should mail 12 slides, biography and SASE. **Response time:** 1 month.
Requirements: Artists should be ready with a complete body of work.

GAGOSIAN

555 West 24 St., 10011.　　　　**T:** (212) 741-1111.
F: (212) 741-9611.　　　　**E:** info@gagosian.com
W: www.gagosian.com　　　　**Open:** Tues.-Sat. 10-6.
Year established: 1991.　　　　**Size:** 22,000 sq. ft.
Owner: Larry Gagosian.　　　　**Director:** Ealan Wingate.
Work shown: Large-scale sculpture and painting.
Artists represented: 15-20.　　　　**Annual exhibitions:** 6-8.
Work by: Douglas Gordon, video and photography; Cecily Brown, painting and drawing; Jenny Saville, painting and photography; Francesco Clemente, painting and drawing; and Mark di Suvero, sculpture; among others.

GALE-MARTIN

134 Tenth Ave., 10011.　　　　**T:** (646) 638-2525
F: (646) 475-6846.　　　　**W:** www.galemartin.com
Open: Tues.-Sat. 11-6.　　　　**Owner:** D. Hamilton Caranda-Martin.
Year established: 1993.　　　　**Work shown:** Contemporary art.
Work by: Francine Tint; Jean Miotte and Jackie Lipton; among others.
Prices: $2,000-150,000.　　　　**Artists represented:** 15. All origins.

GALERIE LELONG

528 West 26 St., 10019.　　　　**T:** (212) 315-0470.
F: (212) 262-0624.　　　　**W:** www.artnet.com/lelong.html
Open: Tues.-Sat. 11-5:30. July Mon.-Fri. 10-5, Aug. by appointment.
Year established: 1978.　 Member of Art Dealers Association of America.
President: Daniel Lelong.　　　　**Vice President:** Jean Fremon.
Vice President: Jacques Dupin.　　　**Director:** Mary Sabbatino.
Work shown: Contemporary and Modern art from the U.S., Europe and Latin America; Contemporary and Modern prints.
Annual exhibitions: 6.　　　　**Advertising:** *Gallery Guide.*
Work by: Andy Goldsworthy: sculpture and photography; Ana Mendieta: photography and installation; Sean Scully: works on paper; Ursula von Rydingsvard: sculpture; and Alfredo Jaar: installation, among others.

GALLERY ALEXIE

529 West 20 St., 4th floor, 10011.　**T:** (212) 741-7957.
Year established: 1996.　　　　**Owner/Director:** Stephen Gang.
Open: Tues.-Sat. 12-6.　　　　**Work shown:** All styles and media.
Work by: Katherine Allen: painting; Orazio Salati: painting; Tamara Wasserman: painting; among others.　　　**Prices:** $500-10,000.
Annual exhibitions: 40 solo/10 group.　**Advertising:** *NY Arts, Gallery Guide.*
Focus/Mission: To show good art in any form. To have a good relationship with the artists and to promote their careers.
Selection process: Artists should mail slides, resumé, prices, and SASE. Artists should also call for an appointment. **Response time:** 2 weeks.
Requirements: Art should be high quality and artists should be agreeable.
Fees: Artists pay a fee for one-year representation.

GALLERY HENOCH

555 West 25 St., 10001.
F: (917) 305-0018.
W: www.galleryhenoch.com
T: (212) 966-6360.
E: ghenoch@earthlink.net
Open: Tues.-Sat. 10:30-6. Closed in Aug.
Year established: 1983.
Owner/Director: George Henoch Shechtman, former painter, degree in art history, Rutgers University.
Work shown: Predominantly Realism in all media.   **Prices:** $1,000-30,000.
Artists represented: 15 male/20 female. **Ages:** 30-50.
Work by: Olga Antonova: oils; Steve Smulka: oils; and Sharon Sprung, oils; Mel Leipzit: oils; and Clifford Smith: oils; among others.
Annual exhibitions: 5 solo/2 group.
Advertising: *ARTnews, Art in America*, and *Gallery Guide.*
Selection process: The best time for artists to submit materials is between January-February, and June-July. The artist should be familiar with the work the gallery represents before they mail slides, biography and SASE.

GALLERY TARANTO

245 West 19 St., 10011.
F: (212) 366-6929.
W: www.tarantolabs.com
Year established: 1993.
T: (212) 691-6070
E: gallery@tarantolabs.com
Open: Mon.-Fri. 9-7, Sat. 11-5.
Owner/Director: Kenneth S. Taranto.
Background: Photographer and photography studio owner. This is a photographic lab that presents exhibitions.
Work shown: Documentary, social, journalistic and other forms of photography.
Work by: Philip Perkis; Roger Ballen; Roger Vail; and Alex Webb; among others.
Annual exhibitions: 4 solo/6 group.
Advertising: *The New York Times.*
Prices: $250-3,000.   **Markets:** Individual, corporate, and museum.
Focus/Mission: To show photography that confronts the social, political, professional, and artistic issues central to today's discourse. Our approach is more didactic than commercial.
Selection process: Artists should call for an appointment to show slides and/or prints. **Requirement:** Artists should have a concise theme.

GALLERY TEN IN ONE

526 West 26 St., #316, 10001.
F: (212) 604-9484.
W: www.artnet/teninone.html
T: (212) 604-9660.
E: teninonegallery@earthlink.net
Open: Tues.-Sat. 11-6; Summer: Tues.-Fri. 11-6.
Year established: 1999 in New York; 1989 in Chicago.
Owner/Director: Joel Leib, MFA in Painting.
Work shown: New and innovative contemporary art in all media.
Size: 1,700 sq. ft.   **Prices:** $500-15,000.
Artists represented: 12, from the U.S.
Work by: Michelle Grabner: painting; John Spear: painting, drawing and mixed media; Rochelle Feinstein: painting: Pam Lins: sculpture and photography; Type A: video and photography; among others.
Annual exhibitions: 8.   **Advertising:** *Gallery Guide, Artforum, Art in America.*
Selection process: Artists should familiarize themselves with at least 3 shows before approaching. Artists should mail slides, photographs, resumé, and SASE.
Response time: 2 months.

STEPHEN GANG

529 West 20 St., 4E, 10011.   **T:** (212) 741-7832.
F: (212) 741-7957.   **W:** www.stephenggallery.ohgolly.com
Open: Tues.-Sat. 12-6.   **Year established:** 1997.
Owner/Director: Stephen Gang.
Work shown: We are an eclectic gallery. We show installation art, Fluxus, Performance, and video.   **Annual exhibitions:** 8 solo/2 group.
Selection process: Artists should send slides, resumé, and SASE.
Additional information: Artists should be prepared to pay exhibition expenses.

KLEMENS GASSER & TANJA GRUNERT

524 West 19 St., 10011.   **T:** (212) 807-9494.
F: (212) 807-6594.   **E:** gassergrunert@earthlink.net
Size: 5,000 sq. ft.
Open: Tues.-Sat 10-6. July Mon.-Fri. 10-6. Closed in Aug..
Year established: 1998.   **Owner/Director:** Klemens Gasser.
Work shown: Contemporary art in all media including Conceptual and film.
Prices: $500-with no limit.   **Artists represented:** 11 international artists.
Work by: Eija-Liisa Ahtilia; Jipka Hanzlova; Thomas Locher; VALIE EXPORT; and Peter Zimmermann; among others.   **Annual exhibitions:** 10.
Selection process: The gallery is not interested in receiving artists' materials.

GENEROUS MIRACLES

529 West 20 St., 8th floor West, 10011.
T: (212) 352-2858.   **F:** (212) 352-2763.
E: genmiracle@aol.com   **Open:** Tues.-Sat. 11-6.
Year established: 1997.   **Size:** 3,000 sq. ft.
Owners: Milagros Maldonado and Generoso Villarreal Garza. International art dealers from Mexico and Venezuela (art foundations).
Work shown: All media by international artists.
Artists represented: 25. 70% male/30% female. 30% are in museum collections.
Work by: Exhibitions have featured artists in collaboration with Galleria L'Atico, Italy; in Cuba; and artists in collaboration with Kukje Gallery in Seoul.
Annual exhibitions: 6 solo/1 group.   **Advertising:** *Flash Art* and *Art Nexus.*
Focus/Mission: A global review of dynamic situations in the arts. Group shows are presented by cities, in collaboration with institutions and private galleries.
Selection process: 30% of the artists are selected from professional referrals; 40% from slides sent to the gallery; and 50% from art seen in exhibitions, publications and artists' studios. Artists should mail slides, resumé and prices with SASE. We review artists' materials every two months. **Response time:** 1 month.
Fees: To be discussed.

SANDRA GERING

534 West 22 St., 10011.   **T:** (646) 336-7183.
F: (646) 336-7185.   **E:** Sandra@geringgallery.com
W: www.geringgallery.com   **Year established:** 1991.
Open: Tues.-Sat. 10-6. Summer: Tues.-Fri. 10-6.
Owner/Director: Sandra Gering, art education at the New School and New York University.
Associate Director: Marianna Baer.   **Work shown:** All styles and media.
Artists represented: 10. Ages 30-60. **Origins**: U.S., Spain, Japan, Venezuela, and U.K. 50% of the artists are in museum collections.

Work by: Meghan Boody: digital photography; Jose Antonio Hernandez-Diez: video installations and sculpture; John F. Simon: digital computer art; Xavier Veilhan: mixed media sculpture and installation; and Matthew McCaslin: video sculpture; among others.

Collectors: Saatchi Collection, Fisher Landau Collection, and Deste Foundation.

Annual exhibitions: 6 solo/2 group.　**Advertising:** *Artforum* and *Gallery Guide*.

Focus/Mission: To exhibit both emerging and established international artists. The artists share the ability to create Conceptual artwork which pushes ideas and materials to controversial lengths. Through technology and innovative materials, these young artists explore the limits in today's world, and what is possible in the future.

Selection process: 98% of the artists are selected from referrals, 2% through publications. Artists should be familiar with the work we show before approaching us. If their work is appropriate, artists should call and see if we are accepting slides.

GET REAL ART

156 Fifth Ave., (entrance on West 20 St.), 10010.
T: (212) 741-2278.　　**F:** (212) 741-9312.
W: www.getrealart.com　　**Open:** Mon.-Sat. 11-7, Sun. 12-6
Year established: 1999.　　**Size:** 3,300 sq. ft.
Owner/Director: Susan Jarrell.　**Work shown:** Contemporary art in all media.
Prices: $20-20,000.　　**Artists represented:** 50, from all origins.
Selection process: Artists should visit or call the gallery.

BARBARA GLADSTONE

515 West 24 St., 10011.　　**T:** (212) 206-9300.
F: (212) 206-9301.　　**E:** info@gladstonegallery.com
W: www.gladstonegallery.com
Open: Tues.-Sat. 10-6; Summer: Call for hours.
Owner: Barbara Gladstone.　　**Work shown:** Contemporary art in all media.
Work by: Matthew Barney; Richard Prince; Vito Acconci; Shirin Neshat; and James Turrell; among others.

CAREN GOLDEN FINE ART

526 West 26 St., #215, 10001.　**T:** (212) 727-8304.
F: (212) 727-8360.　　**W:** www.carengoldenfineart.com
Open: Tues.-Sat. 11-6 through June; July Tues.-Fri. 11-6; Closed in August.
Year established: 1994.　　**Size:** 2,200 sq. ft.
Owner: Caren Golden, former private art advisor.
Director: Collette Blauchard, former Director of David Beitzel Gallery.
Work shown: Work in all media by Contemporary and emerging artists.
Work by: Seong Chun; John Kalymnios; Paul Henry Ramirez; Jean Blackburn; and Tom Burchardt; among others. **Prices:** $500-20,000.
Advertising: *Gallery Guide, Art in America* and *Artforum*.
Focus/Mission: To exhibit the work of established and emerging Contemporary artists. To encourage a dialogue between them and the viewing and collecting public.
Selection process: Artists should contact the gallery for current procedure.
Requirements: Artists who have the right combination of aesthetic appeal, social significance and vision.

RUPERT GOLDSWORTHY

"To show a small group of predominantly emerging and mid-career Conceptual artists. The gallery is also engaged in secondary-market sales. The work we show presents the gallery's role and philosophy best: A commitment to individuality and content-based work. The gallery plans on establishing a project space program in India in 2004.

RUPERT GOLDSWORTHY

453 West 17 St., 2nd floor, 10011.   **T/F:** (212) 414-4560.
E: r_goldsworthy@hotmail.com   **W:** www.artnet/goldsworthy.html
Open: Wed.-Sat 12-6.   **Size:** 500 sq. ft.
Year established: 1997 in New York; 1995 in Berlin, Germany.
Owner/Director: Rupert Goldsworthy, MA Art/Art History from NYU, and worked for Barbara Gladstone.
Work shown: Contemporary, Conceptual, Emerging painting, photography, sculpture, video and installation.
Markets: Individual, corporate and museum. **Prices:** $700-30,000.
Artists represented: 4 +. **Origins:** U.S. and Europe.
Work by: BANK: installation, painting and text; Jane Kaplowitz: painting; Steven Evans: Conceptual, gender-related painting, sculpture, and installation; Stephen Tashjian: Pop-related painting and drawing; and Mr. Leonard: extreme photography; among others.
Annual exhibitions: 6 solo/3 group.
Advertising: *Time Out, Artforum, Flash Art* and *Chelsea Gallery Guide.*
Focus/Mission: To show a small group of predominantly emerging and mid-career Conceptual artists. The gallery is also engaged in secondary-market sales. The work we show presents the gallery's role and philosophy best: A commitment to individuality and content-based work.
Selection process: 20% of the artists are selected from professional referrals; 80% from art seen in exhibitions, publications and artists' studios. The gallery prefers not to be solicited by artists without referral. We are interested initially to see the work, respond to it, and contact the artist ourselves.
Requirement: To be currently showing or somewhat known.
Additional information: The gallery works closely with this small group of artists to bring their work to a wider public. Services include developing a critical and collector base for their work, and developing the artist's profile internationally through connections with other galleries and international art fairs and museums. The gallery program also includes many group shows (curated) of young, emerging artists. The gallery presents some performance events and occasional panel discussions with critics, curators and educators. The gallery plans on establishing a project space program in India in 2004.

GORNEY, BRAVIN & LEE

534 West 26 St., 10001.   **T:** (212) 352-8372.
F: (212) 352-8374.   **E:** info@gblgallery.com
W: www.gblgallery.com   **Open:** Tues.-Sat., 10-6.
Year established: 1998. Member of the Art Dealers Association.
Owners: Jay Gorney, former owner of Jay Gorney Gallery; and Karin Bravin and John Post Lee, former owners of Bravin Post Lee Gallery.   *continued*

Work shown: Painting, drawings, sculpture, photography, video and installations.
Work by: Barbara Bloom; Sarah Charlesworth; David Deutsch; the estate of Moira Dryer; Kenneth Goldsmith; and Fabian Marcaccio; among others.
Markets: Individual, corporate and museum.
Prices: $1,000-60,000. **Annual exhibitions:** 8-9.
Advertising: *Artforum* and *Art in America.*
Selection process: Artists are selected from referrals, slides sent to the gallery, exhibitions, and publications. Artists should send 10 slides, resumé, and SASE.
Response time: 2 months.

BARBARA GREENE

525 West 22 St., 10011.   **T:** (212) 462-4123.
F: (212) 352-0127.   **E:** leafdreams4me@yahoo.com
Open: By appointment.   **Year established:** 1999.
Owner/Director: Barbara Greene, former painter, photographer, and attorney.
Work shown: Contemporary fine art by international artists.
Prices: $500-100,000.   **Artists represented:** 7.
Work by: Ahmad Zakii Anwar: painting; Peter Max Kandhola: photography; Robert Bianchi: photography; Path Soong: painting; Ayano Ohmi: sculpture; and Christopher Wynter: painting; among others. **Annual exhibitions:** 6-8.
Selection process: Artists are selected by referrals only.

GREENE NAFTALI

526 West 26 St., 8th floor, 10011.   **T:** (212) 463-7770.
F: (212) 463-0890.   **Open:** Tues.-Sat. 10-6.
Year established: 1995.   **Size:** 3,000 sq. ft.
Owners: Carol Greene, former Director of the John Good Gallery; and Gloria Naftali.   **Director:** Carol Greene.
Work shown: Contemporary art in all media.
Artists represented: 6, from U.S. and Europe.
Work by: Jacqueline Humphries: Abstract painting; Lucy Gunning: video; Jonathan Horowitz: video; Blake Rayne: painting and installation; and Rachel Harrison: mixed media; among others.
Markets: Individual, corporate, museum.
Collectors: Charles Saatchi, Carol and Arthur Goldberg, MIT, and Eileca Cohen.
Prices: $500-100,000.   **Annual exhibitions:** 4 solo/ 2 group.
Advertising: *Artforum* and *Art in America.*
Focus/Mission: The underlying philosophical principal of the gallery is to exhibit artwork in a range of mediums that presents a visual project that proposes new meaning and provides insight into our current social and cultural times.
Selection process: 50% of the artists are selected from professional referrals, 50% from art seen in exhibitions or artists studios. We are currently not accepting unsolicited artists' materials.

JAY GRIMM

505 West 28 St., 10001.   **T:** (212) 564-7662.
F: (212) 564-8193.   **E:** jay@jaygrimm.com
W: www.jaygrimm.com
Open: Tues.-Sat. 11-6; July and Aug. Tues.-Fri. 11-5:30.
Year established: 1998.   **Size:** 400 sq. ft.
Owner: Jay Grimm, Assistant to President, Pace Wildenstein. Masters in Art History from SUNY Stony Brook.
Work shown: Abstract painting and sculpture, all media.

Artists represented: 5-10, mostly from N.Y.
Annual exhibitions: 8.   **Prices:** $500-10,000.
Work by: Jon McCafferty: oil painting; Patrick Strzelec: sculpture; Bill Scanga: Conceptual art; Jess Von Der Ahe: painting; and Julia Von Eichel: painting; among others.
Selection process: Artists should mail slides, biography and SASE.
Response time: 1 month.

MURRAY GUY

453 West 17 St., 2nd floor, 10011.   **T:** (212) 463-7372.
F: (212) 463-7319.   **E:** murrayguy@mindspring.com
Open: Tues.-Sat. 10-6.   **Year established:** 1998.
Owners: Margaret Murray, previously worked at Bacilico Fine Art, and freelance curator, and Janice Guy, worked at Stern-Gladstone gallery in Milan.
Work shown: Contemporary art in all media by international artists.
Artists represented: 12.
Work by: Fiona Banner: sculpture, drawing and mixed media; Matthew Buckingham: film; Francis Cape: sculpture; Dave Muller: work on paper; and Shirley Tse: sculpture; among others.
Prices: $1,500-25,000.   **Annual exhibitions:** 9.
Selection process: Artists should call the gallery for information.

THE HALF KING

505 West 23 St., 10001.   **T:** (212) 462-4300.
E: exhibits@thehalfking.com   **W:**thehalfking.com
Owners: Owners: Scott Anderson, Nanette Burstein, Jerome O'Connor, Sebastian Junger. This is a classic style pub, serving European flavors.
Work by: Exhibitions have included photography by Teun Voeten; Paul Waldman; and Tobin Russel, in collaboration with a21, which promotes the work of photojournalists worldwide.

SUSAN L. HALPER

505 West 23 St., 10001.   **T:** (212) 473-7166.
F: (212) 473-2558.   **E:** slhaincvdot.net
W: www.artnet.com   **Open:** By appointment.
Owner/Director: Susan L. Harper.
Background: Art historian, former staff member of Guggenheim Museum, curator and private collector.
Work shown: Specializing in brokering fine art of the 20th Century including work on paper, prints, painting and sculpture by American and European master, Postwar and 21st Century emerging artists.
Work by: Current inventories include work by Alfred Jensen; Jacob Lawrence; Damien Hirst; Cecily Brown; and Cesar Domela; among others.

ELIZABETH HARRIS

529 West 20 St., 6th floor, 10011.   **T:** (212) 463-9666.
F: (212) 463-9403.   **E:** ehg@dti.net
Open: Tues.-Sat. 10-6; Summer: July Tues.-Fri. 10-6; Aug. closed.
Year established: 1992.   **Size:** 4,000 sq. ft.
Owner/Director: Elizabeth Harris, former painter and co-owner of Oscarsson-Hood gallery.   **Co-Director:** Bill Carroll.
Work shown: Figurative and Abstract painting and sculpture.   *continued*

Artists represented: 16 artists. 60% are in museum collections.
Work by: Scott Richter: painting; Pat Passlof, painting; Jane Schiowitz: painting; Julian Hatton: painting and Pat Lipsky: painting; among others.
Prices: $1,000-20,000.   **Annual exhibitions:** 7 solo/2 group.
Advertising: *Review, Art in America* and *New York Arts.*
Selection process: The gallery currently has all the artists needed. We are not accepting unsolicited materials.

HELLER

420 West 14 St., 10014.   **T:** (212) 414-4014.
F: (212) 414-2636.   **E:** info@hellergallery.com
W: www.hellergallery.com
Open: Tues.-Sat. 11-6, Sun. 12-5; Summer: Tues.-Sat. 11-6.
Year established: 1972.   **Size:** 7,000 sq. ft.
Owners: Douglas Heller and Michael Heller. Backgrounds: Retail business.
Director: Douglas Heller.   **Assistant Director:** Bob Roberts.
Work shown: Glass art in all styles and contemporary works in wood.
Artists represented: 60.   75male/25 female. **Ages:** 24-74.
90% of the artists are in museum collections.
Work by: Bertil Vallien; Kyohei Fujita; Paul Stankard; Philip Moulphrop; and Lino Tagliapietra; among others.
Prices: $1,000-30,000.   **Markets:** Individual, corporate, and museum.
Collectors: Metropolitan, Toledo Museum, Hokaido Museum of Modern Art, and Corning Museum of Glass.
Annual exhibitions: 10 solo/1 group.
Advertising: *Gallery Guide, American Craft Magazine,* and *Glass Magazine.*
Focus/Mission: To be dedicated to Contemporary glass art and wood and support the field through exhibitions, educational events, as well as working with non-profit artists' organizations. To be an important resource for museums and serious collectors.
Selection process: Artists should have a credible representative body of work before they submit slides, resumé, and SASE. Artists should possess originality, a point of view, command of technique and commitment. **Response time:** 6 weeks.

JOSEPH HELMAN

601 West 26 St., 14th floor, 10001. **T:** (212) 929-1545.
F: (212) 929-1506.   **E:** jhgallery@aol.com
Open: Tues.-Sat.10-6, Summer: Mon.-Fri. 10-6. Aug. by appointment only.
Member of Art Dealers Association of America.
Owner: Joseph A. Helman.   **Director:** Peter Ryan.
Work shown: American and European Contemporary paintings, sculpture drawings and installation.
Artists represented: 13. **Ages:** 25 and above. **Origins:** U.S. and Europe.
Work by: Julie Allen: sculpture; Wes Mills: drawing and painting; Robert Kalka: sculpture; Tom Wesselmann: painting; and Dennis Oppenheim: sculptural and site-specific works; among others.
Collectors: Metropolitan, MoMA, Chase, and Emily Fisher Landau Center.
Annual exhibitions: 6 solo/3 group. **Advertising:** *Art in America* and *NY Times.*
Focus/Mission: To exhibit contemporary art by established and emerging artists.
Selection process: Artists should send up to 20 slides with SASE.
Response time: 3 months.
Requirements: Artistic quality and familiarity with gallery.

I-20

529 West 20 St., 10011.
F: (212) 645-0198.
W: www.I-20.com
Year established: 1997.
Owner/Director: Paul Judelson.
T: (212) 645-1100.
E: Judelson@I-20.com
Open: Tues.-Sat 10-6.
Size: 4,600 sq. ft.
Co-Director: Jill Presti.
Work shown: Contemporary art in all media.
Annual exhibitions: 6.
Work by: Peter Sarkisian: video; and Afrika (Sergei Bugaev), mixed media; Spencer Tunick: photography; Kiki Seror: digital; Marina Kappos: painting; among others.
Selection process: We are always interested in looking for new artists. Artists should visit the gallery and submit slides.
Fees: Artists should be prepared to pay exhibition related expenses.

INDO CENTER OF ART & CULTURE (ICAC)

530 West 25 St., 10001.
F: (212) 462-4437.
W: www.indocenter.org
Open: Tues.-Sat. 11-6.
Owner: Non-profit organization.
Annual exhibitions: 3.
T: (212) 462-4221.
E: mail@indocenter.org

Year established: 2001.
Director: Mahnaz Fancy.
Size: 4,000 sq. ft.
Work shown: Modern and contemporary art & culture of South Asia.
Selection process: Artists from South Asia should send slides and/or photographs, biography and SASE.
Additional information: ICAC curates shows, hosts performances, presents films and hosts lectures.

INTERNATIONAL PRINT CENTER

526 West 26 St., Rm. 824, 10001.
E: contact@ipcny.org
Open: Tues.-Sat. 12-6.
Owner: Non-profit organization.
Work shown: All fine art prints.
T: (212) 989-5090.
W: www.ipcny.org
Year established: 2000.
Director: Anne Coffin.
Annual Exhibitions: 4.
Selection process: We have three juried shows each year. There is a "Call for Submissions" 3 times a year. Artists should visit the website for details.

RENNIE JOHNSON ART / URBAN ARCHITECTURE

210 Eleventh Ave., #401, 10001.
F: (212) 924-3128.
W: www.renniejohnson.com
Open: Tues.-Sat. 12-6; Summer: Tues.-Fri. 11-6.
Year established: 1998 in NY, 1996 in Detroit, MI.
Founder: Keith Johnson, BFA, MFA, Art and Architectural History.
Work shown: Artwork by internationally-renowned artists, designers and architects. Visual and decorative artworks by great visionaries that operate within an art and architectural context. Original drawings, painting, sculpture, public-scale sculpture, limited edition prints, photography, decorative art objects, and art furniture.
Work by: Alessandro Mendini, Patrick Naggar, Ettore Sottsass, Jr., Daniel Buren, and Sandro Chia; among others.
Selection process: Artists should send digital images or photographs.

CASEY KAPLAN

416 West 14 St., 10014.   T: (212) 645-7335.
F: (212) 645-7835.   E: CaseyKaplan@aol.com
Open: Tues.- Sat. 10-6. July Mon.-Fri. 10-6. Closed July 26-August 31.
Year established: 1995.   Size: 2,500 sq. ft.
Owner/Director: Casey Kaplan, previously worked at Pace McGill.
Work shown: Contemporary painting, sculpture, photography and video.
Artists represented: 14, from U.S., U.K., Germany and Sweden.
Work by: Amy Adler: photography; Jeff Burton: photography; Miles Coolidge: photography; Liam Gillick: sculpture; and Anna Jaskell: photography; among others.
Annual exhibitions: 7solo/1 group. Advertising: *Artforum, Frieze &World Art.*
Markets: Individual, corporate, and museum.
Focus/Mission: To introduce and then to represent the work of young artists from California, New York, and Europe.
Selection process: 20% of the artists are selected from professional referrals, and 80% of the artists are selected from art seen in exhibitions or artists studios. We are currently not looking for new artists.

PAUL KASMIN

293 Tenth Ave., 10001.   T: (212) 563-4474.
F: (212) 563-4494.   E: paulkasmin@aol.com
W: www.paulkasmingallery.com
Open: Tues.-Sat. 10-6.   Size: 7,000 sq. ft.
Year established: 1989.   Owner/Director: Paul Kasmin.
Work shown: Contemporary drawing, painting, photography, sculpture and installation.   Prices: $1,000-500,000.
Artists represented: 17. 50% male/female. Ages: mid 20-40's. All of the artists are in museum collections.
Work by: Donald Baechler: painting; Walton Ford: painting; and Nancy Rubins: sculpture; James Wares: painting; and Elliott Puckette: painting; among others.
Collectors: Metropolitan Museum, MoMA, Whitney, and Guggenheim.
Annual exhibitions: 8 solo/1 group.
Selection process: We are currently not looking at new artists' materials.

SEAN KELLY

528 West 29 St., 10001.   T: (212) 239-1181.
F: (212) 239-2467.   E: info@skny.com
WEB SITE: www.skny.com   Size: 9,000 sq. ft.
Open: Tues.-Sat. 11-6.   Year established: 1995.
Owner: Sean Kelly.   Director: Cecile Panzieri.
Work shown: Contemporary art in all media.
Artists represented: 11.   Annual exhibitions: 8.
Work by: Ann Hamilton: mixed media; Lorna Simpson: mixed media; Marina Abramovic: mixed media; Juliao Sarmento: painting; and Callum Innes: painting; among others.
Selection process: Artists should be familiar with the work we show before approaching us.

JIM KEMPNER FINE ARTS

501 West 23 St., 10011.
T: (212) 206-6872.
F: (212) 206-6873.
W: www.artnet.com/jkfa.html
Open: Tues.-Sat. 10-6.
Year established: 1987.
Owner/Director: Jim Kempner.
Work shown: Contemporary Master prints and work on paper.
Work by: Bartlet; Lichtenstein; Johns; Diebenkorn; Rauschenberg; and Hodgkin; among others. **Prices:** $300 and above.
Annual exhibitions: 3-4 solo/continuous group

ANTON KERN

532 West 20 Street, 10011.
T: (212) 367-9663.
F: (212) 367-8135
Open: Tues.-Sat. 10-6.
Contact: Anton Kern.
Work shown: Art by young and emerging American and European artists, with a particular focus on Conceptualism.
Work by: Angus Fairhurst; Lothar Hempel; Lara Schnitger; Sarah Jones; Alessandro Pessoli; and Eberhard Havekost; among others.

THE KITCHEN

512 West 19 St., 10011.
T: (212) 255-5793.
F: (212) 645-4258.
E: info@thekitchen.org
W: www.thekitchen.org
Open: Mon.-Fri., 10-5; Sat. 2-6.
Year established: 1974.
Owner: Non-profit organization.
Director: Elise Bernhardt.
Marketing Director: Isabelle Deconinck.
Work shown: Literature, dance, performance, video, education and more.
Focus/Mission: This is an interdisciplinary laboratory committed to the creation and realization of new ideas by visionary artists. It focuses on the creation and promotion of the cultural vanguard. It has helped foster the careers of such artists as Cindy Sherman, Laurie Anderson, Robert Longo, and Bill Viola.
Selection process: Artists should contact for information about submitting proposals.

NICOLE KLAGSBRUN

526 West 26 St., #213, 10001.
T: (212) 243-3335.
F: (212) 243-1059.
E: gallery@nicoleklagsbrun.com
Year established: 1989.
Owner: Nicole Klagsbrun.
Directors: Ruth Phaneuf and Bruce Hackney.
Work shown: Contemporary international art in all media.
Work by: Hiroshi Sugito: painting; Elaine Reichek: embroidery; Jacob El Hanani: drawings; Wallace Berman: mixed media collage; and Dodi Wexler: paper constructions; among others. **Annual exhibitions:** 8 solo/4 group.
Advertising: *Gallery Guide, Artforum*, and *Frieze*.
Markets: Individual, corporate, and museum. **Prices:** $400-40,000.

KLOTZ/SIRMON

511 West 25 St., 10001.
T: (212) 741-4764.
F: (212) 741-4760.
W: www.photocollect.com
Open: Wed.-Sat. 11-6; Summer: Wed.-Fri. 11-6
Year established: 1998.
Size: 2,200 sq. ft.
Owners/Directors: Alan Klotz and Janet Sirmon
Work shown: Photography in all styles.
Annual exhibitions: 6-7.
Advertising: *Village Voice* and *New Yorker.*

ART OUTDOORS
In NYC sculpture gardens can be enjoyed at
J. Cacciola gallery, Nikolai Fine Art, Metropolitan Museum of Art,
and Isamu Noguchi Garden Museum.

KRAVETS/WEHBY

529 West 21 St., 10011.
F: (212) 352-2239.
Year established: 1996.

T: (212) 352-2238.
Open: Tues.-Sat. 11-6.
Size: 300 sq. ft.

Owners/Directors: Marc Wehby, previously worked at Annina Nosei; and Susie Kravets, worked at John Weber.
Work shown: Contemporary art by primarily young international artists.
Annual exhibitions: 10.
Work by: Irina Alimanestianu: large scale Figurative painting based on personal narratives; Vinnie Angel: a range of media; Manuel Esnoz: lyrical narrative painting; Gajin Fujita: painting with infusions of traditional Japanese iconography and graffiti styles; and Wendell Gladstone: combinations of painting and sculpture that are reminiscent of children's game boards; among others.
Additional information: The gallery also handles art on the secondary market.

ANDREW KREPS

516 A West 20 St., 10011.
F: (212) 741-8163.
Year established: 1996.

T: (212) 741-8849.
Open: Tues.- Sat. 11-6.
Size: 1,500 sq. ft.

Owner/Director: Andrew Kreps, graduate of NYU; worked with Paula Cooper.
Work shown: Young, emerging, cutting-edge art in all media.
Artists represented: 10.
Work by: Meredith Danluck: Abstract wall sculptures with a Minimalist sensibility; Jonah Freeman: video projections on oil painted canvases accompanied by architectural light pieces; Ricci Albenda: text-based work on aluminum panels, accompanied by distorted architectural space wall reliefs; Robert Melee: a variety of painting, video and photography with a mundane suburban sensibility; and Lawrence Seward: Figurative witty sculpture and Abstract painting; among others.
Prices: $200-7,000.
Annual exhibitions: 7 solo/ 2 group. **Advertising:** *Artforum* and *Gallery Guide*.
Focus/Mission: The gallery creates an open forum in which artists, employing a wide variety of media, explore their reactions to life in contemporary society. Kreps exposes the distinctive visions of these emerging artists.
Selection process: Artists should mail slides, biography, resumé, prices, and SASE. **Response time:** 2 weeks. **Requirements:** "It has to be good!"

LFL (LAWRENCE/FEUER/LA MONTAGNE)

531 West 26 St., 4th floor, 10001.
F: (212) 631-7705.
Open: Tues.-Sat. 11-6 and by appointment.
Year established: 2000.

T: (212) 631-7700.
W: www.lflgallery.com

Size: 1,200 sq. ft.

Owners/Directors: Nick Lawrence, Zak Feuor, Russel LaMontagne.
Work shown: Contemporary art by emerging and mid-career artists.

Work by: Danica Phelps: drawing; Dana Schutz: painting; Holly Coulis: painting: Tom McGrath: painting; and Kirsten Stoltmann: video; among others.
Annual exhibitions: 10.
Advertising: *World Art* and *Flash Art*.
Selection process: Artists should send slides and/or photographs, resumé, and SASE.

PATRICIA LALIGANT PHOTOGRAPHS

150 West 28 St., #1702, 10001.   **T:** (212) 252-9922.
F: (212) 627-2993.   **E:** patricialaligant@msn.com
W: www.laligant-photography.com
Open: By appointment.   **Year established:** 1997.
Director: Patricia Laligant.
Work shown: European photography from 1920 to 1940.
Artists represented: Marcel Bovis; Robert Doisneau; Germaine Krull; Emmanuel Sougez; and Laure Albin Guillot; among others.

LIEBMAN MAGNAN

552 West 24 St., 2nd floor, 10011.   **T:** (212) 255-3225.   **F:** (646) 336-9090.
E: liebmanmagnan@rcn.com   **Open:** Tues.-Sat. 11-6.
Year established: 1998.   **Size:** 1,200 sq. ft.
Owners/Directors: Penny Liebman and Kathleen Magnan.
Work shown: Contemporary painting, photography and sculpture by artists from all origins.
Markets: Individual, corporate, museum.   **Prices:** $1,000-200,000.
Work by: Young Sun Lim: sculpture; David Shapiro: sculpture; Valeska Forares: work on paper and sculpture; Tania Bruguera: performance and sculpture; and Tracey Baran: photography; among others.
Annual exhibitions: 10 solo/group.   **Advertising:** *World Art* and *Flash Art*.
Focus/Mission: Cutting-edge, Contemporary international art.

LOMBARD-FREID FINE ARTS

531 West 26 St., 10001.   **T:** (212) 967-8040.
F: (212) 967-0669.   **E:** lomfrd@echonyc.com
Year established: 1995.   **Size:** 2,500 sq. ft.
Owners: Jane Lombard and Lea Freid.
Director: Michael Lieberman.
Work shown: A range of Conceptually-based, and photo-based work, video, installations, objects, and work on paper, by established and emerging, international and contemporary artists.
Annual exhibitions: 10.
Work by: Lee Mingwei: performance-based photographs and sculptural installations.
Focus/Mission: To focus on artists whose work addresses notions of history, natural sciences, technology (as a medium and a subject) and cross-cultural issues. The gallery also provides an exhibition venue for curators to explore challenging contemporary ideas through exhibitions, events and informal salons.
Selection process: Most artists are selected by referrals, although slides are periodically reviewed. Artists should submit materials with SASE.

LONG FINE ART

427 West 14 St., 1st floor, 10014.   **T:** (212) 337-1940.
F: (212) 337-1939.   **E:** longfynart@aol.com
W: www.artnet.com   **Size:** 2,000 sq. ft.
Open: Tues.-Sat. 10-6, Sun. 1-5; Summer closed Sun.
Year established: 1993.
Owner/Director: Stephen Long.   **Associate Director:** Constance Gill.
Work shown: 1st and 2nd generation School of New York Abstract Expressionism.
Work on paper, drawings, painting, and prints (etchings and lithographs).
Artists represented: 12. **Ages:** 47-76. All origins. All are in museum collections
Work by: Robert Motherwell: prints; Milton Avery: drawings and watercolors; Sam
Francis: prints; Helen Frankenthaler: prints; Neil Marshall: painter, printmaker; and
Stanley Boxer, among others.
Collectors: Metropolitan, MoMA, Whitney, and the National Museum of American
Art, Washington, D.C.   **Prices:** $450-90,000.
Annual exhibitions: 5solo/1 group.
Advertising: *The New York Times* and *Gallery Guide.*
Focus/Mission: To specialize in the 12 artists from the School of New York with
whom the gallery has worked with for many years.
Selection process: The Director selects the artists. The gallery is currently not
accepting unsolicited materials.

JOE AND EMILY LOWE

Hudson Guild, 441 West 26 St., 10001.
T: (212) 760-9800.   **F:** (212) 268-9983.
E: hguild@hudsonguild.org   **Open:** Mon.-Fri. 4-7 pm; Sat.-Sun. 1-4.
Year established: 1948.   **Director:** Jim Furlong.
Work shown: Contemporary sculpture, painting and work on paper.
Annual exhibitions: 10.
Focus/Mission: The Guild was founded in 1895. The gallery serves to provide a
wide array of arts programming to the community in Chelsea, especially to the
underserved individuals and low-income families who come to the Guild daily.
Selection process: Artists should send slides, photographs, resumé, and SASE.

LUHRING AUGUSTINE

531 West 24 St., 10011.   **T:** (212) 206-9100.
F: (212) 206-9055.   **E:** info@luhringaugustine.com
W: www.luhringaugustine.com   **Open:** Tues.-Sat. 10-6.
Year established: 1985.
Size: 5,000 sq. ft.
Owners: Roland Augustine and Lawrence Luhring.
Work shown: Contemporary art in all media.
Artists represented: 18.
Advertising: *Gallery Guide* and *Artforum.*
Work by: Christopher Wool: painting; Rachel Whiteread: sculpture; and Larry
Clark: photography; Pipilotti Rist: video; and Gregory Crewdson: photography;
among others.
Collectors: MoMA, Whitney, MoCA Los Angeles, and MoMA Chicago.
Focus/Mission: To work with established artists from Europe, Japan and U.S.
Selection process: Artists are selected from referrals only.

INTERNATIONAL FUSION IN NYC

Marcello Marvelli taught at the University of Florence, Annina Nosei has a doctorate from the University of Rome, Paul Morris worked in a gallery in London, Robert Steele owned a gallery in Australia, and Tatsuhiko Ashida (Radio House Gallery) was a dealer in Japan.

FLORENCE LYNCH

147 West 29 St., 3rd floor, 10001.   **T:** (212) 967-7584.
F: (212) 967-9264.   **W:** www.florencelynchgallery.com
Open: Wed.-Sat. 11-6.   **Size:** 800 sq. ft.
Year established: 1994.   **Owner/Director:** Florence Lynch.
Work shown: Painting, photography, sculpture, and video.
Prices: $1,500-15,000.
Artists represented: 8 from U.S. and Europe.
Work by: Maria Morganti: Abstract and architectural painting; Madeleine Hatz: painting and assemblages; Odili Donald Odita: painting; and Noritoshi Hirakawa: photography; among others.
Annual exhibitions: 5 solo/2 group.
Advertising: *Gallery Guide* and *Art Diary*.
Selection process: Artists are selected from professional referrals and art seen in exhibitions, publications and artists' studios. Artists should mail slides, biography, and SASE. We review artists' materials in early Spring.

LYONS WIER

526 West 26 St., #702, 10001.   **T:** (212) 242-6220.
W: www.lyonswiergallery.com   **Open:** Tues.-Sat. 10-6.
Year established: 2001.   **Owner:** Michael Lyonsweir.
Work shown: Contemporary Realism in all media.
Work by: Louise LeBourgeois: oil on panel; Susan Shatter: watercolor; Jane Fisher: mixed media; Terry Towery: photography; and Chris Cosnowsky: mixed media; among others.
Selection process: Artists should send slides, resumé and SASE.
Response time: 1 month.
Additional information: The gallery's other location is in Chicago, IL.

ROBERT MANN

210 Eleventh Ave., 10th floor, 10001.   **T:** (212) 989-7600.
F: (212) 989-2947.
W: www.robertmann.com
Open: Tues.-Sat. 11-6. July and August Mon.-Fri. 11-6.
Year established: 1985.
Size: 1,200 sq. ft.
Owner: Robert Mann, former Director of the Lunn Gallery, Washington, DC.
Director: Deborah Bosniak.
Work shown: Contemporary and Vintage photography, with an emphasis on masters of the 20th Century. Also 19th Century photographers, camera work gravures.
Artists represented: 12 living artists. All origins. All of the artists are in museum collections. *continued*

Work by: Diane Arbus; Richard Misrach; JoAnn Verburg; O. Winston Link; Aaron Siskind; Lois Guarino; and Leo Rubinfien; among others.
Collectors: Whitney, National Gallery of Art, Goldman Sachs, and Hallmark.
Annual exhibitions: 6-7.
Advertising: *Gallery Guide* and *Photography New York.*
Focus/Mission: To exhibit, educate and sell fine art photography.
Selection process: We are currently not seeking new artists.

GRACIE MANSION

504 West 22 St., 10003.　　　　**T:** (212) 645-7656.
F: (212) 462-4111.　　　　　**E:** gmansion@att.net
W: www.artnet.com/gracemansion.html
Open: Tues.-Sat. 11-6.　　　**Size:** 500 sq. ft.
Year established: 1982.　　　**Director:** Gracie Mansion.
Work shown: Painting, drawing, sculpture and multi-media.
Artists represented: 7. 90% are in museum collections.
Prices: $500-500,000.　　　　**Markets:** Individual, corporate, and museum.
Work by: Ilona Malka Rich: painting, sculpture, and drawings; Al Hansen: Flexus artist, collage; Buster Cleveland: mixed media collage; Sol Lewitt: drawings and sculpture, multiples and original work; and Judy Glantzman: painting, sculpture, drawing, and etchings; among others.
Annual exhibitions: 4 solo/1 group.
Selection process: We are currently not looking for new artists.

KATHRYN MARKEL FINE ARTS

529 West 20 St., 6W, 10001.　　**T:** (212) 366-5368
F: (212) 366-5468.　　　　　**E:** markel@markelfinearts.com
W: www.markelfinearts.com　　**Open:** Tues.-Sat. 10-6.
Year established: 1985.　　　**Size:** 1,500
Owner: Kathryn Markel.　　　**Director:** Kathrine Lord.
Work shown: Work on paper and painting in a variety of media including collage, watercolors, acrylic, and oils.
Artists represented: 40. 40% male/60% female. Ages: 30-50's. All origins.
Work by: Tamar Zinn, oil pastels; collages and watercolors; Elissa Gore: oil pastel and watercolor; Tracey Adams: mixed media and monotype; and Rachel Paxton: collage and oil; and David Wander; among others.
Collectors: Prudential, Reader's Digest, Morgan Guarantee, and Merrill Lynch.
Markets: Corporate and individual.　**Prices:** $300-4,000.
Focus/Mission: To handle unique work on paper in all media.
Selection process: Artists are selected from slides sent to gallery. Artists should send slides and SASE. No calls please. **Requirements:** Art must be excellent quality, accessible and good value, art that is consistent with the gallery's sensibility.

MATTHEW MARKS

522 West 22 St., 10011.　　　　**T:** (212) 243-0200.
F: (212) 243-0047.　　　　　**E:** info@matthewmarks.com
W: www.matthewmarks.com　　**Open:** Tues.-Sat 11-6.
Director: Matthew Marks.
Work shown: Contemporary art.
Work by: Nan Goldin; Elsworth Kelly; Willem de Kooning; Brice Marden; and Terry Winters; among others.

MATTHEW MARKS

523 West 24 St., 10011.
F: (212) 243-0047.
W: www.matthewmarks.com
Director: Matthew Marks.
T: (212) 243-0200.
E: info@matthewmarks.com
Open: Tues.-Sat 10-6.
Work shown: Contemporary art.
Work by: Nan Goldin; Elsworth Kelly; Willem de Kooning; Brice Marden; and Terry Winters; among others.

MARLBOROUGH CHELSEA

211 West 19 St., 10011.
F: (212) 463-9658.
W: www.marlboroughgallery.com
T: (212) 463-8634.
E: publicart@aol.com
Open: Tues.-Sat. 10-5:30; Summer Mon.-Fri. 10-6.
Year established: 1997.
Director: Dale Lanzone.
Work shown: Contemporary art in all media. Artists represented: 5.

MARVELLI

526 West 26 St., 2nd floor, 10001.
W: www.marvelligallery.com
Open: Tues.-Sat. 10-6.
Year established: 2000.
T: (212) 627-3363.
E: info@marvelligallery.com

Size: 1,500 sq. ft.
Owner: Marcello Marvelli, art historian, Ph.D. Art History, Assistant Professor, University of Florence, Italy.
Work shown: Art by intenational contemporary emerging artists.
Work by: Andrea Frank: photography; Manuel Pina: photography; Guy Hindley: painting; Paul Ementa: sculpture; and Yuichi Hibi: photography; among others.
Annual exhibitions: 6-8.
Selection process: Artists should send materials with SASE.

BILL MAYNES CONTEMPORARY ART

529 West 20 St., 8th floor, 10011.
F: (212) 741-3238.
W: www.billmaynes.com
T: (212) 741-3318.
E: bill.maynes@verison.com

Open: Tues.-Sat. 11-6; Summer: Tues.-Fri. 11-6.
Year established: 1994.
Size: 2,700 sq. ft.
Owner/Director: Bill Maynes, previously director of other NYC galleries.
Work shown: Contemporary painting, sculpture and photography.
Artists represented: 10 from U.S. and Europe. 80% are in museum collections.
Work by: Robin Tewes: Figurative and interior painting; Lewis de Soto: sculpture and installation; Susanne Kühn: landscape painting; Stephen Mueller: large format Abstract painting; David Ivie: landscape painting; and Jim Torok: portraiture; among others.
Collectors: Walker Art Museum, Albright Knox Gallery, Herbert and Dorothy Vogel, and Werner Kramarsky.
Annual exhibitions: 8 solo/2 group.
Prices: $1,500-15,000.
Markets: Individual and corporate.
Advertising: *Gallery Guide, Art in America,* and *Artforum.*
Focus/Mission: The development of emerging artists.
Selection process: The gallery selects its artists from professional referrals. We are currently not looking for new artists.

JASON McCOY INC.

525 West 22 St., 10011.
F: (212) 255-5278.
T: (212) 255-5959.
E: jmccoy@mindspring.com
Open: By appointment.
Additional information: This is a satellite gallery to Jason McCoy, on 57th Street.
See Uptown section.

SARA MELTZER

516 West 20 St., 10001.
F: (212) 727-9583.
Open: Tues.-Sat. 11-6.
Year established: 1998.
T: (212) 727-9330.
W: www.sarameltzer.com
Size: 2,400 sq. ft.
Annual exhibitions: 1-2.
Owner/Director: Sara Meltzer, BA in Art History and Fine Art; MA in Arts
Administration; and former private dealer.
Work by: Jan Albers: mixed media and installation; Karen Kimmel: installation,
performance; Daniela Steinfeld: photography; Andrew Bordwin: photography; and
Kara Cressman: drawing and sculpture; among others.
Prices: $200-15,000.
Advertising: *Gallery Guide.*
Focus/Mission: We specialize in the works of emerging artists and a wide range
of media. Most works are Conceptual in nature. The gallery is strongly committed
to encouraging experimentation in the visual arts.
Selection process: 20% of the artists are selected from professional referrals;
10% from slides and other materials sent to the gallery; and 65% from art seen in
artists' studios. Artists should mail slides, biography, resumé, SASE, and a
statement explaining why their work fits into the gallery's program.
Response time: 4-6 weeks.

MESSINEO WYMAN PROJECTS

525 West 22 St., Ste. 5D, 10011. **T:** (212) 414-0827.
Open: Wed.- Fri. 12-6 and by appt.
W: www. Messineo-wyman.com
Year established: 1999.   **Size**: 2,000 sq. ft.
Owner: Meryl Messineo and Helen Greenberg-Wyman.
Work shown: Contemporary American and European photography, painting,
drawings and prints.
Work by: Ruth Liberman: mixed media; Robert Stivers: photography; Kerstin
Roolfs: painting; Sylvia Schuster: painting and work on paper; Rebecca
Weinstein: photography; among others.
Annual exhibitions: 5.

METRO PICTURES

519 West 24 St., 10011.
F: (212) 337-0070.
T: (212) 206-7100.
Open: Tues.-Sat. 10-6.
Year established: 1980.
Owners: Janelle Reiring and Helene Winer.
Work shown: Contemporary art in all media.
Artists represented: 10 male/3 female.
Origins: U.S. and Europe. All of the artists are in museum collections.

Work by: Louise Lawler: photography; Mike Kelly: multi media; Tony Owsler: video and mixed media; Cindy Sherman: photography; and Carroll Dunham: painting; among others.
Annual exhibitions: 8 solo/4 group.
Advertising: *Artforum* and *Freize.*
Selection process: We are currently not looking for new artists.

MILES FINE ART

118 West 27 St., 12th floor, 10001.   **T:** (212) 691-7094.
E: MilesFA@aol.com   **W:** www.milesfineart.com
Open: By appointment.   **Year established:** 1989.
Owner: Shani Miglio.
Work shown: Featuring the work of American Impressionist Matthew Albert Miles. Original painting, etchings, giclées, and limited edition prints.
Prices: $150-20,000.

ROBERT MILLER

524 West 26 St., 10001.   **T:** (212) 366-4774.
F: (212) 366-4454.   **E:** rmg@robertmillergallery.com
W: www.robertmillergallery.com
Open: Tues.-Sat. 10-6; July-August Mon.-Fri. 10-6.
Year established: 1977.   **CEO:** Betsy Wittenborn Miller.
Work shown: Modern and Contemporary painting, sculpture, work on paper; and Vintage and Contemporary photography.
Work by: We represent the estates of Joan Mitchell; Alice Neel; Robert Mapplethorpe; and Diane Arbus.

YOSSI MILO

552 West 24 St., 10011.
T: (212) 414-0370.   **F:** (212) 414-0371.
E: info@yossimilogallery.com   **W:** www.yossimilogallery.com
Open: Tues.-Sat. 11-6.   **Year established:** 1996.
Director: Yossi Milo, background in art history.
Work shown: Contemporary photography and photography based art.
Work by: Shelby Lee Adams; John Dugdale; David Goldes; Simen Johan; and Katherine Turczan; among others.
Annual exhibitions: 7-9.
Selection process: Artists should mail photographs or slides with SASE.
Reponses time: 1-2 months.

MIXED GREENS

601 West 26th Street, 11th Floor, 10001.   **T:** (212) 331-8888.
F: (212) 343-2134.   **E:** artinfo@mixedgreens.com
W: www.mixedgreens.com   **Open:** Mon.-Fri. 10-5 and by appointment.
Work shown: Contemporary art in all media including film.
Focus/Mission: Mixed Greens promotes and supports visual artists and documentary filmmakers by selling art, exhibiting artwork, producing films and cultivating new collector bases. The company also helps create opportunities for artists to reach non-traditional audiences and to find outlets for their creativity outside regular channels.

continued

Work by: Rob Conger; Shoshana Deutz; Bill Feeney; Jerald Freempton and Anne George; among others.

Selection process: Mixed Greens' curatorial team accepts art submissions by mail or email, although mail is preferred. Artists should send a solid representation of current work (slides, color copies, jpegs, videos, etc.); an additional group of selective images from the past 1-2 years; a resumé; an artist's statement; and any related press. Send to the attention of Art Team.

PAUL MORRIS

465 West 23 St., 10011.   **T:** (212) 727-2752.
F: (212) 206-7351.   **Year established:** 1994.
Open: Tues.-Sat. 10-6; July & Aug. Mon.-Fri. 11-6.
Owner: Paul Morris, formerly worked at the Metropolitan Museum, and Hirschl and Adler Modern, in NY, and Anthony d'Offay Gallery, London, U.K.
Work shown: Contemporary art in all media.
Artists represented: 15.   **Annual exhibitions:** 8.
Work by: Tracey Moffatt; Chris Verene; Oliver Boberg; Tom Lussier; and Julian Schnabel; among others.
Prices: $500-25,000.

SARAH MORTHLAND

511 West 25 St., Suite 709, 10001. **T:** (212) 242-7767.
F: (212) 242-7799.   **Open:** Tues.-Sat. 11-5:30.
Year established: 1996.   **Size:** 900 sq. ft.
Owner/Director: Sarah Morthland, former Director of Howard Greenberg, SoHo, NY, and Founder and Director of Gallery 292, SoHo, NY.
Work shown: Eclectic styles of 19th and 20th Century photography, and Contemporary painting.
Prices: $250-25,000.   **Markets:** Individual, corporate, and museum.
Artists represented: 18, from U.S., Canada, and U.K. 40% male/60% female. 55% of the artists are in museum collections.
Work by: Alison Rossiter: Contemporary photography, and installations; Rose Marasco: Contemporary photographs of diaries, quilts, and kitchen implements from past decades; Dan Estabrook: haunting scenes produced by 19th century photographic techniques; Linda Butler: Contemporary photography; Arthur Tress: Contemporary black and white photography; among others.
Annual exhibitions: 8 solo/2 group.
Selection process: 65% of the artists are selected from professional referrals, 30% from slides sent to the gallery; and 5% from art seen in exhibitions and artists studios. We are currently not looking for new artists.
Additional information: We have rare and out of print photographic books.

MUSEUM AT THE FASHION INSTITUTE OF TECHNOLOGY

Seventh Ave. and 27 St., 10011.   **T:** General: (212) 217-5800.
T: Group tours: (212) 217-5708.   **T:** Membership: (212) 217-5701.
F: (212) 217-5978.   **W:** www.fitnyc.suny.edu
Open: Tues.-Fri. 12-8, Sat. 10-5; Summer: Call for hours.
Director: Dorothy Globus.
Focus/Mission: The Museum at FIT is the repository of the world's largest collection of costumes, textiles, and accessories of dress. The collections include 30,000 textiles dating from the 18th to the 20th centuries.

Work shown: Exhibitions consist of a wide spectrum relevant to fashion and its satellite industries. They are selected to appeal to the 30 career majors offered at FIT. They explore both the art and design as well as the business and technology of fashion interior design, toy design, and related industries. Highlighting each season are exhibitions that feature the work by students and faculty.

Selection process: The museum draws upon its extensive collections, develops special projects with outside institutions, and presents traveling exhibitions.

M.Y. ART PROSPECTS

135 West 29 St., Suite 1002, 10001.   **T:** (212) 268-7132.
F: (212) 268-7147.   **E:** MYartpro@aol.com
W: www.myartprospects.com   **Year established:** 1997.
Owner/Director: Miyako Yoshinaga, former Research Associate at the Brooklyn Museum of Art, contributor to Japanese art journals, and independent curator.
Associate Director: Shaheen Rashid.
Work shown: Contemporary painting, drawing, sculpture, photography, and mixed-media. **Prices:** $500-20,000.
Markets: Individual and corporate
Artists represented: 15 from U.S., Asia, Europe. 60% male/40% female.
Work by: Ignacio Burgos, mixed-media drawings and painting; Rodney Dickson, oil and mixed-media painting; Farrell and Parkin, photography; Pouran Jinchi, mixed-media painting, etchings; and Ming Mur-Ray, photography and mixed-media installation; among others.
Annual exhibitions: 4 solo/1-2 group.
Advertising: *Gallery Guide.*
Focus/Mission: The gallery promotes the careers and international reputations of contemporary visual artists. We conduct thorough examination of artists' materials and establish ongoing dialogue with them before representing them.
Selection process: Artists should call for an appointment. We review materials and make studio visits.
Additional information: The gallery actively participates in art fairs both in U.S. and abroad. We also organize collateral art events, such as gallery talks and poetry readings.

NATIONAL DESIGN CENTER, STRATHMORE

164 Fifth Ave., 10010.   **Open:** Mon.-Fri. 11-6, during exhibitions.
T: (212) 807-1990.   **F:** (212) 807-1799.
E: aiga@aiga.org   **W:** www.aiga.org
Year established: AIGA in 1914; the gallery in 2000.
Owner: Non-profit organization the American Institute of Graphic Arts.
Executive Director of AIGA: Richard Grefé.
Work shown: Work by graphic designers and graphic artists including book design, print design.   **Annual exhibitions:** 8.
Focus/Mission: To further excellence in communication design as a broadly defined discipline, as a strategic tool for business, and as a cultural force. AIGA is the place design professionals turn to first to exchange ideas and information, participate in critical analysis and research, and advance education and ethical practice.
Selection process: Several of the exhibitions are a result of competitions conducted by AIGA. Call for information or visit the website.

NEW CENTURY ARTISTS

530 West 25 St., #406, 10011.   **T:** (212) 367-7072.
Open: Tues.-Sun. 11-6.   **E:** newcentyrartists@msn.com
W: www.freeyellow.com/members6/newcenturyartists/
Owner: Membership gallery with over 100 members.
Director: Chana Benjamen. She is also a professional art appraiser, and art photography teacher.
Work shown: Contemporary art in all media.
Annual exhibitions: 27.
Focus/Mission: This is a not-for-profit membership organization which encourages, supports, and exhibits the work of minority artists from under-represented communities, such as gay and lesbian, various ethnic groups, people of color, differently-abled, women, and artists of all ages including seniors and children.
Selection process: Artists may call for information or send slides, resumé and SASE. Membership fees are $300 one year.

NEW YORK THEOLOGICAL SEMINARY

5 West 29 St., 9th floor, 10001.   **T:** (212) 532-4012.
W: www.nyts.com   **Open:** Mon.-Fri. 9:30-4:30.
Year established: 1993.   **Coordinator**: Kathy Ganim.
Work shown: Contemporary art in all media.
Annual exhibitions: 5-6 mostly solo.
Selection process: Artists should call for information.

NIKOLAI FINE ART

505 West 22 St., 10011.   **T:** (212) 414-8511.
F: (212) 414-2763.   **E:** info@nikolaifineart.com
W: www.nikolaifineart.com   **Open:** Tues.-Sat. 11-6.
Year established: 1999.
Owner: Irene Nikolai, former private dealer in NYC.
Director: Cyril Pigot.
Work shown: Contemporary painting, photography and installations and sculpture in the sculpture garden.   **Prices:** $500-25,000.
Artists represented: 12.   **Origins:** International.
Work by: Karin Giusti: sculpture installation; Cornford and Cross: video installation and photography; Allan D. Hasty: photography; and Karl Grimes: photography; among others.
Annual exhibitions: 10.
Selection process: Artists should send visuals, biography, and SASE.
Response time: 1 month.
Additional information: The gallery sponsors public projects throughout NYC.

NOHO

530 West 25 St., 4th Floor, 10001.   **T:** (212) 367-7063
W: www.artincontex.org/NohoGallery
Open: Tues.-Sat. 11-6.
Year established: 1974.   **Owner:** Non-profit cooperative gallery.
Director: Erma Yost.
Work shown: Realism to abstract art in all media.
Artists represented: 27-32 members. 50% male/female. **Ages:** 25-70. All origins   50% of the artists are in museum collections.

Work by: Kate Millet: drawings with commentary; Erma Martin Yost: fabric art; Stephanie Rauschenbusch: painting; Irving Barrett: collage; and Lynne Friedman: painting; among others.
Collectors: School of Visual Arts, University of Kansas, Chicopee Inc., New York Hospital, IBM, Fred James Inc., and Estée Lauder. **Prices:** $500-15,000.
Annual exhibitions: 11.
Advertising: *Art in America, New York Times, Gallery Guide,* and *Village Voice.*
Focus/Mission: To show diversity in aesthetic concerns, styles and media.
Selection process: The gallery welcomes new artists. Artwork is judged the second Wednesday each month. Artists should bring at least 3 paintings and 10 slides to the gallery. Call for delivery information. **Response time:** Immediate.
Fees: Initiation fee: $300 plus 3 month security deposit and first month's rent which totals to $700. Thereafter $100 each month. Within the first year artist will be in a 2-3 member show, have a solo show within two years, and will be included in other group show opportunities outside the gallery. The artist members exhibit at the Albright Knox Museum.
Additional information: The gallery consists of new and emerging artists, many of whom teach at colleges and universities and are exhibited nation-wide.

ANNINA NOSEI

530 West 22 St., 2nd floor, 10011.   **T:** (212) 741-8695.
F: (212) 741-2379.   **E:** annina@earthlink.net
Open: Tues.-Sat. 11-6. June 6-July 31 Mon.-Fri. 11-6. Closed in Aug.
Year established: 1979.   **Size:** 5, 000 sq. ft.
Owner: Annina Nosei. She has a doctorate in Philosophy from the University of Rome, and is an art educator.
Director: Lee Ortega.
Work shown: Figurative and Abstract painting and sculpture.
Artists represented: 20, from all origins. 70% male/30% female. 60% of the artists are in museum collections.
Work by: Heid McFall; Liliana Porter; Myriam LaPlante; and Federico Uribe; among others.
Prices: $2,000-100,000.
Markets: Individual, corporate, and museum.
Collectors: Evan Tawil, Nassau Museum, Norman Dubrow, Marisa Georgio.
Annual exhibitions: 7 solo/ 3 group.
Advertising: *Gallery Guide.*
Focus/Mission: To show national and international Contemporary painting and sculpture.
Selection process: 10% of the artists are selected from professional referrals, 10% from materials sent to gallery, and 80% from art seen in exhibitions or artists studios. Artists should mail slides or photographs, resumé, biography, and SASE.

ROBERT PARDO

210 Eleventh Ave., #503, 10001.   **T:** (212) 242-8523.
F: (212) 242-8582.   **E:** robertpardogallery@yahoo.com
W: www.robertpardogallery.com   **Open:** Tues.-Sat. 10-6.
Year established: 1998.   **Size:** 1,200 sq. ft.
Owner/Director: Robert Pardo, gallery owner for over 20 years.
Work shown: Sculpture and installation.
Prices: $5,000 and above.

continued

Artists represented: 25 international artists.
Work by: Alastair Noble: multi-media; Migulel Berrocal: sculpture; Ted Kurahara: painting; and Casper Henselmann: sculpture; among others.
Annual exhibitions: 12.
Selection process: Artists should mail slides or photographs, biography and SASE. **Response time:** 2 months.

STUART PARR

231 Tenth Ave., 2nd floor, 10011.   **T:** (212) 206-6644.
F: (212) 206-6646.   **E:** parrstudio@aol.com
W: www.warrenmcarthur.com
Open: Tues.-Sat. 10-7; Summer: Mon.-Fri. 10-7.
Year established: 1999.   **Owner:** Stuart Parr.
Director: Luca Scalisi.
Work shown: 20th Century decorative art, Vintage furniture and sculpture. Primarily furniture by Warren McArthur.

FRIEDRICH PETZEL

535 West 22 St., 10001.   **T:** (212) 680-9467.
F: (212) 680-94   **E:** info@petzel.com
W: www.petzel.com
Open: Tues.-Sat. 10-6 and by appointment.
Year established: 1993.   **Size:** 1,200 sq. ft.
Owner: Freidrich Petzel, former Director of Metro Pictures.
Directors: Blaire Dessant and Maureen Sarro.
Work shown: Contemporary American and European art. A range of artistic media from painting to installation art. In addition to representing 12 artists, FPG organizes thematic exhibitions with outstanding works from the 1970s and 1980s.
Artists represented: 12, from all origins.   50% male/female. 50% of the artists are in museum collections.
Work by: Charlene von Heyl; Keith Edmier; Jorge Pardo; Richard Phillips; and Dana Hoey; among others.
Markets: Individual, corporate, and museum.
Prices: $1,000-30,000.
Collectors: Whitney, Walker Art Institute, Susan and Lewis Manilow, and Carlos and Rosa de la Cruz.
Annual exhibitions: 6 solo/2 group.
Advertising: *Gallery Guide* and *Artforum*.
Additional information: Regularly, we invite well-known artists like Louise Lawler, Albert Oehlen, and Allan McCollum who create a conceptual frame for our younger artists.
Selection process: We are currently not looking for new artists.

PLEIADES

530 W. 25 St., 4th floor, 10001.   **T/F:** (646) 230-0056. **Open:** Tues.-Sat. 11-6.
Owner: Non-profit cooperative gallery.
Year established: 1974.   **Directors:** Ellen Bradshaw and Frank Dosne.
Work shown: All styles and media.
Annual exhibitions: 26 solo/6 group.
Advertising: *Gallery Guide*.

Artists represented: 40 members. 50% male/female. **Ages:** 20-80. All origins.
Focus/Mission: To have freedom of artistic choice and freedom of operation.
Selection process: All artists are selected from slides sent to the gallery. Work is usually reviewed the second Sunday of each month, except for July and August. Artists should submit 12 slides and 2-3 original works. Call for delivery information.
Fees: Initiation fee: $500. Monthly: $100. Each member has a one-person show every 18-24 months and periodic group shows. There is no gallery commission.

PLUM BLOSSOMS

555 West 25 St., 10001.   **T:** (212) 719-7008.
E: infony@plumblossoms.com   **W:** www.plumblossoms.com
Open: Tues.-Sat. 10:30-6:30.   **Size:** 4,500 sq. ft.
Year established: 1987 in Hong Kong; 2001 in N.Y.
Mananging Director: Stephen McGuiness.
Director: Paul Fudor.
Work shown: Asian Contemporary art and Asian antiques.
Work by: C.C. Wang: painting, Chinese ink on paper; Zhu Wei: painting, sculpture, ink on paper, bronze and fiberglass; Wu Shaoxiang: painting, sculpture, Hong Kong and Austrian coins, oil on canvas, wood and stone; Tran Trong Vu: painting, installation, painting; Hong Zhu An: painting and Chinese ink on paper; and Jimmy Ong: charcoal on paper; among others.
Annual exhibitions: 10.
Selection process: Artists should send images and letter to the Director. The Director will call for appointment. **Response time:** 2-3 weeks.

POSTMASTERS

459 West 19 St., 10011.   **T:** (212) 727-3323.
F: (212) 229-2829.   **E:** postmasters@thing.net
W: www.postmastersart.com   **Open:** Tues.-Sat. 11-6.
Year established: 1989.   **Size:** 4,000 sq. ft.
Director: Magdalena Sawon, MA in Art History.
Work shown: Contemporary, Conceptual installations, sculpture and painting and New Media.   **Prices:** $1,000-40,0000.
Artists represented: 16.   **Annual exhibitions:** 8-9.
Work by: Sylvie Fleury: mixed media; Paul Ramirez Jonas: mixed media; David Nyzio: mixed media; Christian Schumann: painting; Alix Pearlstein: mixed media; Mary Kelly: mixed media; and Diana Cooper: painting/installation; among others.
Focus/Mission: To show new emerging artists' work, while continuing to work with mid-career artists.
Selection process: Artists should submit slides and SASE.
Response time: 1-2 months. **Requirements:** A unique vision and commitment.

PRINCE STREET

530 West 25 St., 4th floor, 10001.   **T/F:** (646) 230-0246.
Open: Tues.-Sat. 11-6.
W: www.princestreetgallery.com   **E:** psg@aol.com
Year established: 1972.   **Size:** 1,000 sq. ft.
Owner: Non-profit cooperative gallery.
Director: Mark Webber.
Work shown: Primarily Figurative; some Abstract. Painting and sculpture.

continued

Markets: 90% individual, 10% corporate.
Prices: $200-20,000.
Artists represented: 30 from NY and its environs.   **Ages:** 20-50's.
Work by: Nancy Prusinowski: mixed media painting; Mary Salstron: painting; Marion Lerner-Levine: painting; and Gerald Marcus: painting; among others.
Annual exhibitions: 15 solo/2 group.
Advertising: *Gallery Guide.*
Focus/Mission: This gallery was formerly devoted to figurative art only. In the past few years it has expanded its range of styles.
Selection process: Artists should call to obtain policies and procedures. Slides and original works are reviewed by the members. **Response time:** 1 month.
Requirements: Maturity, development and responsibility.
Fees: Initiation fee: $500. Monthly fee: $100 for in town members, and $130 for a select few out of town members. Each member has a one-person show every 2-3 years and a group show every year. Commission for group show: 10%. Commission for solo show: 5%, after deducting $2,500 for expenses.

MAX PROTECH

511 West 22 St., 10011.   **T:** (212) 633-6999.   **Open:** Tues.-Sat. 10-6.
E: info@maxprotech.com   **W:** www.maxprotech.com
Year established: 1969.   **Size:** 3,000 sq. ft.
Owner: Max Protech.   **Director:** Josie Browne.
Work shown: Contemporary painting, sculpture, ceramics, and architectural drawings.
Work by: Inigo Manglano Ovalle; Oliver Herring; Scott Burton; Betty Woodman; David Reed; and Byron Kim; among others.
Selection process: We are currently not looking for new artists.

RADIO HOUSE

601 West 26 St., 14th floor, 10001. **T:** (212) 620-7630.
F: (212) 620-7638.   **E:** radiohouse@earthlink.net
W: artnet.com/radiohouse.html **Open:** Tues.-Sat. 12-5.
Year established: 1998.   **Size:** 3,000 sq. ft.
Owner/Director: Tatsuhiko Ashida, former dealer from Japan.
Work shown: Contemporary fine art.
Artists represented: 20 international artists.
Work by: Christina Ray: mixed media; Christina Lanzl: painting, sculpture and video installation; Hanako Matsumoto: Japanese painting on wood; Koji Kinutani: painting; and Anthony Makepeace: black and white photography; among others.
Annual exhibitions: 7.   **Prices:** $500-6,000.
Selection process: Artists should submit materials with SASE.
Response time: 2 months.

RARE

435 West 14 St., 10014.   **T:** (212) 645-5591.
F: (212) 645-5594.   **E:** raregallery@earthlink.net
W: rare-gallery.com   **Open:** Tues.-Sat. 11-6, Mon. by appointment.
Year established: 1997.   **Size:** 2,000 sq. ft.
Owners/Directors: Peter Ted Surace: Background as a lawyer, marketing and public relations in financial services; and Alexis Hubshman: Artist and inventor.

Work shown: Contemporary art in all media by emerging and mid-career artists.
Prices: A range of prices that serves beginning through advanced collectors.
Artists represented: 10, from all origins. 30% are in museum collections.
Work by: Anthony Goicolea: photography; Daisuke Nakayama: Neo-Pop work that explores double-edged nature of personal relationships and banality of violence in modern society; Roger Kelly: painting; Chris Johanson: painting/drawings; and Paul Johnson: video that explores issues of high versus low technology, industrialization of American landscape; among others.
Annual exhibitions: 6 solo/1 group. **Advertising:** *Artforum* and *Gallery Guide.*
Focus/Mission: To promote and help grow the careers of emerging artists.
Selection process: 10% of the artists are selected from referrals; 30% from slides and other materials sent to the gallery; 60% from art seen in exhibitions, publications and artists' studios. Artists should familiarize themselves with several shows before approaching. If their work is appropriate artists should mail slides, photographs, biography, resumé, artist's statement, prices, and SASE.
Response time: 1 month.
Fees: Artists are expected to pay for their framing. All sales are split 50/50 between the gallery and the artist.
Additional information: They are founders of Scope, an annual art fair at the Gershwin Hotel in New York City. The gallery is on the Board of Directors of the Bronx Museum and Art in General.

RICCO/MARESCA
"To show masters of American Self-Taught, Outsider Art and Contemporary Photography."

RICCO/MARESCA

529 West 20 St., 3rd floor, 10011.   **T:** (212) 627-4819.
F: (212) 627-5117.   **E:** info@riccomaresca.com
W: www.riccomaresca.com   **Open:** Tues.-Sat. 11-6.
Year established: 1979.   **Size:** 6,000 sq. ft.
Owners: Roger Ricco and Frank Maresca.
Directors: Sarah Hasted and Stephen Romano.
Work shown: American Vernacular, Self-Taught and Outsider art, and Folk sculpture, drawings, furniture and Contemporary photography, by mostly American artists.
Work by: William Hawkins: enamel, collage and mixed-media constructions on masonite; Charles A.A. Dellschau: mixed-media on paper; Ken Grimes: acrylic on canvas; Gerald Slota: unique silver gelatin prints; and Jayne Hinds Bidaut: tintypes photography; among others.
Collectors: Museum of American Folk Art, Newark Museum, Milwaukee Museum, and MoMA, NY.
Annual exhibitions: 10 solo.
Advertising: *ARTnews, Art in America, Folk Art Museum, Gallery Guide,* and *Photography New York.*
Focus/Mission: To show masters of American Self-Taught, Outsider Art and Contemporary Photography.
Selection process: We are currently only accepting photography. Photographers may mail photographs/slides, resumé and SASE. **Response time:** 6 months.

YANCEY RICHARDSON

535 West 22 St., 10011.
T: (646) 230-9610.
F: (646) 230-6131.
E: yrg@mindspring.com
W: yanceyrichardson.com
Open: Tues.-Sat. 11-6.
Year established: 1995.
Size: 1,150 sq. ft.
Owner/Director: Yancey Richardson, previously a private dealer, also a photographer since 1982.
Work shown: 20th Century and Vintage photography.
Artists represented: 20. 15% of the artists are in museum collections.
Annual exhibitions: 8 solo/2 group.
Advertising: *Photography in New York* and *Artforum*.
Markets: Individual, corporate, and museum.
Prices: $400-20,000.
Focus/Mission: To show new and interesting contemporary work in addition to the work of previously overlooked and recently re-discovered, 20th century photographers.
Selection process: There is a portfolio review 4-5 times a year. Artists should call for schedule, then drop off portfolio and pick up the following day.

RIVA

529 West 20 St., 11th floor, 10011.
T: (212) 242-3434.
F: (212) 242-3322.
E: riva@aol.com
Open: Tues.-Sat. 11-6.
Size: 3,000 sq. ft.
Year established: 1997.
Owners/Directors: Dr. Stefan Stoyanov.
Work shown: Contemporary art with a focus on installation, painting, sculpture, photography and mixed media.
Artists represented: 10. All origins.
Work by: Exhibitions have featured: Odili Donald Odita; Lucas Mancione; Tim White; Lazarczyk; among others. Artists are given the space for a 5 week period for an installation.
Selection process: De Folin chooses artists he believes in. They are 30-40 years old who are under recognized. Artists should mail slides and resumé with SASE.
Response time: 2 months.

ROCKINGHORSE CAFÉ MEXICANO

182 Eighth Ave., 10011.
T: (212) 463-9511.
F: (212) 243-3245.
Open: Daily 11:30-11.
Work shown: This is a café that also presents changing exhibitions of artwork by Deb Mill.

PAUL RODGERS/9W

529 West 20 St., 10011.
F: (212) 414-9844.
W: www.paulrodgers9w.com
Year established: 2000.
Owner: Paul Rodgers.

T: (212) 414-9810.
E: info@paulrodger9w.com
Open: Tues.-Sat. 11-6 and by appointment.
Size: 3,000 sq. ft.

Work shown: Contemporary art in all media.
Artists represented: 6.
Work by: Lucinda Devlin: photography; Margaret Evangeline: painting; James Hegge: sculpture and video; Win Knowlton: sculpture; John Powers: sculpture; and Richard Rothman: photography; among others.
Annual exhibitions: 8.
Advertising: *Artforum* and *Art in America*.
Selection process: Not currently accepting new artists.

ANDREA ROSEN

525 West 24 St., 10011.
F: (212) 627-5450.
W: www.andrearosengallery.com

T: (212) 627-6000.
E: andrea@rosengallery.com

Open: Tues.-Sat. 10-6; July and first half of Aug.: Mon.-Fri. 10-6.
Year established: 1990.   Size: 5,000 sq. ft.
Owner/Director: Andrea Rosen, Art History background.
Directors: Michelle Reyes, and John Connelley.
Work shown: Content-oriented work in all media.
Artists represented: 12.   60% male/40 female. Ages: late 20's to 70's. All origins. All of the artists are in museum collections.
Work by: John Currin: painting; Felix Gonzalez-Torres: mixed media; Sean Landers: mixed media; Miguel Calderon: mixed media; and Andrea Zit: mixed media; among others.
Markets: Individual, corporate, and museum.
Annual exhibitions: 7-8 solo; 1-2 group.
Advertising: *Flash Art* and *Artforum*.
Selection process: 90% of the artists are found through gallery or museum exhibitions. Artists must follow exhibitions for several months and only artists that feel their work is appropriate should apply. Gallery reviews slides 3-4 times a year. Artists should inquire about current policy and schedule.

PERRY RUBINSTEIN

521 West 23 St., 9th floor, 10011.
F: (212) 206-9782.
Year established: 1986.
Owner: Perry Rubinstein.

T: (212) 206-7348.
Open: By appointment.

Director: Michael Toledo.
Work shown: Contemporary works by artists including: Salle; Bleckner; Clemente; Fischl; Polke; Twombley; and Warhol; among others.

RUSH ARTS

526 West 26 St., #311, 10011.
F: (212) 691-9304.
Open: Tues.-Sat. 11-6. Closed in July and Aug.
Year established: 1996.

T: (212) 691-9552.
E: rusharts@phatfarm.com

Size: 1,500 sq. ft.
Owner/President: Daniel Simmons, artist and President of Rush Philanthropic Arts Foundation.   *continued*

Director: Quashell Curtis.
Work shown: Alternative exhibition of painting, sculpture, video, and photography.
Annual exhibitions: 1 solo/ 5 group.
Markets: Individual and corporate.
Prices: $500- 3,000.
Selection process: Artists are selected from professional referrals, from slides and other materials sent to the gallery, and from art seen in exhibitions and artists' studios. Artists should mail slides, photos, biography, resumé, prices, and SASE.

JULIE SAUL

535 West 22 St., 6th floor, 10011.   **T:** (212) 627-2410.
F: (212) 627-2411.   **E:** mail@saulgallery.com
W: www.saulgallery.com
Open: Tues.-Sat. 11-6; July-Aug. Tues.-Fri., 11-6
Year established: 1984.   **Size:** 1,000 sq. ft.
Owner/Director: Julie Saul.   **Assistant Director:** Edna Cardinale.
Work shown: Contemporary photography.
Artists represented: 20. 50% male/female. **Ages:** 30-60's. All origins. All of the artists are in museum collections.
Work by: Sally Gall; Andrew Bush; Penelope Umbrico; Bill Jacobson; and the estate of Tseng Kwong Chi; among others.
Collectors: Metropolitan, MoMA, San Francisco Museum, and International Center for Photography.
Prices: $500-5,000.
Annual exhibitions: 10.
Advertising: *Photography in New York* and *Gallery Guide*.
Selection process: Artists should mail slides and SASE.
Response time: 2 weeks.

SCHOOL OF VISUAL ARTS WEST SIDE

141 West 21 St., 10010.   **T:** (212) 592-2145.
F: (212) 592-2095.   **E:** galleries@sva.edu
W: www.sva.edu.   **Open:** Mon.-Thurs. 9-8, Fri. and Sat. 9-5.
Owner: School of Visual Arts.   **Size:** 2,000 sq. ft.
Director: Francis DiTommaso.   **Associate Director:** Rachel Gugelberger.
Work shown: All styles and media. **Prices:** $100-2,500.
Artists represented: Full-time students of SVA from all departments.
Origins: International.
Annual exhibitions: 60.   **Advertising:** *Gallery Guide* and *Time Out*.
Selection process: Exhibitions are juried by student committees. Artists should submit 10-15 slides according to deadlines which are posted by the gallery.
Response time: 6 weeks. **Requirements:** Artists must be full time students at SVA. **Additional information:** There is no gallery commission.

LUCAS SCHOORMANS

508 West 26 St., 11B, 10001.   **T:** (212) 243-3159.
F: (212) 243-5069.   **W:** www.artnet.com
Open: Tues.-Sat. 10-6. July and August Mon.-Fri. 10-6.
Year established: 1997. Originally located in the East Village.
Owner/Director: Lucas Schoormans.

Work shown: Contemporary art in all media. Also resale secondary market.
Prices: $2,000-15,000 (contemporary). $10,000-1,000,000 (secondary market).
Artists represented: 6, primarily from the U.S.
Work by: Michael Brennan: painting; Antonio Murado: painting; the estate of Leendert Blok: photography; Bing Wright: photography; and Liz Ridal: photography; among others.
Annual exhibitions: 8.
Advertising: *Gallery Guide, Photography New York* and *Artforum.*
Selection process: We are currently not interested in new artists.

HOWARD SCOTT

529 West 20 St., 7th floor, 10011.   **T:** (212) 646-486-7004.
F: (212) 646-486-7005.
Open: Tues.-Sat. 10:30-6; July: Tues.-Sat 11-6; Aug. by appointment.
Year established: 1983.   **Size:** 2,500 sq. ft.
Owner/Director: Howard Scott.
Work shown: Minimalism, Gestural Abstraction and aspects of Figuration. Painting, drawing and sculpture.   **Artists represented:** 16.
Ages: 30-70's. 20% of the artists are in museum collections.
Work by: Toon Kuijpers: painting; Robin Rose: painting; Ford Crull: painting; and Woong Kim: painting; among others.
Prices: $3,500-20,000.
Collectors: IBM, Prudential Bache, Masslow Industries, and Westinghouse.
Annual exhibitions: 8 solo/3 group.
Advertising: *Art in America* and *Artforum.*
Selection process: Artists are selected from referrals and slides sent to the gallery. Artists should send slides, resumé, and SASE. **Response time:** 2 weeks.
Requirements: Artists must be committed to creating art with a firm understanding of color, composition, and content.

SILAS SEANDEL STUDIO

551-3 West 22 St., 10011.   **T:** (212) 645-5286.
F: (212) 741-9627.   **E:** silas551@nyc.rr.com
W: www.silasseandel.com   **Open:** Mon.-Sat. 10-4:30.
Year established: 1982 this location; 1963 on 47 St.
Owner/Director/Artist: Silas Seandel.
Work shown: Sculpture in all sizes in metal, stone and combinations by Silas Seandel. **Prices:** $1,000 and above.

SEARS-PEYTON: WORK ON PAPER

210 11th Avenue, 8th Floor, 10012. **T:** (212) 966-7469.
F: (212) 966-7431.   **W:** www.searspeyton.com
Open: Tues.-Sat 10-6.   **Year established:** 1999.
Size: 1,500 sq. ft.
Owners: Gaines Peyton and Macy Sears.
Work shown: Unique work on paper by contemporary American artists.
Prices: $300-4,000.
Work by: Carol Anthony, Susan Hambleton; Michael Abrams; Cecil Touchon; and Shawn Dulauney; among others.
Selection process: We are happy to look at submissions anytime. Artists may mail slides, biography, prices, and SASE. **Response time**: 3 weeks.

SEPIA INTERNATIONAL & THE ALKAZI COLLECTION OF PHOTOGRAPHY

148 West 24 St., 11th floor, 10014.
F: (212) 645-9449.
E: ealkazi@interport.net
Year established: 1999.
Director: Esa Epstein.
T: (212) 645-9444.
Open: Tues.-Sat. 10-6.
W: www.sepia.org
Size: 2,000 sq. ft.
Work shown: Contemporary photography and 19th & 20th Century photography from Southeast Asia.
Work by: Solomon Ed Grazda, Stuart Rome, and Jung-Jin Lee; among others.
Selection process: Artists should consult the gallery's web site for detailed information about the selection process.

JACK SHAINMAN

513 West 20 St., 10011.
F: (212) 645-8316.
T: (212) 645-1701.
E: Jshainman@aol.com
Open: Tues.-Sat. 10-6. Closed in August.
Year established: 1986.
Size: 4,500 sq. ft.
Owner/Director: Jack Shainman.
Work shown: Contemporary sculpture, photography, painting, and video.
Artists represented: 27. 50% male/female.
Origins: Primarily from Europe, Canada and U.S.
Work by: Kerry James Marshall: painting; Claude Sinard: sculptural installation; Leslie Wayne: painting; and Shimon Attie: photography; Prudencio Irazabal: painting; among others.

ALLEN SHEPPARD

135 West 24 St., 10011.
F: (413) 669-4472.
T: (212) 989-9919.
W: www.artbackroom.com
Open: Tues.-Sat. 12-6.
Year established: 1998.
Owner/Director: Allen Sheppard.
Work shown: Representational, Contemporary painting.
Artists represented: 30, from all origins.
Work by: Shoichi Akutsu: oil painting; Grace Mitchell: oil painting; Ellisa Gore: oil pastel; David Konigsburg: pastel and oil; and Mary Beth Thielhelm: oil painting / encaustic; among others.
Focus/Mission: To represent new and emerging artists.
Annual exhibitions: 10.

BRENT SIKKEMA

530 West 22 St., 10011.
F: (212) 929-2340.
Year established: 1991.
Owner: Brent Sikkema.
T: (212) 929-2262.
Open: Tues.- Sat. 11-6.

Director: Michael Jenkins.
Work shown: Contemporary art and photography.
Work by: Carol Kara Walker: drawings and installations; Arturo Herrera: drawings and installations; Vik Muniz: conceptual photography; Amy Sillman: drawings and painting; and Jeff Gauntt: painting and drawings; among others.
Annual exhibitions: 8.
Selection process: We are currently not accepting unsolicited artists' materials.

SILVERSTEIN

520 West 21 St., 10011.
F: (212) 929-7902.
W: www.silversteingallery.com
Year established: 1991.
Owner: Daniel Silverstein.
Work shown: Contemporary art.

T: (212) 929-4300.
E: info@ silversteingallery.com
Open: Tues.-Sat. 10-6.
Size: 2,000 sq. ft.

MERTON D. SIMPSON

38 West 28 St., 5th floor, 10011.
F: (212) 686-7573.
W: www.mertonsimpsongallery.com
Open: Tues.-Sat. 10:30-5:30.
Owner: Merton D. Simpson. Background: painter.
Director: Miya Rakotoarivony.
Work shown: Contemporary, African and Tribal Oceanic.

T: (212) 686-6735.
E: simpson@inch.com

SKOTO

529 West 20 St., 5th floor, 10011.
F: (212) 352-8079.
Year established: 1999.
Director: Skoto Aghahowa and Alix du Serech.
Work shown: Contemporary African art.
Work by: El Anatsui; Bright Bimpong; Diako; Rosemary Karuga; Khalid Kodi; among others.

T: (212) 352-8058.
Open: Wed.-Sat. 11-6.

GARY SNYDER FINE ART

601 West 29 St., 10001.
F: (212) 871-1262.
W: www.garysniderfineart.com
Open: Tues.-Sat. 10-6, Summer Mon.-Fri. 10-6.
Year established: 2001.
Owner: Gary Snyder, specialist in American art from 20's-60's.
Director: Elizabeth Moore.
Work shown: American art from 20's-60's, Abstract and some Contemporary art.
Work by: Janet Sobel; Beatrice Maudelman; Karl Benjamin; Norman Bluhm and Hilla Rebay; among others.
Prices: 2,500-200,000.
Annual exhibitions: 8.
Advertising: All major magazines.
Selection process: We are not currently looking for new artists.

T: (212) 871-1077.
E: gven@gallerysniderfineart.com

Size: 4,500 sq.ft.

SOHO20 CHELSEA

511 West 25 St., Suite 605, 10001.
F: (212) 367-8984.
W: www.soho20gallery.com
Year established: 1973.
Owner: Non-profit cooperative gallery.
Director: Suzanne de Vegh.
Work shown: Contemporary art in all media.

T: (212) 226-4167.
E: soho20@earthlink.net
Open: Tues.-Sat. 12-6.
Size: 1,600 sq. ft.

Annual exhibitions: 16-18.
Artists represented: Approximately 25 members. All women. All origins.
Selection process: Artists should contact the gallery for guidelines. Do not mail materials without a proper application.
Fees: Artists are expected to incur exhibition/membership costs. There is no gallery commission.
Additional information: The gallery conducts annual juried shows judged by a museum curator. It also presents panel discussions and lecture series.

SOLO IMPRESSION

601 West 26 St., 10011.
F: (212) 229-9595.
W: www.soloimpression.com
Year established: 1980.
T: (212) 229-9292.
E: prints@soloimpression.com
Open: By appointment.
Size: 4,500 sq. ft. including print shop.
Owner/Director: Judith Solodkin, a Tamarind master printer.
Work shown: This is a fine art print publisher of works by contemporary artists.
Artists represented: 40. **Origins:** International.
Work by: Louise Bourgeois; Joe Andoe; Petah Coyne; Maya Lin; and Betye Saar; among others. **Prices:** $300-5,000.
Collectors: MoMA, Whitney, Metropolitan, and The New York Public Library.
Advertising: *Gallery Guide* and *On Paper*.
Selection process: Artists are selected by their reputations and from other gallery exhibitions. We are currently not accepting unsolicited artists' materials.

HOLLY SOLOMON

Chelsea Hotel, 222 West 23 St., Room 425, 10011. **T:** (212) 924-1191.
F: (212) 924-8545. **E:** hollysolomongallery@hotmail.com.
Open: By appointment. **Size:** 900 sq. ft.
Year established: 1975. **Owner/President:** Holly Solomon.
Work shown: Contemporary painting, sculpture, video, photography, drawings.
Artists represented: 15, from all origins. All artists are in museum collections.
Work by: Nam June Paik: video sculpture and installations; Susan Graham: sculpture and photography; Izhar Patkin: mixed media; Rob Wynne: painting, photography, installations; and Virgil Marti: mixed media; among others.
Advertising: *Art in America, Artforum* and *Gallery Guide*
Selection process: We are currently not looking at new artists' materials.

SONNABEND

536 West 22 St., 10011.
F: (212) 627-0489.
Year established: 1971.
Owner: Ileana Sonnabend.
T: (212) 627-1018.
Open: Tues.-Sat. 10-6. Aug. by appointment.
Size: 4,000 sq. ft.
Director: Antonio Homem.
Work shown: Contemporary American and European painting, sculpture and photography.
Artists represented: More than 20.
Annual exhibitions: 9.
Work by: Bernd and Hilda Becher; Gilbert and George; Robert Rauschenberg; Robert Morris; Barry Le Va; and Haim Steinback; among others.
Selection process: We are currently not looking at new artists' materials.

SPACE 504

150 West 26 St., Suite 301, 10011. **T:** (212) 206-1800.
F: (212) 206-6266. **Open:** By appointment.
Owner: Rebecca Alston: Architect, Rebecca Alston Inc.
Director: Angela Danielle.
Year established: The architectural firm in 1986; the gallery in 1994.
Work shown: Modern, non-objective art with an emphasis on architecture-related works. Special exhibitions have been curated by Peter Frank. Artists shown have a color background with special emphasis on spatial and architectural relationships.
Work by: Kramer; Alston; Cunningham; Hinman; Harington; and Mohr; among others.
Prices: $800-25,000.
Selection process: Most artists are selected by referral, however, artists may mail slides, photographs, resumé and SASE. **Response time:** 1 month.

SPACED: GALLERY OF ARCHITECTURE

31 West 26 St., 10011. **T:** (212) 213-1720.
F: (212) 787-6350. **E:** jyorknewman@earthlink.net
Open: Tues.-Sat. 12-5. **Year established**: 1976.
Owner: Judith York Newman, background in architecture.
Work shown: Historical and Contemporary work by architects, architectural subjects and design-related material.
Work by: James Heron; Frank Lloyd Wright; LeCorbusier; Paolo Soleri; and David McCauley; among others. **Annual exhibitions**: 8.

STARK

555 West 25 St., 2nd floor, 10001. **T:** (212) 807-1051.
F: (212) 807-0642. **E:** starkgall@aol.com
W: www.starkgallery.net
Open: Tues.-Fri. 10-5, Sat. 11-6; June and July Tues.-Fri. 10-5; Closed in Aug.
Year established: 1986. **Size:** 25000 sq. ft.
Owner: Eric Stark, background in international banking.
Director: Karolyn Hatton.
Work shown: Contemporary American and European art in all media.
Prices: $2,000-30,000. **Artists represented:** 16. **Ages:** 27-65.
Work by: Nancy Haynes: painting; Winston Roeth: painting; Frank Gerritz: sculpture; Jene Highstein: sculpture; and Phil Sims: painting; among others.
Collectors: Brooklyn Museum, MacArthur Foundation, and Panza Collection.
Annual exhibitions: 9 solo/2 group.
Advertising: *Artforum, Art in America* and *Gallery Guide*.
Selection process: Most artists are selected from referrals. Artists must fit in with the personal vision of the gallery. We are not seeking new artists at this time. Please call before mailing slides, biography, and SASE.

ROBERT STEELE

547 West 27 St., 3rd floor, 10001. **T:** (212) 736-5565.
F: (212) 736-4911. **E:** info@robertsteelegallery.com
W: www.robertsteelegallery.com **Open:** Tues.-Fri. 10-6, Sat. 11-6.
Year established: 1997. **Size:** 10,000 sq. ft.
Owner: Robert Steele, former owner and director of Anima Gallery in Australia.

continued

Work shown: Contemporary Aboriginal, Australian, American and European art by emerging and established artists.
Artists represented: 50% male/female. All artists are in museum collections.
Work by: Emily-Kame Kngwarreye: Aboriginal painter; Lee Tribe: sculptor; Elizabeth Castagna: painter; Susan Schwalb: painter; David Seerisier: painter; among others.
Markets: Individual, corporate and museum.
Prices: $1,500-55,000.
Advertising: *Art in America.*
Selection process: Artists should mail slides, photos, biography, resumé, and SASE. **Response time:** 4 weeks. Artists should call for an appointment. Please, no walk-ins with art work; a studio visit is required.

JOHN STEVENSON

338 West 23 St., 10011.   **T:** (212) 352-0070.
F: (212) 741-6449.   **E:** mail@johnstevenson-gallery.com
W: www.johnstevenson-gallery.com
Open: Tues.-Sat. 11-6; July and Aug.Tues.-Fri. 12-6.
Year established: 1993.   **Size:** 700 sq. ft.
Owner/Director: John Stevenson, more than 35 years as a collector, dealer and gallery owner.
Work shown: Fine photography in rare handcrafted media, especially platinum prints and gravure.
Prices: $400-20,000.   **Markets:** Individual, corporate, museum.
Artists represented: 40, all origins. 80% male/20% female.
Work by: Edward Weston: vintage platinum prints; Alfred Stieglitz: vintage gravures; Marcus Leatherdale: Contemporary platinum prints; and Imogen Cunningham: platinum prints, vintage and modern; and Cy DeCosse: Contemporary; among others.
Annual exhibitions: 3 solo/3 group.
Advertising: *Photography in New York, Gallery Guide* and *Chelsea Art.*
Focus/Mission: We specialize in the exceptional 19th and 20th Century images. Classic gravure, fine press books, and the most sumptuous collection of platinum prints ever shown. Handcrafted prints, in which the artist is passionately involved, not only in the taking, but the making.
Selection process: Artists are selected from professional referrals, from materials sent to the gallery, and from art seen in exhibitions, publications and artists' studios. Artists should call for an appointment. We review artists' materials in July and Aug. **Response time:** 2-6 weeks. **Requirements:** Originality, made with outstanding skill, for which we believe we have a constituency.

STRICOFF FINE ART

564 W 25 St., 10001.   **T:** (212) 219-3977.
F: (212) 219-3240.   **E:** info@stricoff.com
W: www.stricoff.com   **Open:** Tues.-Sat. 11-6.
Year established: 1986.   **Size:** 3,500 sq. ft.
Owners/Directors: Jeffrey Stricoff and Gloria Stricoff, background as collectors.
Work shown: Contemporary art in all media.
Artists represented: 8-10.
Work by: Gary Mirabelle: sculpture; David Gerstein: sculpture; Peter Malkin: painting; Voytek: painting; Greg Lauren: oil stick on paper; Volker Kuhn: mixed media; and Yoel Ben Harrouche: painting; among others.

Prices: $400-40,000   **Annual exhibitions:** 8-10 group.
Selection process: Artists are selected from referrals and materials sent to the gallery. Artists should send slides or photographs, resumé and SASE. Walk-ins if not busy. **Response time:** Immediate.

STEFAN STUX

529 West 20 St., 9th floor, 10011.   **T:** (212) 352-1600.
F: (212) 352-0302.   **E:** stuxgall@aol.com
W: www.stuxgallery.com   **Open:** Tues.-Sat. 10-6.
Year established: 1986 in New York; 1980 in Boston.
Size: 3,000 sq. ft.
President: Stefan Stux, former gallery owner in Boston.
Director: Mike Weiss.
Work shown: Contemporary art in all media.
Annual exhibitions: 7-8.
Work by: James Croak; Joel Fisher; Jay Davis; Patrick Wilson; Su-en Wong; and Brenda Zlamany; among others.
Selection process: We are currently not looking for new artists.

SYNCHRONICITY FINE ARTS

106 West 13 St., 10011.   **T:** (646) 230-8199.
F: (646) 230-8198.   **E:** synchspa@bestweb.net
Open: Tues.-Sat. 12-6 or by appointment.
Year established: 1988.   **Owner:** Not-for-profit organization.
Director: John Smith-Amato, an internationally exhibited artist.
Artists Represented: 44 from all origins.
Work shown: Semi-abstract/ semi-representational painting, sculpture, photography and graphics.   **Prices:** $350-$15,000.
Work by: Rosalyn Jacobs: oils on linen, semi-abstract: landscapes, still lifes, personages; Diana Postel: oils on linen, semi-abstract, still lifes, personages; Andrew Gottleib: semi-representational oils, watercolors, graphic illustration; John Smith-Amato: all media, principally oils on linen; landscapes and personages, Douglas Doubler: digital photography, semi-abstract; among others.
Annual exhibitions: 10.
Focus/Mission: To develop and maintain a working relationship between the local and the international art community.
Selection process: Artists should call the gallery to arrange a portfolio review that are offered Wed. and Thurs. 12-6 by appointment only. A studio visit is arranged usually 3-5 weeks after first meeting.
Additional information: We provide numerous services including helping artists find and submit for funding and support. We also recruit artists for international exchange projects.

TAI

The Actors Institute, 159 West 25 St., 9th floor, 10001.   **T:** (212) 924-8888.
F: (212) 627-5045.   **E:** gb@tairesources.com
W: www.tairesources.com   **Open:** Mon.-Fri. 10-6 and by appointment.
Year established: 1990.   **Director:** Gifford Booth.
Work shown: Contemporary art in all media. Painting, sculpture, photography, video, computer arts, collage, assemblages and performance art.
Work by: Exhibitions have featured: Barbara Bachner; Frank Boros; Anne Finkelstein; Ginger Levant; and A.J. Nadel; among others.   *continued*

Focus/Mission: To introduce the works of emerging artists to New York. To offer visual artists a community in which they can nurture creativity and hone their unique visions. To create a space where the visual and performing arts can interact. We have been committed to exhibiting works in all media and to offering unique seminars and roundtable discussions based on self-discovery and self-expression.
Selection process: Artists should call for an appointment.

TAPESTRIES, ETC.

151 West 25 St., 8th floor, 10001.   **T:** (212) 242-0525.
F: (212) 242-0988.   **E:** marsha@tapestries.com
W: www.tapestries.com
Open: Mon.-Fri. 12-5 and by appointment. Best to call for hours.
Year established: 1996.
Owner/Director: Marsha Vander Heyden, MFA, painting and sculpture, Cornell University; also background in woodworking.
Work shown: A selection of several hundred tapestries from all historical periods. Tapestries are both reproduction and original works.
Prices: $100-thousands. Custom work is also available.
Origins: Mostly European with a selection from the U.S., Africa and Native American works.
Additional information: Artists should inquire about the costs and arrangements for reproducing their art.

GARY TATINTSIAN

508 West 26 St., 10001.   **T:** (212) 633-0110.
F: (212) 633-0516.   **E:** tatunz@rcn.com
W: www. tatintsian.com   **Open:** Tues.-Sat. 10-6.
Year established: 1999.   **Size:** 1,700 sq. ft.
Owner: Gary Tatintsian, collector and dealer for 25 years.
Work shown: Contemporary art and Modern photography by artists from all origins.
Work by: William Anastasi: Conceptual art; Thomas Florschutz: photography; Elizabeth Zavada: Conceptual art; Leon Tarasevitch: painting, sculpture, installation; and Olive Ayhens: painting.
Annual exhibitions: 6-7.
Advertising: *Gallery Guide, Photo Guide* and *Art in America.*
Selection process: Artists should send slides, photographs and other visual materials with resumé and SASE.

TATISTCHEFF and CO.

529 West 20 St., 6th floor, 10011.   **T:** (212) 627-4547.
F: (212) 627-4596.   **E:** tatistch@bigplanet.com
Open: Tues.-Sat. 10-6; Summer: Mon.-Fri. 10-6.
Year established: 1976.
Owner: Peter A. Tatistcheff.
Work shown: Contemporary Figurative painting, drawing, oil, pastel, graphite, and watercolor.
Artists represented: 25, from North America. 50% male/female. 80% of the artists are in museum collections.

Work by: John Stuart Ingle: watercolor; Gabriel Laderman: oil and pastel; Damon Lehrer: oil; David Turner Harmon: oil; and Edgard Herins: charcoal drawing; among others.

Prices: $1,000-150,000. **Annual exhibitions:** 10 solo/2 group.

Advertising: *Gallery Guide.*

Selection process: 50% of the artists are selected from slides sent to the gallery, 50% from exhibitions. Artists should send slides, biography, resumé, prices and SASE. **Response time:** 3 weeks.

FREDERIEKE TAYLOR

535 West 22 St.,6th floor, 10013. **T:** (646) 230-0992.
F: (646) 230-0994. **E:** frederieketaylor@rcn.com
W: www.tzart.com **Open:** Tues.-Sat. 11-6.
Year established: 1993.

President: Frederieke Taylor, former Director of Skowgegan School of Painting and Sculpture, and exhibition organizer.

Co-Director: Jamina Achour.

Work shown: Installation, architecture, sculpture, photography and painting in all media.

Artists represented: 6+. 50% male/female. Ages 30's and up. All origins. 50% of the artists are in museum collections.

Work by: Armando: painting and sculpture; Jeremy Adams: painting; Asymptote; and Lilla Locurto & William Outcault: collaborative sculpture; others.

Collectors: MoMA, Ronald Lauder, and High Museum.

Prices: $1,000-30,000.

Annual exhibitions: 8. **Advertising:** *Gallery Guide.*

Focus/Mission: To show highly Contemporary, Conceptual work, combining architectural and spatial concerns with a tendency toward irony and formal beauty.

Selection process: Artists should mail slides, biography, and other materials with SASE. No calls, please. **Response time:** 2-3 months.

TEAM

527 West 26 St., 10001. **T:** (212) 279-9219.
E: office@teamgal.com **W:** www.teamgal.com
Open: Tues.-Sat. 10-6. **Size:** 3,200 sq. ft.
Year established: 1996. **Work shown:** Contemporary art in all media.
Markets: Individual, corporate, museum.

Prices: $500-10,000.

Artists represented: 9 international artists. 85% male/15% female. All of the artists are in museum collections.

Annual exhibitions: 6 solo/2 group.

Selection process: All artists are selected from professional referrals.

TENRI CULTURAL INSTITUTE

43 West 13 St., 10011. **T:** (212) 645-2800.
F: (212) 925-8501. **E:** tci@tenri.org
W: www.tenri.org **Year established:** 1991.
Owner: Non-profit organization. **Director:** Toshiko Okui.

Work Shown: Contemporary and traditional art in all media by artists from all origins.

Annual exhibitions: 6-7, solo and group.

MARGARET THATCHER PROJECTS

529 West 20 St., 9th floor, 10011. **T:** (212) 675-0222.
F: (212) 675-1121. **Open:** Tues.-Sat. 11-6.
Year established: 1998. **Size:** 900 sq. ft.
Owner/Director: Margaret Thatcher, former Administrator for Dia Center for the Arts; and more than 10 years as a private dealer.
Work shown: Abstract reductive painting and sculpture and Conceptual art. Primarily painting; also work on paper, sculpture.
Markets: Individual, corporate, and museum.
Prices: $1,000-20,000.
Artists represented: 8-10, from the U.S. and Europe. 40% of the artists are in museum collections.
Work by: Frank Badur: Reductive Abstraction, painting; Fran Siegel: Reductive Abstraction painting and installation; Max Gimblett: Reductive Abstraction painting; William Steiger: landscape and architectural painting; and Markus Linnenbrink: Reductive Abstraction painting; among others.
Annual exhibitions: 9.
Advertising: *Gallery Guide.*
Focus/Mission: The gallery exhibits high-quality works of emerging and middle-career artists. The gallery is committed to the exploration of issues of formal and non-formal abstraction.
Selection process: Nearly all of the artists are selected from referrals. Unsolicited artists' materials are reviewed in July only. Artists should call for an appointment.

EDWARD THORP

210 Eleventh Ave., 6th floor, 10001. **T:** (212) 691-6565.
F: (212) 691-4933. **Open:** Tues.-Sat. 10-6. Closed in Aug.
Owner/Director: Edward Thorpe.
Work shown: Contemporary painting, drawing and sculpture.
Work by: Deborah Butterfield: sculpture; Judith Linhares: painting; Christopher Brown: painting and drawing; Beatriz Milhazes: painting; and Joseph Santore: painting; among others.
Annual exhibitions: 3-4 solo/2 group.
Advertising: *Gallery Guide* and *Artforum.*

303

525 West 22 St., 10011.
F: (212) 255-0024.
W: www.303gallery.com
Year established: 1984.
Owner: Lisa Spellman.

T: (212) 255-1121.
E: infor@303gallery.com
Open: Tues.-Sat. 10-6.

Director: Mari Spirito.

Artists represented: 8 male/9 female. Ages: 25-50. Origins: U.S., U.K., Germany, Austria and Canada. 30% of the artists are in museum collections.
Work by: Sue Williams: painting/installation; Collier Schorr: photography; Karen Kilimnik: drawing/installation; Daniel Oates: sculpture; Doug Aitken: film and photography; among others.
Collectors: Whitney, MoMA, and Metropolitan.
Annual exhibitions: 9 solo/1 group.
Selection process: 90% of the artists are selected from referrals, 10% from exhibitions. We are currently not looking for new artists.

TIBET HOUSE CULTURAL CENTER

22 West 15 St., 10011.
F: (212) 807-0565.
Open: Mon.-Fri. 12-5.

T: (212) 807-0563.
W: www.tibethouse.org
Year established: 1998.

Coordinator of in-house exhibitions: Eric Mendelow.
Traveling Exhibitions: Sarah Fogel.
Work shown: Contemporary and traditional exhibitions of Tibetan art and art related to Tibet.
Annual exhibitions: 2-3.
Selection process: An informal committee of curators and consultants review submissions as well as make suggestions for exhibitions. Artists are invited to mail slides, photographs, resumé, biography, and SASE.

LESLIE TONKONOW ARTWORKS + PROJECTS

535 West 22 St., 10001.
F: (212) 414-8744.
W: www.tonkonow.com
Year established: 1997.

T: (212) 255-8450.
E: lt@tonkonow.com
Open: Tues.-Sat. 11-6.
Size: 1,000 sq. ft.

Owner/Director: Leslie Tonkonow, former Director, Paula Cooper Gallery and Director, Zabriskie Gallery.
Work shown: Contemporary art. Photography, painting, and work on paper.
Work by: Kunie Sugiura: photography; Betsy Kaufman: painting; Mary Kelly: mixed media; Tokihiro Sato: photography; and Nikki S. Lee: photography; among others.
Annuual exhibitions: 7.
Selection process: We are currently not accepting submissions.

2/20

220 West 16 St., 10011.
F: (212) 255-1562.
Year established: 1989.

T: (212) 807-8348.
Open: Tues.-Sun. 2-7.
Size: 400 sq. ft.

Owner/Director: Miguel Herrera, MFA, Pratt Institute; painting and drawing instructor; recipient of a Fulbright Grant.
Work shown: Contemporary art in all media.

continued

Artists represented: 10. 50% male/female. 50% are in museum collections.
Work by: Christine Amarger: color etchings, painting, box constructions, whimsical, representative, light colors, and joyful; John D'Agostino: painting/collages in Abstract Expressionism; Vincent Arcilesi: oil painting/pastel drawings in Contemporary Realism; Edward Swift: mixed media objects; and Alan Wells: Abstract painting; among others.
Markets: Individual and corporate. **Prices:** $100-7,000.
Collectors: Sanofi, Paris, France; Carton de Venezuela, Caracas; and Princess of Holenhoe, Madrid, Spain.
Annual exhibitions: 8 solo/3 group. **Advertising:** *New York Art World.*
Focus/Mission: To give new emerging artists of all ages the opportunity to exhibit their work in New York City.
Selection process: 50% of the artists are selected from professional referrals, 50% from materials sent to gallery. Artists should mail slides, photos, biography, resumé, prices, and SASE, and call for an appointment.
Response time: 1 month.
Fees: $900 for individual artist for 2 weeks; and $1,100 for a group of artists for two weeks. Artists are expected to pay for their framing and advertising.

UNIVERSAL CONCEPTS UNLIMITED

507 West 24 St. 10011.　　　　**T:** (212) 727-7575.
F: (212) 727-7676.　　　　**E:** ucu1@rcn.com
W: www.U-C-U.com　　　　**Open:** Tues.-Sat. 11-6.
Year established: 2000.　　　　**Size:** 2,500 sq. ft.
Owners/Directors: Marian Ziola and Wolf-Dieter Stoeffelmeier. Ziola was director of ACE Gallery, NY, NY, and Stoeffelmeier was director of galleries in Austria.
Work shown: Contemporary art focusing on art & technology. Painting, sculpture and video installation.
Work by: Suzanne Anker; Matthias Groebel; Steve Miller; Joseph Nechvatal; and Michael Zansky; among others.
Additional information: The gallery also presents lectures and special events.

HENRY URBACH ARCHITECTURE

526 West 26 St., #1019, 10001.　　**T:** (212) 627-0974.
F: (212) 645-7222.　　　　**E:** hua@huagallery.com
Open: Tues.-Sat. 11-6; Summer: Closed July 21-Labor Day.
Year established: 1998.　　　**Owner/Director:** Henry Urbach.
Work shown: Contemporary art and architecture by international artists.
Work by: Richard Barnes: photography; Marco Brambilla: video; E.V. Day: sculpture; Stephen Dean: sculpture and video; and LOT/EK; among others.
Annual exhibitions: 8-10.
Selection process: Send slides and SASE. **Response time:** 1-2 months.

VAN DE WEGHE FINE ART

521 West 23 St., 10001.　　　**T:** (212) 929-6633.
F: (212) 929-6632.　　　　**E:** info@vdwfineart.com
W: www.vdwfineart.com
Open: Tues.-Sat. 10-6 and by appointment; Summer: Closed July 21-Labor Day.
Year established: 2000.　　　**Owner/Director:** Christophe Van De Weghe.
Work shown: Postwar contemporary.
Work by: Richard Serra; Andt Warhol; Lucio Fontana.
Annual exhibitions: 3.

THE VIEWING ROOM

114 West 17 St., 10011. **T:** (646) 298-5261.
Open: Call for hours. **W:** www.wallstreetviewingroom.com
Year established: 2000.
Owners/Directors: Margaret Bodell and Caroline Kerrigan.
Work shown: Contemporary art in all media.
Work by: John Coffer; Mary McDonnell; Michael Ackerman; David Taylor; and Susan Mayr; among others.
Annual exhibitions: 4 or more.
Advertising: *Photography in New York* and *Time Out.*
Selection process: Artists should call for an appointment.

VIRIDIAN

The gallery offers artists the opportunity to do everything their way.
It is not dictated by style, but rather by quality.

VIRIDIAN

530 West 25 St., #407, 10001. **T/F:** (212) 414-4040.
W: www.viridianartists.com
Open: Tues.-Sat. 10:30-6; July: Mon.-Fri. 10:30-6; Closed in Aug.
Year established: 1969. **Owner:** Non-profit, cooperative gallery.
Director: Vernita Nemec, artist, with extensive gallery and museum experience.
Work shown: All styles and media. **Prices:** $200-15,000.
Artists represented: 30 plus members from all origins. **Ages:** 25-75.
Annual exhibitions: 14 solo/2 or more group. **Advertising:** *Gallery Guide.*
Focus/Mission: The gallery offers artists the opportunity to do everything their way. It is not dictated by style, but rather by quality.
Selection process: The gallery has a jurying committee that considers new artists' submissions. Artists should submit 10-20 slides, resumé and SASE.
Fees: There are annual dues and exhibition expenses.
Additional information: The gallery sponsors an annual National Competition open to all artists. Artists should inquire about it in January.

VON LINTEL

555 West 25 St., 2nd floor, 10001. **T:** (212) 242-0599.
F: (212) 242-0803. **E:** gallery@vonlintel.com
W: www.vonlintel.com
Open: Tues.-Sat 10-6; July Mon.-Fri. 10-6; Aug. by appointment.
Year established: 1999 in New York, 1993 in Munich.
Size: 2,400 sq. ft.
Owner: Thomas Von Lintel, former owner, Galerie Thomas Von Lintel, in Munich.
Director: Elizabeth Culbert.
Work shown: Contemporary New-York School Abstract Contemporary Painting; photography, sculpture and video.
Work by: David Row; Stephen Ellis; Lydia Dona; John Zinsser; and Roland Fischer; among others.
Annual exhibitions: 11. **Advertising:** *Artforum* and *Art in America.*

PAUL WEINSCHENK

15 West 20 St., 10011.
T: (212) 206-1644.
F: (212) 206-1753.
W: www.cloneachrome.com
Open: Mon.-Fri. 9-7, Sat. 10-3; Summer: Closed on Sat.
Year established: 1997. **Owner/Director:** Paul Weinschenk.
Work shown: Photography in all styles and themes.
Prices: $1,500-3,000. **Annual exhibitions:** 5-10.
Artists represented: 8-10 international artists.
Selection process: Photographers should contact Paul Weinschenk to make arrangements to show slides or larger transparencies.

WESSEL + O'CONNOR

242 West 26 St., 10001.
T: (212) 242-8811.
F: (212) 242-8822.
E: wesselocon@aol.com
W: www.wesseloconnor.com
Open: By appointment.
Year established: 1985. **Size:** 3,500 sq. ft.
Owners: John Wessel, former Arts administrator; and William O'Connor: Architect.
Work shown: Contemporary and vintage photography.
Markets: 98% individual, 2% museum.
Prices: $500-5,000.
Artists represented: 30. All origins. 30% are in museum collections.
Work by: John Dugdale: photography, cyanotypes; David Halliday: toned still lifes; Wouter Deruytler: cowboy photographs; and Mark Beard: erotic photographs; among others.
Annual exhibitions: 9 solo/1 group.
Advertising: *Photography in New York* and *Artforum*.
Focus/Mission: To show art we like.
Selection process: 50% of the artists are selected from referrals, 10% from materials sent to the gallery, 40% from art seen in exhibitions and artists studios. Artists should mail slides and SASE. Please do not call for an appointment. We review artists' materials in January and July. **Response time:** 1 week.

WHITE BOX

525 West 26 St., 10001.
T: (212) 714-2347.
F: (212) 714-2349.
E: whitebox@earthlink.net
W: www.whiteboxny.org
Open: Tues.-Sat. 12-6.
Year established: 1998. Original location in PA.
Size: 2,500 sq. ft.
Owner: Not-for-profit alternative art space.
Director: Juan Puntes. **Exhibitions Coordinator**: M. Vitale.
Work shown: Contemporary, New Media, Conceptual and Video by international artists.
Work by: Exhibitions have included Herman Nitsch; Brian Magure; Michael Snow; Martha Rosler; and Carolee Schneeman; among others.
Annual exhibitions: 4.
Focus/Mission: This is a vibrant, non-profit space whose mission is to stage Conceptually-driven shows of emerging, established and historically significant artists.
Selection process: Guest curators make proposals of exhibitions directly to the gallery.

WHITE COLUMNS

320 West 13 St. (entrance on Horatio), 10014.
T: (212) 924-4212.   F: (212) 645-4764.
E: info@whitecolumns.org   W: www.whitecolumns.org
Open: Wed.-Sun. 12-6. June 9-July 15: Wed.-Sat. 12-5. Closed in August.
Year established: 1969.   Size: 2,600sq. ft.
Owner: Not-for-profit organization. Director: Lauren Ross.
Work shown: All styles and media including video art.
Annual exhibitions: 12 solo/6 group.
Focus/Mission: This is New York's oldest not-for-profit space. It provides an
ongoing program of culturally diverse exhibitions and services for visual artists.
Many of America's most prominent artists received their first major exposure here.
Selection process: Artists should call or send a letter with SASE for guidelines,
anytime except summer.

WOOSTER PROJECTS

421 West 14 St., 10014.   T: (646) 336-1999 or (646) 336-1177.
F: (646) 336-0349.   W: www.woosterprojects.com
Open: Tues.-Sat. 12-6.   Owner: Michael Haber.
Director: Jennifer Johnson.
Work shown: Prints, paintings and works on paper by Andy Warhol. Also
featuring work by: Christo; Dine; Haring; Hockney; and Johns; among others.

WORLD FINE ART

511 West 25 St., 8th floor, 10001.   T: (646) 336-1677.
F: (212) 995-2993.   E: worldfineart@yahoo.com
W: www.worldfineart.com   Open: Tues.-Sat 12-6; Closed in Aug.
Year established: 1991.   Size: 3,000 sq. ft.
Owner/Director: O'Delle Abney, artist, MFA, Carnegie-Mellon University.
Work shown: All styles and media. Primarily painting, photography and prints.
Artists represented: 30-50 annually.   All origins.
Collectors: Individual, corporate and museum.   Prices: $500-5,000.
Annual exhibitions: 11.   Advertising: Soho Arts magazine.
Focus/Mission: This is an Artist Collective Gallery with selected members who
exhibit their artwork in our gallery and on the Internet.
Selection process: Slide submissions and referrals. Artists may request
information online at: www.worldfineart.com. Artists may submit jpeg or gif
images via email to worldfineart@yahoo.com or mail slides, biography and SASE.
Fees: Artists should be prepared to pay exhibition fees.

WRIGHT

529 West 20 St., 8th floor, 10011.   T: (646) 336-5070.
F: (646) 336-5065.   W: www.wrightgallery.com
E: wrightgallery@aol.com   Open: Tues.-Sat. 10-6.
Year established: 1993.   Owner/Director: Jack Wright.
Work shown: Contemporary Realist painting.
Work by: Donald Roller Wilson; John Nava; Oris Robertson; Humberto Aquino;
and Sally Michaels.
Selection process: Artists should mail slides, photographs, biography, resumé
and SASE. Materials will be reviewed for consideration for both gallery locations.
Additional information: The gallery has another location in Palm Beach, FL.

YESHIVA UNIVERSITY MUSEUM

15 West 16 St., 10011.　　　　**T:** (212) 294-8330.
F: (212) 294-8335.　　　　**E:** rwulkan@yum.cjh.org
W: www.yu.edu/museum
Open: Sun, Tues., Wed. 11-5, Thurs. 11-8.
Admission: $6 general; $4 seniors and children, free for members.
Year established: 1973.
Director: Sylvia Herskowitz.
Work shown: Contemporary and historical art. Varied styles and media.
Annual exhibitions: 12.
Focus/Mission: To preserve, enrich and interpret Jewish life, history, art and culture. To address the needs of a culturally diverse neighborhood. In addition to its exhibitions, tours, public lectures, videos and performances for adults, its arts workshops and experimental programs foster improved multi-cultural understanding.
Selection process: Artists should mail slides, photographs, resumé and SASE to the attention of "Contemporary Exhibition Coordinator."

ANDRE ZARRE

515 West 20 St, 6th floor, 10011.　　**T:** (212) 255-0202.
Open: Tues.-Sat. 12-6.　　　　**Year established:** 1974.
Owner: Andre Zarre.
Director: Rosemary Aldin.
Work shown: Contemporary painting, sculpture and photography.
Artists represented: 6-10.
Work by: Elena Borstein; Brad Covington; Sonia Delaunay; Irene Rice Pereira; and Doug Ohlson; among others.
Prices: $3,000-70,000.
Selection process: Artists should mail materials including slides, photographs, resumé, biography and SASE.

MIDTOWN

30 – 59 STREET

FORUM

"A founding member of the Art Dealers Association of America, it has an aggressive exhibition program in Contemporary Figurative art as well as a history and reputation for showing American and European Modernists, Surrealists and Figurative material."

THIRTIES & FORTIES

A RAMONA STUDIO

65 West 37 St., Suite 402, 10018.   **T:** (212) 398-1904.
E: Ramona@aromastudio.com   **W:** aramonastudio.com
Open: Call for hours.
Owner/Director: Denise Melroy.   **Year established:** 1999.
Owner/Director: Denise Melroy.   **Annual exhibitions:** 6-8.
Work shown: Contemporary art in all media by artists from all origins.
Work by: Bari Goodman; Augusto Murrillo; Stacy Douglas; Hilary Lorenz; and David Stess; among others.

ARTLINK

Elizabeth Foundation for the Arts, 323 West 39 St., 5th floor, 10018.
T: (212) 564-2760.   **W:** www.artlink.com
Open: Call for hours.   **Year established:** 2002.
Size: 1,000 sq. ft.   **Director:** Tal Danai.
Work shown: Contemporary art by emerging international artists.
Selection process: Visit the website or send an email for more information.
Additional Information: Artlink is an international art company based in Israel, which has a residency program.

K. CARACCIO PRINT SHOP AND GALLERY

208 West 30 St., Suite 803, 10001. **T/F:** (212) 594-9662.
Open: By appointment Tues., Thurs., and Fri. 2-5, and Sat. 12-6.
Owner/Director: Kathy Carraccio, Master printer.
Year established: 1999.
Work shown: Intaglio, etching, mezzotint, monoprint, and silk collograph.
Artists represented: 4.   **Annual exhibitions:** 5.
Prices: $200-1,200.   **Advertising:** *Gallery Guide.*

Work by: Tanja Softic; Jeff Gordon; Adam Pitt; Jackie Felix; William Behnken and Lynn Newcomb; prints printed by Kathy Carraccio.

Additional information: Kathy Carraccio conducts weekend workshops in printmaking and welcomes studio visits by appointment.

DAHESH MUSEUM

601 Fifth Ave., 2nd floor, 10017.
F: (212) 759-1235.
W: www.daheshmuseum.org
Year established: 1995.

T: (212) 759-0606.
E: information@daheshmuseum.org
Open: Tues.-Sat. 11-6.
Director: David Farmer.

Work shown: 19th and early 20th Century academic art.

Focus/Mission: To collect, preserve, exhibit and interpret European academic art of the 19th and early 20th Centuries.

Additional information: The Museum, named after Dr. Dahesh, the late Lebanese writer and philosopher, presents a wide variety of talks ranging from scholarly academic subjects to broader public programs.

FOUNTAIN

702 Ninth Ave., 10019.
F: (212) 265-5482.
Open: Tues.-Sat., 11-8; Sun., 1-5.
Size: 800 sq. ft.

T: (212) 262-2756.
W: www.fountaingallerynyc.com
Year established: 2000
Director: Kenn Dudek.

Owner: Fountain House, a non-profit psychiatric rehabilitation organization.

Work shown: Contemporary art in all media.

Work by: Marty Cohen; Jeffrey Fields; Amy Koy; Mario Reyes; and Tony Cece.

Annual exhibitions: 7-8.

Focus/mission: To exhibit and sell works of art by Fountain House members as active participants in the creative community.

GALLERY DAI ICHI ARTS

249 East 48 St., 10017.
F: (212) 230-1618.
Year established: 1993.

T: (212) 230-1680.
W: www.Daiichiarts.com
Owner/Director: Beatrice Lei Chang.

Open: Tues.-Sat. 10:30-5:30; Summer: Call for hours.

Work shown: Contemporary ceramic art in clay, porcelain and stoneware.

Work by: Shimaoka Tatsuzo (Living National Treasure); Mingei style ceramics: wood fired, slip, glazed vase; Chinese influenced glazed work, such as Temmoku and Celedon; Kamada Koji; Korean influenced work: Kohiki (white slip); Six ancient Japanese kilns; sculptures; and tea ceremony.

Artists represented: 40.   **Annual exhibitions:** 6-7.

Origins: Japan and U.S. 80% are in museum collections.

Advertising: *ARTnews, New York Times*, and Asian art newspapers.

Markets: Individual, corporate, and museum.

GALLERY @ 49

322 West 49 St., 10019.
F: (212) 664-1534.
W: www.gallery49.com
Year established: 1998.

T: (212) 767-0855.
E: info@gallery49.com
Open: Tues.-Sat. 12-6.
Size: 880 sq. ft

Owner: Monica Rotaru, Art Historian.

Work shown: Contemporary international art in all media.

Artists represented: 12.   **Annual exhibitions:** 11.
Work by: Barda: sculpture; Jill Freedman: photography; Melisa Meyer: painting; Librado Romero: painting; and Judith Wilde: painting.
Advertising: *Gallery Guide and Art News.*
Focus/Mission: To offer collectible art.
Selection process: Artists should mail slides/photographs, resumé and SASE.
Response time: 1-2 months.

GERMAN CONSULATE
871 United Nations Plaza, 10017.   **T:** (212) 610-9700.
F: (212) 610-9703.   **W:** www.germanconsulate.org/newyork
Open: Mon.-Fri. 9-4.   **Size:** 2,100 sq. ft.
Year established: 1978.   **Owner:** German Consulate.
Vice Consulate for Cultural Affairs: Hans-Juergen Paschke.
Work shown: Modern and Contemporary German paintings and.
Work by: Exhibitions have featured paintings by Dolf Bissenger; Anette Venzlaff; H.N. Semjon; and Klaudia Smolarz; among others.   **Annual exhibitions:** 12.
Focus/Mission: To show the work of emerging German Contemporary artists.
Selection process: Artists should submit 20 slides, artist's statement, biography and SASE. Call for an appointment.
Requirements: Artists must be German or German-American who have not had the opportunity to exhibit their work in the New York area.

HUNTER COLLEGE/TIMES SQUARE GALLERY
450 West 41 St., 10036.   **T:** (212) 772-4991.
F: (212) 772-4554.
Open: Tues.-Sat. 1-6 September-May; Summer: Closed July and Aug.
Year established: 1990.   **Curator:** Tracy Adler.
Work shown: All styles and media. **Annual exhibitions:** 6, mostly group.
Selection process: Exhibitions are selected by a committee. Artists should mail the curator slides, biography and SASE September through May.

INTAR LATIN AMERICAN
420 West 42 St., 2nd floor, 10036.   **T:** (212) 695-6135 ext. 14.
F: (212) 268-0102.   **Year established:** 1979.
Open: Mon.-Fri. 1-6 or by appointment; Summer: Call for hours.
Size: 600 sq. ft.   **Owner:** INTAR, a non-profit exhibition space.
Director/Curator: Eduardo Casares. **Annual exhibitions:** 3 solo/2 group.
Work shown: Contemporary paintings, work on paper, photography and Conceptual art.
Artists represented: Predominantly Latino and Latin American artists.
Work by: Ernesto Pujol: mixed media; Consuelo Castaneda: painting; Michael Bramwell: mixed media; and Kukuli Velarde: clay sculpture; among others.
Advertising: *Gallery Guide, Village Voice*, and *Association of Hispanic Art Newsletter.*
Focus/Mission: To explore through exhibitions, publications, symposia, and educational activities, the work of emerging and mid-career artists of dual identity, primarily Latino artists, who act as catalysts for new thinking and new dialogue.
Selection process: 30% are selected from referrals, 35% from slides sent to the gallery, 20% from exhibitions, and 15% from publications. Artists should approach the gallery anytime. **Response time:** 3-4 weeks.

INTERNATIONAL CENTER OF PHOTOGRAPHY MIDTOWN

1133 Ave. of the Americas, 10036. **T:** (212) 857-0000.
F: (212) 857-0090. **E:** info@icp.org
W: www.icp.org **Year established:** 1989.
Director: Willis Hartshorn.
Open: Tues.-Thurs. 10-5, Fri. 10-8, Sat.-Sun. 10-6.
Work shown: Early photographs to avant-garde and digital photography.
Annual exhibitions: At least 8.
Selection process: We review portfolios for exhibition purposes on the first Monday of each month. Work can be submitted either by leaving a portfolio for Drop-Off Review, or by mailing slides. For Drop-Off, include a cover letter, addressed to General Submissions/Exhibitions Dept., resumé, artist's statement and, if necessary, a project description. Portfolios must be delivered to the receptionist at ICP by noon on the given Monday. After it is reviewed by the Exhibitions Department's Curatorial Committee, the portfolios should be picked up on the following day, Tuesday, after noon. Portfolios should be limited to 20 photographs and should preferably be no larger than 20x24". The exterior of the portfolios must be labeled clearly with your name, address and telephone number. We do not recommend mailing prints, however, you may send 20-40 slides, along with the other materials listed above and SASE. All slides should be labeled and accompanied by a slide list. **Response time:** 6-8 weeks.

THE JAPAN SOCIETY

333 East 47 St., 10017. **T:** (212) 715-1223.
F: (212) 715-1262. **W:** www.japansociety.com
Size: 2,900 sq. ft. **Open:** Tues.-Sun. 11-5 during exhibitions.
Year established: Japan Society in 1907; the gallery in1971.
Owner: Japan Society, Inc., an educational, non-profit, cultural institution.
Director: Alexandra Munroe, in consultation with Fluxus scholar Jon Hendricks.
Work shown: All styles of Japanese art in all media by Japanese artists, in addition to artists from other parts of Asia. **Annual exhibitions:** 3.
Advertising: *The New York Times, The Art Newspaper,* and *Village Voice.*
Focus/Mission: As one of the few U.S. museums dedicated solely to exhibiting the arts of Japan, we bridge the traditional and contemporary fields of Japanese art, and explore the breadth and diversity of Japanese aesthetics. Exhibitions contribute to the scholarship, connoisseurship and general appreciation of Japanese and East Asian art and culture.
Selection process: Exhibitions are organized by the Japan Society gallery in association with leading museums and arts institutions. Artists should send slides, photographs, resumé, and SASE. A committee judges the applications.
Additional information: The Gallery also publishes scholarly catalogues and conducts educational programs devoted to Japan's finest religious and classical, traditional and folk, and modern and contemporary arts.

LIMNER

870 Ave. of the Americas, 10001. **T:** (212) 725-0999.
E: slowart@aol.com **W:** www.slowart.com
Open: Wed.–Sat.12-6 **Size:** 2,000 sq. ft.
Year established: 1987. **Owner/Director:** Tim Slowinski, painter.
Artists represented: 30. **Ages:** 20-40's.

Prices: $200-10,000.   Annual exhibitions: 6 solo/6 group.
Work shown: Non-traditional Figurative painting and sculpture in all media.
Work by: Tim Slowinski: painting; Kevin O'Neill: painting and mixed media; Jeremy Eagle: sculpture; Euphema Robinson: painting; among others.
Advertising: Gallery Guide, Direct Art, and Village Voice.
Focus/Mission: To exhibit unique types of artwork not represented in the commercial market place.
Selection process: Artists are selected from referrals and slides sent to gallery. Artists should send slides and SASE. Education and the artist's career history are not important. Response time: 2-3 weeks.
Fees: Artists should be prepared to pay exhibition expenses.
Additional information: The gallery has two annual, open art competitions in April and October.

MEDIALIA

335 West 38 St., 4th floor, 10018.   T: (212) 971-0953
F: (212) 967-9827.   E: medialia@cs.com
W: www.medialia.com   Open: Sat.-Tues. 12-5. By appointment only.
Year established: 1997.
Owner/Director: Mashiko Nakashima, sculptor, printmaker, book-artist, and independent curator.
Work shown: Primarily metallic sculpture.
Markets: Individual, corporate, and museum.   Prices: $35-5,000.
Artists represented: over 100. All origins. 50% male/female. 90% of the artists are in museum collections.
Work by: João Duarte (Portugal): untraditional metallic and small scale sculpture; Robert Donahue (U.S.): painting on canvas, paper and 3-dimensional, self-built objects; Irving Masse (U.S.): gem engraving; and Jeanne Stevens-Sollman (U.S.): transformable small scale sculpture; among others.
Annual exhibitions: 4-5 group.   Advertising: Gallery Guide.
Focus/Mission: To develop closer relationships between artists and collectors. To offer the opportunity to collect the works of internationally-known artists at very affordable prices.
Selection process: Artists are selected from art seen in exhibitions, publications, and artists' studios. Artists should send slides or photographs, resumé and SASE.

MORGAN LIBRARY

29 East 36 St., 10016.   T: (212) 685-0008.
W: www.morganlibrary.org
Open: Tues.-Thurs. 10:30-5, Fri. 10:30-8, Sat., 10:30-6, Sun. 12-6.
Admission: $8; $6 seniors and students. Free for children 12 and under.
Year established: 1924.   Director: Charles E. Pierce, Jr.
Annual exhibitions: 3 major exhibitions/other smaller exhibitions.
Work shown: Rare books, manuscripts, and drawings focus on the history, art, and literature of Western civilization from the Middle Ages to the 20th century. The Morgan Library is a museum and a center for scholarly research.
Additional information: There is a Morgan Court Café and The Morgan Library Shop. Group tours and historic tours are available; call (212) 590-0332.

NATIONAL SCULPTURE SOCIETY AT AMERICAS TOWER,

237 Park Avenue, 10017.
F: (212) 764-5651.
W: nationalsculpture.com
T: (212) 764-5645.
E: nss1893@aol.com
Director: Gwen Pier.
Open: Lobby Mon.-Fri. 10-6.
Work shown: Realist and Figurative Contemporary sculpture in all media.
Collectors: Metropolitan, MoMA, Boston Museum, Philadelphia Museum.
Annual exhibitions: 6-7/mostly group.
Advertising: Sculpture Review, Sculpture and Gallery Guide.
Focus/Mission: To promote sculpture.
Selection process: Artists should send SASE for a prospectus. The membership committee looks for quality, originality and maturity in artwork.
Additional information: The NNS provides the National Sculpture Society Annual Exhibition Prizes, Young Sculptors Awards, Scholarships, The Alex J. Ettl Grant, and The Henry Hering Medal: Art and Architecture Award. Professional membership is open to all sculptors. All exhibitions are juried. General membership is open to everyone interested in sculpture.

NEW YORK PUBLIC LIBRARY

Fifth Ave., between 40 & 42 St., 10018. T: (212) 869-8089.
W: www.nypl.org
President: Dr. Paul LeClerc.
Year established: 1911.
Manager of Exhibitions: Susan Rabbiner.
Open: Mon., Thurs.-Sat. 10-6, Tues., Wed., 11-7:30.
Four galleries: D. Samuel and Jeane H. Gottesman Exhibition Hall, Edna Barnes Salomon Room, Charles Adams Gallery and the Print and Stokes Gallery, have changing exhibitions. The Jill Kupin Rose Gallery contains a permanent exhibition.
Work shown: Rare books, manuscripts, drawings, photographs, and maps from Historical to Contemporary.
Additional information: The library also presents a lecture series and other events. Free tours begin at 12:30 and 2:30. For group tours call (212) 930-0501.

OCTAVIO PAZ

At The Mexican Cultural Institute of New York, 27 East 39 St., 10016.
T: (212) 217-6422.
E: rvasquez@5re.gov.nxmx
Open: Mon.-Fri. 10-5.
F: (212) 217-6425.
W: www.lavitrina.com.
Year established: 1994.
Owner: Mexican Cultural Institute. Executive Director: Hugo Hiriart.
Work shown: Contemporary art in all media by emerging and established Mexican artists presented in mostly group exhibitions.
Focus/Mission: To enhance in the U.S. a deeper understanding of Mexico's culture, history, art and public affairs by developing events that celebrate Mexico's rich cultural heritage and contemporary artistic expression. The Institute also supports the growing Mexican community that has established itself in the New York area by organizing educational, sports and cultural programs aimed at reinforcing the cultural identity of Mexican and Mexican-Americas while improving the quality of life.
Selection process: Artists should send slides, resumé, and SASE to Carlos Gutierrez, Director of Cultural Programs. Artists may apply individually as well as in artists' groups. Response time: 1 month.

POLISH ART

333 West 38 St., 10018.

F: (212) 594-2383.

Open: Mon.-Fri. 10-6.

Year established: 1993.

T: (212) 594-2266.

W: www.dzinnik.com

Size: 800 sq. ft.

Owner: Bicentennial Publishing Corp.

Work shown: Permanent installation of Contemporary art. All styles and media.

Work by: Polish artists. All of the artists are in museum collections.

Collectors: MoMA, NY; and Museum Narodowe, Poland.

Prices: Moderate.   Advertising: *Gallery Guide* and *New Horizon*.

Focus/Mission: The gallery's role is to promote Polish art, and its artistic profile is shaped by all styles, given the professional standards of the artists.

Selection process: Artists are selected in Poland.

SCANDINAVIA HOUSE

The Nordic Center in America, 58 Park Ave. at 38 St., 10016

T: (212) 879-9779.   Open: Tues.-Sat. 12-6.

E: info@amscan.org   W: www.scandinaviahouse.org

Size: 2 floors of gallery space.   Owner: American Scandinavian Foundation.

Curator: Ann Sass, Director of Cultural & Educational Programs.

Admission: Free admission to Scandinavia House. Suggested donation for admission to exhibitions: $3 general; $2 students / seniors; free for ASF members.

Work shown: Contemporary Scandinavian art and design.

Annual exhibitions: 3 group.

Focus/Mission: Scandinavia House/The American-Scandinavian Foundation, have been promoting education and cultural exchange between the U.S. and Nordic countries since 1910.

Selection process: Artists should mail slides, photographs, resumé and SASE to the attention of Ann Sass.

Additional information: The Scandinavia House presents performances and lectures in the Victor Borge Hall. It also contains the Heimbold Family Children's Learning Center and Halldor Laxness Library. It presents films, concerts and other programs. Gift shop hours are Mon.-Sat. 12-6. AQ Café hours are Mon.-Sat. 10-5.

ROGER SMITH

501 Lexington Ave., 10017.

F: (212) 319-9130.

Year established: 1994.

Director: Jill Brienza.

T: (212) 832-8831.

Open: Tues.-Fri. 11-6, Sat. 11-3.

Size: 700 sq. ft.

Work shown: Contemporary/Emerging artists from all origins. Primarily painting.

Work by: Elizabeth Cooper: Abstract Expressionist oil on canvas; Isidro Blasco: photography installation; Alan Shields: mixed media; Luis Macias: painting, drawing, object installation; and Magdalena Z' Graggen: oil on wood, and painting installations; among others.   Annual exhibitions: 7.

Prices: $1,000-12,000.   Advertising: *Artforum* and *Gallery Guide*.

Focus/Mission: To introduce new/emerging talent into New York. To be a public-friendly and education space.

Selection process: Artists should mail slides, photographs, biography, resumé, artist's statement and SASE. Response time: 3-6 months.

Additional information: The gallery coordinates book and poetry readings, film screenings, lectures, and artist salons. Two glass walls and continuous lighting permit exhibitions to be viewed 24-hours a day.

STUDIO ANNEX

Satellite Gallery of The Studio at Madison Ave., Madison Industries Inc., 279 Fifth Ave. 10016.	**T:** (914) 273-1452
E: thestudio@aol.com	**W:** www.thestudionyalternative.com
Open: Mon.-Thurs., 10-3.	**Year established:** 2000
Director: Katie Stratis, background in art management.
Size: 400 sq. ft.
Work shown: Painting, drawing, prints, mixed media, collage and photography by emerging and established artists.
Work by: Marcy B Freidman: photography and mixed media; John Maggiotto: photography; Judith Steinberg: sculpture; Tedd Stratis: painting and work on paper; and Joyce Wenglowski: photography and mixed media; among others.
Prices: $400 – $20,000.
Annual exhibitions: 4.
Advertising: *Art in America, Gallery Guide.*
Focus/mission: To present solo exhibitions of contemporary art in a corporate lobby.
Selection process: Artists should send slides, SASE and resumé June - Sept. Response time: Up to 4 months.

THE TIMES SQUARE LOBBY

255 West 43 St., 10036.	**T:** (212) 247-2359
Open: Wed.-Sat. 4-7 pm.	**Owner:** Not-for-profit organization.
Curator: Cyn McLean, independent curator, painter, lecturer, and art reviewer.
Work shown: Contemporary paintings, works on paper, sculpture and mixed media.
Annual exhibitions: 3-4.
Focus/Mission: To exhibit art dealing with social issues. The Times Square is a project of Common Ground Community HDFC.
Selection process: Artists should call Cyn McLean: (212) 247-2359.

VIS-À-VIS

St. Clement's Church, 423 West 46 St., 10036. **T:** (212) 246-7277.
F: (212) 307-1442.	**Size:** 3 walls, each 10' in length.
Open: Mon.-Fri. 10-5, Sun. 9-5. Visitors should call first regarding access.
Work shown: Contemporary painting, photography, drawing, mixed media, and collage.
Focus/Mission: As the lobby of the Church sanctuary which is also an Off-Broadway Theatre, we provide exposure of the artwork to a theater audience.
Annual exhibitions: More than 6.

Selection process: Proposals may be submitted for solo and group shows. Artists should submit 20 slides, resumé, and SASE. Religious subjects encouraged. **Response time:** 2 months.

WHITNEY MUSEUM OF AMERICAN ART AT PHILIP MORRIS,
120 Park Ave., at 42 St., 10017. **T:** (917) 663-2453.
Open: Mon.-Fri. 11-6, Thurs. 11-7:30.
The Sculpture Court: Mon.-Sat. 7:30-9:30, Sun. 11-7.
Director: Shamin Momin. **Admission:** Free.
Work shown: Exhibitions of 20th century American painting, sculpture, drawing, photography, prints, film, and video. Also education programs and performances. Free gallery talks are presented Mon., Wed. and Fri. at 1.

FIFTIES

GEORGE ADAMS
"Artists may bring their slides, photographs, and resumé on Wednesday mornings at 9:15, October-April. Call first to confirm."

GEORGE ADAMS
41 West 57 St., 7th floor, 10019.   **T:** (212) 644-5665.
F: (212) 644-5666.   **E:** gadamsgal@aol.com
W: www.artnet.com/gadams.html
Open: Tues.- Sat. 10-6, Mon. by appointment; Summer: Mon.-Fri. 10-5.
Year established: 1952.   **President:** George Adams.
Member of Art Dealers Association of America.
Work shown: Realist, California Bay Area, Latin American and the figure.
Work by: Robert Arneson; Jose Bedia; Lesley Dill; Peter Saul; and James Valerio; among others.
Selection process: Artists may bring their slides, photographs, and resumé on Wednesday mornings at 9:15, October-April. Call first to confirm.

AMERICAN CRAFT MUSEUM
40 West 53 St., 10019.   **T:** (212) 956-3535.
F: (212) 459-0926.   **W:** www.americancraftmuseum.org
Open: Tues., Wed., Fri.-Sun. 10-6, Thurs. 10-8.
Admission: $7.50 adults; $4 students and seniors, children under 12 and members, no charge. Thurs. 6-8 pay as you wish.
Year established: 1956.
Annual exhibitions: 7-10.

continued

Focus/Mission: The foremost museum of craft in the U.S., its purpose is to collect, conserve, exhibit, interpret, and document craft. While American craft is the primary focus, the Museum's mandate embraces the international world of craft and considers the related disciplines of design, architecture, interior decoration, painting, and sculpture. Through its collections, exhibitions, publications, and education programs, the Museum seeks to encourage, for both scholar and the general audience, a love of the art of craft and an understanding of craft as a vital contributor to our cultural life.

Selection process: Artists should submit slides and C.V./Biography to the Curatorial Department.

Additional Information: The museum has a store and hosts annual benefit events.

AMERICAN FOLK ART MUSEUM

45 West 53 St., 10019.
F: (212) 977-8134
W: www.folkartmuseum.org
Year established: 1961.
T: (212) 265-1040
E: info@folkartmuseum.org
Open: Tues.-Sun. 10-6; Fri. 10-8.
Director: Gerard C. Wertkin.

Admission: $9 adults, $5 seniors/students; Free Fri. 6-8pm; Free to members.

Work shown: Folk art, mostly American, including contemporary folk art.

Focus/Mission: To exhibit, preserve, promote, conserve works by self-taught artists form the U.S and abroad.

Additional information: The museum has a café, a gift store, an auditorium and a library. The museum also has programs for families and children, and publishes *Folk Art Magazine*.

AMERINGER - HOWARD - YOHE FINE ART

20 West 57 St., 2nd floor, 10019.
F: (212) 455-0102.
W: www.artnet.com
T: (212) 455-0051.
E: nycgallery@ameriger-howard.com
Year established: 1999.

Open: Tues.-Fri. 10-6, Sat. 10-5. July and Aug. Mon.-Thurs. 10-5, Fri. 10-3.

Owners/Directors: Will Ameringer, former Owner/Director of Ameringer Gallery; Loretta Howard, formerly with Andre Emmerich Gallery; Jim Yohe, an expert of the Hans Hofman estate, formerly with Andre Emmerich Gallery. Member of Art Dealers Association of America.

Work shown: The estates of Hans Hofmann, Friedel Dzubas, John McLaughlin and Esteban Vicente. Also work of Kenneth Nolan and Helen Frankenthaler.

Artists represented: 24.

Advertising: *The New York Times, Artforum* and *Art in America*.

Selection process: We are currently not looking for new artists.

HERBERT ARNOT, INC.

250 West 57 St., 10107.
W: www.arnotart.com
T: (212) 245-8287.
Open: Mon.-Fri. 9-5:30 and by appointment.

Owners/Directors: Peter and Vicki Arnot.

Year established: 1946 in New York; 4 generations of art dealers originating in Austria in 1863.

Work shown: Dealers of Fine Original European and American oil paintings, specializing in traditional Impressionistic oil paintings.

Advertising: *Gallery Guide*.

ART FOR HEALING
*"To educate the public with current art of a healing nature,
for example, artwork that has a pleasant aesthetic,
food for the soul, which then heals the body and mind."*

ART FOR HEALING

405 West 50 St.,10019.
E: lorenellis2000@yahoo.com
Year Established: 2000.
Owner: Not-for-profit organization.
Prices: $50-$5000.

T: (212) 977-1165
Open: By appointment.
Size: 300sq ft.
Director: Loren Ellis, M.F.A., artist.

Mission: To educate the public with current art of a healing nature, for example, artwork that has a pleasant aesthetic, food for the soul, which then heals the body and mind. To teach artists how to market and present their work, and to learn to work with others. To educate the public about their art.

Selection process: Independent curators select the artists.

Additional information: We also present poetry and theatrical readings, Meditation on Tues. nights. For information call Debra Kursh (212) 996-4755. We allow video artists to use the space for showings. Our exhibitions are two weeks so the rest of the month we allow artists and actors to meet with curators or people interested in their work by appointment.

ARTEMIS, GREENBERG, VAN DOREN FINE ART

730 Fifth Ave., 7th floor, 10019.
F: (212) 445-0442.
Year established: 1999.

T: (212) 445-0444.
E: info@agvdgallery.com
Size: 3,000 sq. ft.

Open: Tues.-Sat. 10-6. After July 4 Mon.-Fri. 9-5:30 until Labor Day.
Owners: Artemis, Ronald Greenberg, and John Van Doren, owners of a gallery in St.Louis, MO.
Director: Dorsey Waxter.
Work shown: American Modern masters and Contemporary artists.
Artists represented: 10, international.
Work by: Richard Diebenkorn: oil on canvas; Sam Francis: oil on canvas; Malerie Marder: photography; Katy Grannan: photography; and Ben Edwards: acrylic on canvas; among others.
Annual exhibitions: 10.
Advertising: *Art in America* and *Artforum.*
Selection process: The gallery is currently not reviewing new artists' materials.

ARTSFORUM

24 West 57 St., 10019.
F: (212) 333-5379.
W: artsforumonline.com
Year established: 1998.

T: (212) 333-5952.
E: artsforum@earthlink.net
Open: Tues.-Sat. 12-6.

Owner/Director: Serge Gregoryan, background in visual arts administration.
Work shown: Contemporary art in all media.

continued

Markets: Individual, corporate, museum.
Prices: $1,000-20,000.
Artists represented: 20. All origins. 60% male/40% female.
Annual exhibitions: 12 solo/4 group.
Advertising: *Gallery Guide, Photography in New York* and *ARTnews.*
Focus/Mission: Dedicated to the promotion of emerging Contemporary artists.
Selection process: 20% of the artists are selected from professional referrals; 80% from materials sent to the gallery. Artists should mail materials and SASE.
Response time: 3 month.
Fees: Artists should be prepared to pay exhibition-related fees.

ART STUDENTS LEAGUE OF NEW YORK

215 West 57 St., 10019. **T:** (212) 247-4510.
F: (212) 541-7024. **Year established:** 1928.
Curator: Pam Koob **Administrative Manager:** Ira Goldberg.
Archivist: Stephanie Cassidy.
Open: Mon.-Fri. 8:30-8:30, Sat. 8:30-3, Sun. 8:30-4; Summer: closed.
Work shown: All styles of painting, prints, and sculpture.
Focus/Mission: We have exhibitions of current students, instructors, members and special invited exhibitions, essentially of an educational nature. During the month of December we present the Holiday Art Exhibition and Sale.
Selection process: Artists should not approach the school for exhibitions.

AUSTRIAN CULTURAL FORUM

11 East 52 Street, 10022. **T:** (212) 759-5165.
W: www.acfny.org **Open:** Mon.-Fri. 9-5.
Director: Christoph Thun-Hohenstein.
Work shown: Contemporary art by Austrian artists. Mostly installation.
Annual exhibitions: 2-4.
Focus/Mission: To present young, promising Austrian artists with the purpose of opening the door for them and exposing them to the New York market. We focus on installations. The exhibitions complement our virtual gallery on the Internet which features 75 artists in group shows of 10 each month. There are special projects each month of original artwork – mostly digital art.

AXA

787 Seventh Ave., 10019. **T:** (212) 554-4818.
F: (212) 554-2456. **W:** axa-financial.com/gallery.html
Open: Mon.-Fri. 11-6 and Sat. 12-5.
Year established: 2000. Formerly known as Equitable Gallery founded in 1992.
Owner: AXA Financial Inc.
Director: Pari Stave, previously worked for Equitable.
Work shown: All fields of the visual arts.

BABCOCK

724 Fifth Ave., 10019. **T:** (212) 767-1852.
F: (212) 767-1857. **W:** artnet.com\babcock.html
Open: Mon.-Fri. 10-5. **Year established:** 1852.
Director: John Driscoll: Museum professional with a PhD in Art History.
Member of Art Dealers Association of America.

Work shown: American historical art, specializing in the 1840-1945 period. Studio ceramics by international Master artists. Occasional Contemporary exhibitions.

Annual exhibitions: 3.

Collectors: Metropolitan, Nelson Atkins Museum, Art Institute of Chicago, and the Glen C. Janns Collection.

Selection process: We are currently not accepting unsolicited materials.

J.N. BARTFIELD GALLERIES & BOOKS

30 West 57 St., 3rd floor, 10019.   **T:** (212) 245-8890.
E: bartfield@aol.com   **W:** www.artnet.com
Open: Mon.-Fri.10-5, Sat. 10-3; Summer: Mon-Fri. 10-5.
Year established: 1937.   **Size:** 5,000 sq. ft.

Owners: Michael Frost and George Bartfield. Member of Art and Antique Dealers League of America Inc., Member of The Appraisers Association of America, and Art Dealers Association of America.

Work shown: 19th and 20th Century American Western and Sporting art in oils and watercolors, and bronze sculpture.

Artists represented: 12 male/3 female contemporary artists.

Ages: 30-75. All origins. 50% of the artists are in museum collections.

Work by: Michael Coleman: painting and sculpture; William Acheff: painting; Arthur Shilstone: watercolor; Carl Hantman: painting; and Adriano Manocchia: painting. Also: America's most select collections of old original western art, by Russell, Remington, and other masters.

Collectors: Buffalo Bill Historical Museum, Rockwell-Corning Museum, Cowboy Hall of Fame, and Gene Autry Museum.

Prices: $1,000-several million.   **Annual exhibitions:** Continuously changing.

Advertising: *Antiques* and *Southwest Art.*

Focus/Mission: To introduce high quality Contemporary artists that can hang well next to the 19th and early 20th century Masters of painting and sculpture.

Selection process: 65% are acquired from referrals, 10% from slides sent to gallery, 25% from exhibitions. Artists should approach the gallery when they have a good cross-section of works that are similar to the field we handle. Artists must have an individualistic style, and be easy to communicate with.

Additional information: The gallery also specializes in leather bound sets and single volumes, color plate books, rare books, and much more.

BEADLESTON

724 Fifth Ave., 4th floor, 10019.   **T:** (212) 581-7544.
F: (212) 581-7545.   **Open:** Mon.-Fri. 10-5.
E: beadleston@aol.com   **W:** www.beadleston.com
Year established: 1997.   **Director:** Susanna Allen.

Owner: William Beadleston, formerly a private dealer.

Work shown: Impressionist and 20th Century Masters and Contemporary art.

Artists represented: 4 contemporary. Many earlier masters.

Work by: Wolf Kahn: paintings and pastels; Victor Koulbak: silverpoint drawings; Dominque Rousserie: paintings; and Robert Kippness: paintings and drawings; among others.

Advertising: *ARTnews, The New York Times* and *The New York Observer.*

BERNARDUCCI . MEISEL

37 West 57 St., 10019.   **T:** (212) 593-3757.
F: (212) 593-3933.   **E:** bernarducci@meiselgallery.com
W: www.newrealism.com   **Open:** Tues.-Sat. 10-5:30; closed in Aug.
Year established: 2001.   **Size:** 3,000 sq. ft.
Owners: Frank Bernarducci and Louis K. Meisel, owner, Louis Meisel Gallery, SoHo.
Work shown: Contemporary realist paintings.
Artists represented: 20, from all origins.
Work by: Daniel Tennant; Ben Schonzeit; Ken Danby; Mark Workman and Mel Ramos; among others.
Annual exhibitions: 11.
Advertising: *ArtNews* and *Gallery Guide.*
Selection process: Artists should mail slides and resumé with SASE.

MARY BOONE

745 Fifth Ave., 4th floor, 10151.   **T:** (212) 752-2929.
F: (212) 752-3939.   **Year established:** 1977.
Open: Tues.-Fri. 10-6, Sat. 10-5; July and Aug. by appointment.
Owner/Director: Mary Boone. Member of Art Dealers Association of America.
Work shown: Contemporary art.
Work by: Richard Artschwager; Ross Bleckner; Leonardo Drew; Eric Fischl; and Barbara Kruger; among others.

CHINA 2000 FINE ART

5 East 57 St., 10022.   **T:** (212) 588-1198.
F: (212) 588-1882.   **E:** c2000fa@aol.com
W: www.china2000fineart.com
Open: Mon.-Sat. 10-6; Summer: Tues.-Sat. 11-5.
Year established: 1997, from another location in Manhattan.
Work shown: Sculpture, painting, works on paper, traditional painting from 15th Century to living Contemporary Chinese painters.
Work by: Arlan Huang; Nina Kuo; Mel Chin; Bing Lee; and Xu Xi, among others.
Prices: $3,000 and above.
Advertising: *New York Times,* and *Orientations* magazine.
Focus/Mission: The purpose is to show how well the traditional aspects of Chinese painting stand side-by-side with Contemporary Chinese art movements.
Selection process: Chinese artists should send slides and SASE.
Response time: Up to our discretion.

GARTH CLARK

24 West 57 St., 3rd floor, 10019.   **T:** (212) 246-2205.
F: (212) 489-5168.   **E:** info@garthclark.com
W: www.garthclark.com   **Year established:** 1981.
Size: 1,200 sq. ft.   **Director:** Mark Del Vecchio.
Owners: Garth Clark and Mark Del Vecchio.
Open: Tues.-Sat. 10-5:30; July and Aug. Mon.-Fri. 10-5:30.
Work shown: Modern and Contemporary Ceramic Art.
Artists represented: All origins.   80% of the artists are in museum collections.
Work by: Adrian Saxe; Beatrice Wood; Claudi Casanovas; Lucio Fontana; and Ron Nagle; among others.

Prices: $1,000 and above.

Advertising: *Gallery Guide.*

Collectors: Metropolitan, Los Angeles County Museum, Victoria and Albert Museum, and Everson Museum.

Focus/Mission: To make available the best ceramic vessels in the world.

JAMES COHAN

41 West 57 St., 2nd floor, 10019.   **T:** (212) 755-7171.

F: (212) 755-7177.   **E:** info@jamescohan.com

W: www.jamescohangallery.com   **Year established:** 1999.

Open: Tues.-Sat. 10-6; July and Aug. Mon.-Fri. 10-5.

Owner: James Cohan, former Director at Anthony d'Offay Gallery and previous Director of Paula Cooper gallery.

Work shown: Contemporary art in all media.

Prices: $1,000 and above.   **Artists represented:** 20, from all origins.

Work by: Bill Viola; Ron Mueck; Fred Tomaselli; Richard Patterson; and the estate of Robert Smithson; among others.

Advertising: *Art in America, Artforum,* and *Gallery Guide.*

Selection process: Artists should send slides, resumé and SASE to the attention of James Cohan. **Response time:** 10 weeks.

RENATO DANESE

41 East 57 St., 6th floor, 10022.   **T:** (212) 223-2227.

E: contact@danesegallery.com   **W:** www.danesegallery.com

Year established: 1997.

Owner/Director: Renato Danese, former Executive Director of Pace Gallery, and partner at C & M Arts.

Open: Tues.-Sat 10-6; Summer: June-August: Mon.-Thus 10-6, Fri 10-4.

Work shown: 20th Century Contemporary and Historical art.

Annual exhibitions: 8-10.

MAXWELL DAVIDSON

41 East 57 St., 3rd floor, 10022.   **T:** (212) 759-7555.

F: (212) 759-5824.   **E:** md4@davidsongallery.com

W: www.davdisongallery.com   **Year established:** 1968.

Size: 2,000 sq. ft.

Open: Mon.-Sat. 10-5:30. July and Aug. Mon-Fri 10-5:30.

Owner: Maxwell Davidson III, background in Art History, Williams College. Member of Art Dealers Association of America.

Director: Mary Davidson.

Work shown: 20th Century Master paintings, drawings, watercolors and sculpture.

Artists represented: 14 male/3 female. **Ages:** 20's-80's.

Origins: American, Japanese and British. All of the artists are in museum collections.

Work by: George Rickey: sculpture; Carol Anthony: painting; David Hollowell: painting; Fré Ilgen: sculpture; and Pedro de Movellan: sculpture; among others.

Prices: $2,000-300,000.

Annual exhibitions: 7 solo.

continued

Collectors: Metropolitan, Guggenheim, MoMA, and National Gallery.
Advertising: *Gallery Guide, ARTnews, Artforum* and *The New York Times*.
Focus/Mission: Primarily a kinetic sculpture gallery with a core of young contemporary artists. The gallery presents major shows periodically for secondary market artists including Matta, Matisse, Dufy, Leger, Wesselmann; and Sam Francis.
Selection process: The history of the gallery has been to look at new work, but they are currently not looking.

DC MOORE

724 Fifth Ave., 10019.   **T:** (212) 247-2111.
F: (212) 247-2119.   **E:** www.artnet.com/dcmoore.html.
Year established: 1995.   **Size:** 4,500 sq. ft.
Open: Tues.-Sat. 10-5:30; Summer: Mon.-Fri. 10-5:30.
Owner: Bridget Moore. Her background: Former Director, Midtown Galleries.
Director: Edward DeLuca.
Work shown: 20th Century and Contemporary American paintings, sculpture, drawings, prints, and photographs.
Artists represented: 21 in addition to artists' estates. 55% male/45% female.
Origins: North America and Europe. 90% are in museum collections.
Work by: The estate of Paul Cadmus: egg tempera on panel, crayons on paper: satirical paintings, lyrical drawings, and studies of the nude; Janet Fish: oil on canvas and watercolor: still-life and landscape painting in a painterly Realist style; the estate of Jacob Lawrence: tempera on panel and gouache on paper: works that depict episodes of everyday life; David Bates: sculpture, wood and metal wall reliefs, oil paintings and works on paper; and George Tooker: egg tempera paintings and prints.
Annual exhibitions: 8-9 solo/ 1-2 group.
Advertising: *ARTnews, Art in America, Gallery Guide* and *The New York Times*.
Markets: Individual, corporate, museum.
Focus/Mission: The gallery is not formed around a particular artistic movement but around a group of strong artists who are the best at their particular stylistic and philosophical approach to art.
Selection process: 69% of the artists are selected from professional referrals, 30% from art seen in exhibitions or artists studios, 1% from materials sent to the gallery. The gallery is currently not accepting unsolicited artists' materials.

TIBOR DE NAGY

724 Fifth Ave., 12th floor, 10019.   **T:** (212) 262-5050.
F: (212) 262-1841.   **Open:** Tues.-Sat. 10-5:30.
Year established: 1950 by Tibor de Nagy and John Bernard Myers.
Owners: Eric Brown and Andrew Arnot.
Director: Daniene Decker.
Member of Art Dealers Association of America.
Work shown: Primarily Representational art, some Abstract art, Modern and Contemporary art. Paintings, sculpture, and photography.
Size: 4,500 sq. ft.
Artists represented: 20. **Ages:** 30-75. Predominantly U.S. 80% of the artists are in museum collections.

Work by: Nell Blaine: painting; Fairfield Porter: painting; Edwin Dickinson: painting; Rudy Burckhardt: photography and painting; Jane Freilicher: painting; among others.
Prices: $1,000-50,000.
Annual exhibitions: 6-7 solo/2-3 group.
Collectors: Metropolitan, Guggenheim, Parish Art Museum, and The Arkansas Art Center.
Advertising: *Art in America* and *Gallery Guide.*
Focus/Mission: To promote pioneering work concentrating on exhibiting contemporary painting, sculpture and photography while presenting works from the gallery's rich history.
Selection process: We are currently not accepting any unsolicited materials.

RUSS ELLIOTT

405 East 54 St., 10022.   **T:** (212) 758-6632.
F: (212) 759-6750.   **E:** eld405@aol.com
Open: By appointment.
Owner/Director: Russ Elliott, residential and commercial muralist, painter, and designer.
Assistant Director: John Lauruska.
Collectors: Joan Crawford, Copacabana, and Robert Ploncky.
Markets: Individual, corporate, and museum.
Prices: $250-40,000.
Advertising: *House Beautiful, Art Business News,* and *Interior Design.*

FELISSIMO DESIGN HOUSE

10 West 56 St., 10019.   **T:** (212) 247-5656.
W: www.felissimo.com   **Open:** Tues.-Sun. 12-6, Fri. 12-8.
Owner: This is a Lifestyle Store catering to the Mind, Body and Soul, with a gallery on the 5th floor of a turn-of-the-century townhouse built by architects Warren and Wetmore and restored by designer Clodagh.
Vice President: Sachi.   **Creative Director:** Mitria Di Giacomo.
Work shown: Handmade textiles.
Selection process: Artists should contact Kim Rogan in the Corporate office for an appointment and current policy: (212) 956-4438.

DAVID FINDLAY JR. FINE ART

41 East 57 St., #1115, 10022.   **T:** (212) 486-7660.
F: (212) 980-2650.   **E:** gallery@findlayart.com
W: www.findlayart.com
Year established: 1870.
Open: Mon.-Sat. 10-5:30 and by appointment; Summer: Mon-Fri 10-5:30.
Member of Art Dealers Association of America.
Work shown: 19th and early 20th Century American painting and sculpture including Hudson School painters, Tonalism, Impressionism, Ash Can School, 1930's and 1940's American Abstraction, and Contemporary Realism.
Work by: Contemporary artists Trey Friedman and Jeffrey Blones in addition to earlier masters such as George Bellows, James Whistler and George Inness.
Annual exhibitions: 5.

WHERE TO FIND IT
Animal paintings at William Secord, Portraiture at Portraits, Inc.,
Abstract at Anita Shapolsky, African-American at Bill Hodges,
Post-Impressionism at Soufer, and Ashcan at Hollis Taggart.

PETER FINDLAY
41 East 57 St., 3rd floor, 10022. T: (212) 644-4433.
F: (212) 644-1675. E: gallery@findlay.com
W: www.findlay.com **Year established:** 1970.
Owner/Director: Peter Findlay.
Open: Mon.-Sat. 10-6, Summer: Mon.-Fri. 10-5.
Work shown: Contemporary art, in addition to 19th and 20th Century Master work, painting, sculpture, and prints.
Work by: Cesar; Lester Johnson; Kubach-Wilmsen; Robert Birmelin; and Simon Gaon; among others.
Annual exhibitions: 4 one-person/6 group.
Advertising: *The New York Times* and *The Observer*.

FITCH-FEBVREL
5 East 57 St., 12th floor, 10022. T: (212) 688-8522.
F: (212) 207-8065. E: fitch@earthlink.net
W: www.fitch-febvrel.com **Year established:** 1971.
Owner/Director: Andrew Fitch.
Open: Tues.-Sat. 11-5:30. July Tues.-Fri. 11-5:30. Aug. by appointment.
Work shown: 19th and 20th Century European and American prints and drawings.
Work by: Odilon Redon; Louis Legrand; Erik Desmazières; Gunnar Norrman; and Friedrich Meckseper; among others.
Advertising: *Gallery Guide*.
Selection process: Artists should mail slides, photographs, biography and SASE. The gallery hasn't accepted new artists in a while, but Mr. Fitch tries to refer artists to other galleries when appropriate.

FORUM
745 Fifth Ave., 4th & 5th floors, 10151. T: (212) 355-4545.
F: (212) 355-4547. E: gallery@forumgallery.com
W: www.forumgallery.com **Owner/Director:** Robert S. Fishko.
Associate Director: Simone Garber.
Year established: 1961. Member of Art Dealers Association of America.
Open: Tues.-Sat. 10-5:30; Summer: Mon.-Fri. 10-5:30.
Work shown: Realist Figurative Contemporary and American Modernism paintings, drawings and sculpture.
Size: 5 rooms on 2 floors totaling 2,000 sq. ft.
Artists represented: 20 or more. 75% male/25% female. Predominantly American; some international artists. 75% of the artists are in museum collections. The gallery also represents 5 artists' estates.

Work by: Gregory Gillespie: painting; William Beckman: painting; Odd Nerdrum: painting; Alan Feltus: painting and Raphael Soyer; among others.
Collectors: Metropolitan, Whitney, Brooklyn Museum, and Hirshhorn.
Prices: $2,000-250,000.
Annual exhibitions: 8 solo/1 group.
Advertising: *Art in America* and *Gallery Guide*.
Focus/Mission: Forum is a founding member of the Art Dealers Association of America, Inc. It is a gallery of 20th century art, and has an aggressive exhibition program in Contemporary Figurative art as well as a history and reputation for showing American and European Modernists, Surrealists and Figurative material.
Selection process: The gallery is currently not actively looking for new artists, however, artists may contact the gallery for more information.
Additional information: The gallery has another location in Los Angeles, CA.

GALERIA RAMIS BARQUET
41 East 57 St., 5th floor, 10022.   **T:** (212) 644-9090.
F: (212) 702-9538.   **E:** mail@ramisbarquet.com
W: ramisbarquet.com   **Year established:** 1997.
Owner: Ramis Barquet, former owner of a gallery in Mexico.
Director: Virgilio Garza.   **Size:** 2,000 sq. ft.
Open: Tues.-Fri. 10-6, Sat. 12-5:30; Summer: Mon.-Fri. 10-6.
Work shown: International contemporary art with an emphasis on Latin American art by emerging and well-established artists. All styles and media.
Artists represented: 15.   **Annual exhibitions:** 10 solo and group.
Work by: Ray Smith: painting; Jose Bedia: painting and drawings; Daniel Senise: painting; Marta Maria Perez Bravo: photography; and Marco Arce: painting and drawings; among others.
Advertising: *Artforum, Art Nexus* and *Art in America*.
Selection process: We are currently not reviewing artists' materials.

GALERIE ST. ETIENNE
24 West 57 St., 10019.   **T:** (212) 245-6734.
F: (212) 765-8493.   **E:** gallery@gseart.com
W: www.gseart.com
Open: Tues.-Sat. 11-5; Summer: Tues.-Fri. 11-5.
Year established: 1939. Member of Art Dealers Association of America.
Directors: Jane Kallir and Hildegard Bachert.
Work shown: Austrian and German Expressionism and 19th and 20th Century Naive Art.
Work by: Sue Coe: paintings and prints; Egon Schiele: drawings and paintings; Gustav Klimt: paintings and drawings; Grandma Moses: paintings; and Kätha Kollwitz; among others.
Focus/Mission: To introduce the best contemporary Japanese art to U.S.A.
Selection process: 20% of the artists are selected from professional referrals; 20% from slides and other materials sent to the gallery; and 60% from art seen in exhibitions, publications and artists' studios. Artists should mail slides, photographs, biography, resumé, artist's statement, prices and SASE.
Response time: 2 weeks.
Additional information: The gallery has extensive information and library books on contemporary Japanese ceramics.

GALLERY KOREA

460 Park Ave., 6th floor, 10022. **T:** (212) 759-9550.
F: (212) 688-8640. **E:** NYKocus@koreanculture.org
W: www.Koreanculture.org **Open:** Mon.-Fri. 10-5.
Year established: 1979. **Size:** 2,150 sq. ft.
Owner: Korean Cultural Service, a government institution.
Director: Gerard McCarthy. **Annual exhibitions:** 1 solo/12 group.
Work shown: Contemporary art in all media and traditional Korean cultural
objects. **Advertising:** *Gallery Guide.*
Focus/Mission: To exhibit art objects created by Korean artists and artists of
other nationalities. Special attention is given to the development and
encouragement of Contemporary and Modern Korean artists. We also emphasize
mutual understanding between the U.S. and Korea through culture and art.
Selection process: There are several exhibitions each year that are selected
from submitted materials. Artists should mail slides, photos, biography, resumé,
artist's statement and SASE. We provide gallery space for Korean artists and
artists of other nationalities free of charge.

GEMINI G.E.L. at JONI MOISANT WEYL

58 West 58 Street, #21B 10019. **T:** (212) 308-0924.
F: (212) 308-0528. **E:** gemini@joniweyl.com
W: www.joniweyl.com **Open:** Tues.-Sat. 10-6.
Year established: 1985. **Size:** 2,500 sq. ft.
Owner/Director: Joni Moisant Weyl.
Work shown: Contemporary prints and multiples.
Prices: $2,000 and above. **Artists represented:** 40.
Origins: 95% male. All artists are in museum collections.
Work by: Richard Serra: etchings, paintstiks, and lithographs; Elizabeth Murray:
etchings, lithographs, and unique pastels; Robert Rauschenberg: lithographs,
screenprints, and multiples; Roy Lichtenstein: lithographs and screenprints; and
Bruce Nauman: etchings and lithographs; among others.
Selection process: All artists are selected from professional referrals. The gallery
is currently not looking for new artists.

JAMES GOODMAN

41 East 57 St., 10022. **T:** (212) 593-3737.
F: (212) 980-0195. **W:** www.jamesgoodmangallery.com
E: jamesgoodman@jamesgoodmangallery.com
Size: 2,600 sq. ft. **President:** James N. Goodman.
Director: Katherine K. Goodman. **Assistant Director:** Charles Conkright.
Executive Director: Patricia H. Tomkins.
Open: Tues.-Sat. 10-6, Mon. by appointment; Summer: Mon.-Fri. 10-5:30.
Year established: 1958. Member of Art Dealers Association of America.
Work shown: 19th and 20th Century European and American Modern and
Contemporary masters. Painting, sculpture and works on paper.
Work by: Exhibiting artists have included: Fernando Botero: paintings, drawings,
watercolors and sculpture; Roy Lichtenstein: paintings, drawings and sculpture;
Pablo Picasso: paintings, drawings and sculpture; and Henri Matisse: drawings;
among others. **Prices:** $15,000-4,000,000.
Annual exhibitions: 2 solo/4 group. **Advertising:** *The New York Times.*

MARIAN GOODMAN GALLERY, MULTIPLES

24 West 57 St., 4th floor, 10019.   **T:** (212) 977-7160.
F: (212) 581-5187.   **E:** goodman@mariangoodman.com
W: www.mariangodman.com   **Open:** Mon.-Sat. 10-6.
Owner: Marian Goodman.   **Director:** Jeannie Freilich.
Year established: 1977. (Multiples was established in 1965).
Member of Art Dealers Association of America.
Work shown: Contemporary paintings, sculpture and prints.
Work by: Lothar Baumgarten; Rebecca Horn; Juan Munoz; Thomas Struth; and
Gerhard Richter; among others.   **Annual exhibitions:** 5 or more.

GRANT SELWYN FINE ART

37 West 57 St., 10019.   **T:** (212) 755-0434.
F: (212) 759-9039.   **Year established:** 1998.
Open: Tues.-Sat. 10-5; Summer: Mon.-Fri. 10-5.
Owners: Anthony Grant and Marc Selwyn, formerly directors at Pace gallery.
Work shown: Contemporary art in all media.
Artists represented: 15 international artists.
Work by: Claes Oldenburg; Coosjee Von Bruggen; Donald Judd; Alexander
Calder; George Stoll; and Anthony Hernandez; among others.
Annual exhibitions: 8-10.   **Advertising:** *Artforum.*
Additional information: The gallery's other location is in Beverly Hills, CA.

NOHRA HAIME

41 East 57 St., 6th floor, 10022.   **T:** (212) 888-3550.
F: (212) 888-7869.   **E:** nohrahaime@aol.com
W: www.artnet/nohrahaime.html   **Director:** Nohra Haime.
Open: Tues.-Sat. 10-6; Summer: Mon.-Fri. 10-6.
Year established: 1982. Member of Art Dealers Association of America.
Work shown: Contemporary European, American, and Latin American painting
and sculpture.
Artists represented: 18. All of the artists are in museum collections.
Work by: Luis Caballero; Lika Mutal; Adam Straus; Francisca Sutil; and Sophia
Vari; among others.
Collectors: Metropolitan, Guggenheim, MoMA, and Hirshhorn.
Prices: $500-500,000.   **Annual exhibitions:** 9 solo/2 group.
Selection process: Artists should mail slides, resumé and SASE.
Response time: 1month.

MARTINA HAMILTON FINE ART

T/F: (212) 722-3311.   **Open:** By appointment.
Work shown: Oil paintings and prints by Odd Nerdrum, and Contemporary prints
and photography by other artists.

HAMMER

33 West 57 St., 10019.   **T:** (212) 644-4400.
F: (212) 832-3763.   **W:** www.hammergalleries.com
Owner: Michael Hammer.   **Director:** Richard Lynch.
Assistant Director: Howard Shaw. **Size:** 10,000 sq. ft.
Open: Mon.-Fri. 9:30-5:30, Sat. 10-5; Summer: Mon.-Fri. 9:30-5.
Year established: 1928 by Dr. Armand Hammer.

Work shown: Realism: Landscapes, still life and portraiture in all media.
Artists represented: 10 male.   **Ages:** 40-82. All origins.
Markets: Individual, corporate, and museum.
Collectors: Art Institute of Chicago, Hermitage, AT & T, and Smithsonian.
Prices: Several thousand to above several hundred thousand.
Annual exhibitions: 6 solo/4 group.
Advertising: *The New York Times, Art & Auction* and *ARTnews.*

HAMMER GRAPHICS

33 West 57 St., 3rd floor, 10019.   **T:** (212) 644-4405.
F: (212) 832-3763.   **Director:** Rhoda Altman.
Open: Mon.-Fri. 9:30-5:30, Sat. 10-5; Summer: Mon.-Fri. 9:30-5.
Work by: Leroy Neiman: paintings, watercolors, drawings, and serigraphs.
Collectors: Art Institute of Chicago, Hermitage Museum, Baltimore Museum of Fine Art, and Museo de Bella Artes, Caracas.
Advertising: *The New York Times* and *ARTnews.*

BILL HODGES

24 West 57 St., 10019.   **T:** (212) 333-2640.
F: (212) 333-2644.   **W:** www.billhodgesgallery.com
E: behodges@erols.com   **Size:** 1,000 sq. ft.
Year established: 1979.   **Owner/Director:** Bill Hodges.
Open: Tues.-Fri. 10-6 and Sat. by appointment; Summer: Tues.-Fri. 10-6.
Work shown: Contemporary art in acrylic, oil, steel and wood, with an emphasis on Abstraction.
Artists represented: 4. Predominantly African-American, and Asian artists.
Work by: Norman Lewis: paintings; Tomiko Kato: Nihonga painting; Maceo Mitchell: paintings; Linda Touby: paintings; and Benny Andrews: collages.
Collectors: Metropolitan, MoMA, The Tate, and High Museum, GA.
Annual exhibitions: 4 solo/3 group.   **Prices:** $1,200-110,000.
Markets: Individual, corporate, and museum.
Focus/Mission: To show work by prominent and established artists and to expose emerging artists.
Selection process: 55% are selected from referrals, 10% from slides sent to the gallery, 30% from exhibitions, and 5% from publications. Artists should approach the gallery during the Winter and Summer months. They should send slides, photographs, resumé and SASE. **Response time:** 2 months.
Requirements: Heavy abstractions. There are no exhibition expenses.

SO HYUN

41 West 57 St., 3rd floor, 10019.   **T:** (212) 355-6669.
F: (212) 355-4334.   **W:** www.sohyungallery.com
Open: Tues.-Sat. 10-6.   **Year established:** 2000.
Size: 2,500 sq. ft.   **Annual exhibitions:** 12.
Director: Sohyun Bai, former Owner/Director of Gallery BAI in SoHo.
Work shown: Contemporary art in all media, paintings, drawings, sculpture and photography.
Selection process: Artists should mail slides and resumé with SASE.
Response time: 2-3 weeks.
Fees: Artists should be prepared to pay the gallery for promotion expenses.

CORPORATE ART ADVISORS
These individuals play a crucial role in locating art for corporations.
Corrine Shane (InvestinArt); Shirley Reece (Reece Gallery),
Judith Selkowitz (Art Advisory Services), James Cavello (Corporate Art
Associates), and Alan Spanier (Images Gallery), among others.

INVESTINART
136 East 57 St., 10022. **T:** (212) 752-5307.
F: (212) 794-4071. **Open:** By appointment.
Founder/President: Corinne Shane.
Member of the National Association of Corporate Art Managers.
Focus/Mission: InvestinArt is an independent art consulting firm that specializes in locating art for corporations, professionals, and service firms.
Work shown: All styles and media. 75% of the artists are emerging artists.
Selection process: Artists should mail slides, resumé, price list and SASE.

THE IRISH ARTS CENTER
553 West 51 St., 10019. **T:** (212) 757-3318.
F: (212) 247-0930. **W:** www.irishartcenter.org
Open: Mon.-Fri. 10-6, Sat. and Sun. by appointment.
Year established: 1972. **Curator:** Megan Arney.
Work shown: Contemporary Irish art. Painting, sculpture and Conceptual.
Annual exhibitions: 10.
Focus/Mission: To promote a wide-range of contemporary Irish art, showcasing emerging and mid-career artists and curators working or born in Ireland. The Center also presents student and adult educational programs such as lectures, films and video screenings, thereby linking contemporary Irish artists with current U.S. and global aesthetic and ethical issues found in New York.
Selection process: Artists should send resumé and portfolio. Decisions are made by a committee.

ELSA MOTT IVES
YWCA of the City of New York, 610 Lexington Ave., 10022.
T: (212) 735-9732. **Open:** Mon.-Fri. 9-7, Sat. 10-3.
Year established: 1991. **Size:** 536 sq. ft.
Director: Frances Perrone.
Owner: Not-for-profit gallery located at and affiliated with the YWCA of the City of New York. The Craft Student's League is also located at the YWCA.
Annual exhibitions: 7 group. **Work shown:** A wide variety of art and crafts.
Focus/Mission: The gallery seeks to promote social awareness and provide inspiration through fine art and craft exhibitions, and provides a forum for emerging, minority and women artists. The purpose of the Craft Student's League is to provide continuing education in the visual arts and crafts to adults of diverse social, economic and ethnic backgrounds.
Selection process: Artists should send slides, artist's statement, exhibition proposal and SASE to Frances Perrone to be reviewed by a gallery advisory committee comprised of artists, art administrators, collectors and curators, which meets 4-5 times each year. Group shows only. **Response time:** 2 months.

JADITE

413 West 50 St., 10019.
F: (212) 315-2793.
W: www.jadite.com
T: (212) 315-2740.
E: jaditeart@aol.com
Year established: 1985.
Owner/Director: Roland Sainz, previously in banking.
Assistant Director: Katalina Petrova.
Open: Mon.-Sat. 12-6; Closed Aug. 12-Sept. 7.   **Size:** 1,100 sq. ft.
Work shown: Contemporary Figurative and Abstract paintings, watercolors, sculpture and photography.
Artists represented: 25. **Ages:** 20-50's. All origins.
Annual exhibitions: 12-15.
Advertising: *ARTnews, Latin American Art,* and *Gallery Guide.*
Focus/Mission: To exhibit the best possible art at reasonable prices.
Selection process: Artists may approach the gallery anytime. They should call or send slides, biography and SASE. **Response time:** 2-3 weeks.
Requirement: We require the best possible art there is.
Fees: The gallery and exhibiting artists share expenses.

JOHN JAY ATRIUM

John Jay College of Criminal Justice, 899 Tenth Ave., 10019.
T: (212) 237-8737.
Year established: 1985.
Open: Mon.-Fri. 9-5.
Contact: Hank Smit, Dean.
Selection process: All exhibitions are sponsored by groups within the college.

JOHN JAY WALL

John Jay College of Criminal Justice, 445 West 59 St., 10019.
T: (212) 237-8737.
Year established: 1985.
Open: Mon.-Fri. 9-5.
Contact: Hank Smit, Dean.
Selection process: All exhibitions are sponsored by groups within the college.

JEANMARIE

1057 Second Ave., 10022.
F: (212) 826-7164.
Year established: 1955.
Owner: Marie Kalisch.
T: (212) 486-8150.
Open: Mon.-Sat. 10-5.
Size: 1,000 sq. ft.
Director: Helene Singer.
Work shown: Contemporary Art and French Impressionist oil paintings.
Work by: H. Claude Pissarro: oil paintings; Michel Henry: oil paintings; J.P. Dubord: oil paintings; and Charles Levier: oil paintings; among others.

LEO KAPLAN MODERN

41 East 57 St., 7th floor, 10022.
F: (212) 872-1617.
W: www.lkmodern.com
Size: 4,000 sq. ft.
T: (212) 872-1616.
E: lkm@lkmodern.com
Year established: 1990.
Artists represented: 20.
Owner/Director: Scott Jacobson, Background: Wall Street.
Open: Mon.-Sat. 10-5:30. Memorial Day-Labor Day Mon.-Fri. 10-5:30.
Work shown: Contemporary art glass and furniture.
Prices: $10,000-200,000.
Work by: Wendell Castle; Albert Paley; Dan Dailey; Richard Jolley; and Tommy Simpson; among others.

Advertising: *American Craft* and *ARTnews.*
Selection process: Artists should mail materials with SASE.
Response time: 3 months.

KENNEDY

730 Fifth Ave., 10019.   **T:** (212) 541-9600.
F: (212) 977-3833.   **E:** Kennedygal@aol.com
W: www.kgny.com   **President:** Martha Fleischman.
Vice President: Lillian Brenwasser.
Year established: 1874. Member of Art Dealers Association of America.
Open: Tues.-Sat. 9:30-5:30 and Monday by appointment; Summer: Mon.-Fri. 9:30-5:30.
Work shown: 18th, 19th and 20th Century American paintings, watercolors, drawings, sculpture and prints.
Work by: Carolyn Plochmann: painting; Clarice Smith: painting; Joseph O'Sickey: painting; Carol Wald: painting; and George Sorrels: painting; among others.

KRAUSHAAR

724 Fifth Ave., 10019.   **T:** (212) 307-5730.
E: kraushaarg@aol.com   **W:** ww.artnet.com
Year established: 1885.   **Size:** 4,500 sq. ft.
Open: Tues.-Fri. 9:30-5:30, Sat. 10-5; Summer: Mon.-Fri. 10-5; Aug. by appointment.
Owner/President: Carole M. Pesner. Member of Art Dealers Association of America and International Fine Art Print Dealers Association.
Director: Katherine Kaplan.
Work shown: 20th Century and Contemporary American paintings, drawings, graphics and sculpture.
Artists represented: 15 living artists: 50% male/female. **Ages:** 30-90's.
Origins: U.S. All of the artists are in museum collections. Also: 15 artists' estates.
Work by: William King: sculpture; John Sloan: painting; John Heliker: painting; Linda Sokolowski: paintings and graphics; and John Koch: painting; among others.
Collectors: Metropolitan, MoMA, Whitney, and National Gallery.
Annual exhibitions: 6 solo/3 group.
Advertising: *Gallery Guide, Antiques* and *The New York Times.*
Focus/Mission: This is one of the oldest galleries in NYC that focuses on American art.

JAN KRUGIER

41 East 57 St., 6th floor, 10022.   **T:** (212) 755-7288.
F: (212) 980-6079.
Open: Tues.-Sat. 10-5:30. June and July: Mon.-Fri. 10-5; August closed.
Year established: 1987.   **Director:** Tzila Krugier.
Member of Art Dealers Association of America.
Work shown: 19th and 20th Century Masters including Marina Picasso's collection of works by Pablo Picasso. Painting, drawing, sculpture, and Picasso graphics.
Annual exhibitions: 4 solo/2 group.
Selection process: We are currently not looking for new artists.

LITTLEJOHN CONTEMPORARY

41 East 57 St., 10022.
T: (212) 980-2323.
F: (212) 980-2346.
W: www.littlejohncontemporary.com
Year established: 1992.
Size: 1,500 sq. ft.
Open: Tues.-Sat. 10-5:30; Summer: July and Aug. Mon.-Fri. 10-5:30.
Owner/Director: Jacquie Littlejohn, Rhode Island School of Design graduate, artist, and private dealer.
Work shown: Painterly Abstraction, Reductive painting and sculpture, and content-oriented Figuration. Paintings, mixed media and drawing.
Artists represented: 26, primarily from the U.S. **Ages:** 32-56.
Work by: Julie Heffernan: painting; Phyllis Bramson: painting and collage; Alison Moritsugu: painting and sculpture; Catherine Howe: painting; and Elena Sisto: painting; among others.
Markets: individual, corporate, museum.
Prices: $2,000-50,000.
Collectors: MoMA, Brooklyn Museum, Wadsworth Atheneum, and Boston Museum of Fine Arts.
Annual exhibitions: 10 solo/2 group.
Advertising: *Gallery Guide, Artforum,* and *Art in America.*
Focus/Mission: To show work that has a strong personality and does not restrict the gallery to a specific stylistic agenda. The gallery's Project Room presents special exhibitions which may be more adventurous in spirit.
Selection process: We are currently not actively taking on any new artists.

LOBBY

31 West 52 St., 10022.
T: (212) 586-1757.
Open: 7 days 8-8.
Year established: 1990.
Owner: Non-profit organization.
Size: 1,500 sq. ft.
Work shown: All styles and media. **Annual exhibitions:** 10.
Focus/Mission: The gallery was established with the mandate of providing unique exhibitions to be viewed in the architectural setting designed by Kevin Roche. It reflects a commitment of the occupants to support and encourage a deeper understanding and appreciation of the arts. Through exhibitions it is hoped that the gallery will enrich the lives of employees of the building and the general public.
Selection process: Application to the exhibition program is open to all artists working in all media. Artists must submit a proposal, 10 slides and SASE, and take into consideration that this is a corporate space. **Response time:** 3 months.
Additional information: There are no exhibition fees and no commission fees.

MARLBOROUGH GALLERY and MARLBOROUGH GRAPHICS

40 West 57 St., 2nd floor, 10019
T: (212) 541-4900.
F: (212) 541-4948.
E: mny@marlboroughgallery.com
W: www.marlboroughgallery.com
Director: Pierre Levai.
Year established: New York in 1963; London in 1946.
Open: Mon.-Sat. 10-5:30; Summer: Mon.-Fri. 10-5:30.
Work shown: Contemporary paintings, sculpture and graphics.
Size: 19,000. This is one of the largest galleries in NYC.
Artists represented: More than 16 artists and 2 estates.

Work by: Fernando Botero: painting; John Alexander, painting; Red Grooms: mixed media; and Larry Rivers: painting.

Additional information: The gallery has been publishing prints for more than 35 years. It offers secondary market prints including important prints by 20th Century Masters such as Matisse and Picasso, and Contemporary artists Hockney, Johns, and Rauschenberg.

JAIN MARUNOUCHI

24 West 57 St., 6th floor, 10019.   **T:** (212) 969-9660.
F: (212) 969-9715.   **E:** jainmar@aol.com
W: www.jainmargallery.com   **Size:** 700 sq. ft.
Year established: 1991.   **Owner/Director:** Ashok Jain.
Open: Tues.-Sat. 11-5 and by appointment.
Work shown: Contemporary art in all media.
Markets: Individual, corporate, and museum.
Prices: $500-25,000.
Artists represented: 39, from the U.S., Europe, Asia, and South America. 50% male/female. 30% are in museum collections.
Work by: Richard Vaux: carbon drawing, polymar on canvas, sculpture; Fernando Pomalaza: collages on canvas and paper, prints, and monotypes; Pauline Gagnon: all media; Claus Eben: canvas, paper, and prints; and Emily Wei: paper and canvas; among others.
Annual exhibitions: 16 solo/4 group.
Advertising: *ARTnews, New York Arts* and *Gallery Guide.*
Selection process: We are not accepting artist's submissions at this time.

BARBARA MATHES

41 East 57 St., 3rd floor, 10022.   **T:** (212) 752-5135.
F: (212) 752-5145.   **E:** art@bmathesgallery.com
W: www. bmathesgallery.com
President: Barbara Mathes.
Director: Jill Bishins.
Open: Tues.-Sat. 9:30-5:30; Summer: July and August Mon.-Fri. 10-5:30.
Year established: 1978. Member of Art Dealers Association of America.
Work shown: Modern and Contemporary European and American paintings, sculpture and drawings.

EARL MC GRATH

20 West 57 St., 3rd floor, 10019.   **T:** (212) 956-3366
F: (212) 956-6761.   **Year established:** 1995.
Open: Tues.-Sat. 10-6; Summer: Tues.-Sat. 10-5. Aug. by appointment.
Owner/Director: Earl McGrath, owner of a gallery in California.
Work shown: Modern and Contemporary art in all media.
Artists represented: 10.
Work by: Gabrielle Bakker; Marina Karella; Allesandro Twombly; Fernando Bengoechea; and Amato; among others.
Selection process: Most of the artists are selected from artist studio visits, however, the gallery will look at artists' materials mailed with SASE.

MC KEE

745 Fifth Ave., 4th floor, 10151.   **T:** (212) 688-5951.
F: (212) 752-5638.   **E:** gallery@mckeegallery.com
W: www.mckeegallery.com
Size: 10,000 sq. ft.
Open: Tues.-Sat. 10-6. July Mon.-Fri. 10-5. August by appointment.
Year established: 1974. Member of Art Dealers Association of America
Owners: David and Renée McKee.
Work shown: Contemporary painting, drawing, and sculpture. Also secondary market sales.
Artists represented: 14. **Ages:** 30s-60.
Work by: Martin Puryear: sculpture; Vija Celmins: painting; Leonid Lerman: sculpture, painting. We represent the Philip Guston Estate, painting; and Jake Berthot.
Collectors: Metropolitan, MoMA, Guggenheim, Art Institute of Chicago.
Annual exhibitions: 8-10 solo.
Advertising: *Artforum* and *Gallery Guide*.
Selection process: Artists should mail slides with SASE.

MERIDIAN FINE ART - MAX LANG, RITA KRAUSS

41 East 57 St., 8th floor, 10022.   **T:** (212) 980-2400.
F: (212) 223-9981.   **W:** www.meridianfa.com
E: info@meridianfa.com   **Open:** Mon.-Fri. 10-5.
Year established: 1997.   **Owners:** Max Lang, more than 15 years in
the international art market and Rita Krauss, more than 26 years experience as a private art advisor.
Work shown: 20th Century art in all media. Primarily secondary market.
Work by: Picasso; Warhol; Haring; Basquiat; and Wesselman; among others.
Advertising: *Gallery Guide*.

LAURENCE MILLER

20 West 57 St., 10019.   **T:** (212) 397-3930.
F: (212) 397-3932.   **E:** lmg@laurencemillergallery.com
W: www.laurencemillergallery.com **Year established:** 1983.
Size: 2,500 sq. ft.
Open: Tues.-Fri. 10-5:30, Sat 11-5:30; Summer: Closed Saturday.
Owner/President: Laurence Miller, former Director, Light Gallery.
Co-Director: Vicki Harris.
Work shown: Contemporary and Vintage fine art photography.
Photography by: Ray K. Metzker; Helen Levitt; Zeke Berman; Lois Conner; and Stephane Couturier; among others.
Advertising: *Gallery Guide* and *Photography in New York*.
Focus/Mission: To exhibit and represent the finest in Contemporary and Vintage fine art photography.
Collectors: Metropolitan, and Museum of Fine Arts, Houston.
Prices: $750-100,000.
Markets: Individual, Corporate, and museum. **Selection process:** Artists should call for current procedure.

MODERNAGE CUSTOM COLOR LABS
1150 Ave. of the Americas, 2nd floor, 10036. Main Office: **T:** (212) 997-1800.
F: (212) 869-4796.   **E:** zmorin@modernage.com.
W: www.modernage.com   **Open:** Mon.-Fri. 8:30-6.
Owner: K. Troiano.   **Director:** Joe Smith.
Assistant Director: Zee Morin.   **Size:** 250 sq. ft.
Work shown: Photographic and Digital Prints.
Annual exhibitions: 10 solo/1 group.
Work by: Exhibitions have included Dianne Arndt: duratrans (backlighted) images reflecting social/urban issues; Bill Perlmutter: silver-gelatin vintage prints of post WWII Europe; Ralph Gross: ethnic portraits; Paul Seligman: silver-gelatin vintage prints and Maria Callas' Metropolitan Opera Debut; and Susan Islam: silver-gelatin and C-prints on varied themes of travel; among others.
Prices: $125-2,500.
Focus/Mission: To provide an interesting atmosphere for clients by showcasing photographic art. To give photographers a place to exhibit.
Selection process: Artists should call for an appointment.
Response time: 3 weeks.
Requirements: Photos must be ready to hang.
Fees: Artists are responsible for mounting, framing and opening reception costs.

MUNICIPAL ART SOCIETY URBAN CENTER
457 Madison Ave., 10022.   **T:** (212) 935-3960.
W: www.mas.org   **Open:** Daily 11-5. Closed Thurs. and Sun..
Year established: 1893.   **President:** Kent Barwick.
Exhibitions Director: Aimee Molloy. **Annual exhibitions:** 5.
Focus/Mission: The Municipal Art Society is a membership organization which aggressively champions excellence in urban design, sanity in planning, and the preservation of the best of the City's past. This program emphasizes NYC's cultural and geographic diversity, providing entree to often inaccessible resources.
Additional information: The Society conducts "Discover New York" historical walking tours, bus tours, lectures, courses and other programs.

MUSEUM OF MODERN ART
11 West 53 St., 10019. This location is closing May 22, 2002 for renovations and will reopen in 2005. The Museum of Modern Art in Queens will open for exhibitions in the Summer 2002. See Queens section for more information.
T: (212) 708-9480.   **Group tours:** (212) 708-9658.
W: www.moma.org   **Director:** Glenn D. Lowry.
Year established: 1929.   **Annual exhibitions:** over 60.
Open: Sat.-Tues., Thurs., 10:30-5:45, and Fri. 10:30-8:15.
Size: 67,000 sq. ft. permanent collection; 20,000 sq. ft. temporary exhibitions.
Admission: $10. adults; $6.50 seniors / full-time students with current identification; free for members and children under 16 years old if accompanied by an adult. Pay what you wish Fri. 4:30-8:15.
Additional information: MoMA has a sculpture garden behind the front entrance. There is a MoMA book and gift store. The museum also offers lectures, workshops and films. Sette MoMA is an Italian restaurant upstairs overlooking the sculpture garden. T: (212) 708-9710.

NEUHOFF

41 East 57 St., 10022.　　**T:** (212) 838-1122.
F: (212) 838-1250.　　**E:** info@neuhoffgallery.com
W: www.neuhoffgallery.com　　**Owner/Director:** Heidi Neuhoff.
Open: Tues.-Sat. 10-6. Memorial Day-Labor Day: Mon.-Fri. 10-6.
Work shown: Contemporary Art.　**Annual exhibitions:** 4.
Work by: Hanneke Beaumont; Jeffrey Brosk; David Remfry; Norman Sunshine; and Roy Gussow; among others.

NIPPON

145 West 57 St., 10019.　　**T:** (212) 581-2223.
F: (212) 581-3332.　　**W:** www.jcciny.org/nipponclub
Open: Mon.-Sat. 10-6.　　**Owner:** Not-for-profit organization.
Director: Yuko Y. Royer.
Work shown: Contemporary art and traditional Japanese art in all media.
Annual exhibitions: 10 solo/2-3 group.
Advertising: *Gallery Guide.*
Selection process: Artists should send proposal, slides, resumé and SASE.

O'HARA

41 East 57 St., 13th floor, 10022.　　**T:** (212) 355-3330.
F: (212) 355-3361.　　**E:** info@oharagallery.com
Open: Mon.-Fri. 10-5:30, Sat. 10-5; Summer: Mon.-Fri. 10-5:30.
Year established: 1990. Member of Art Dealers Association of America.
President: Ruth O'Hara, art dealer for over 40 years.
Work shown: Modern, Impressionism and Contemporary art. European and American master paintings, works on paper, and sculpture.
Work by: Calder; Chagall; Basquiat; Botero; Lichtenstein; Warhol; and Picasso; among others. The inventory is constantly changing, with an increase in contemporary masters as well as traditional.

PACE PRINTS and PACE PRIMITIVES

32 East 57 St., 10022.　　**T:** Prints (212) 421-3237.
T: Old Master, Modern and Primitive (212) 421-3688.
F: (212) 832-5162.　　**W:** www.paceprints.com
Size: 6,000 sq. ft.　　**Owner:** Richard Solomon.
Open: Tues.-Fri. 9:30-5:30, Sat. 10-5; Summer: Mon.-Thurs. 9:30-5:30, Fri. 9:30-4.
Year established: 1968. Member of Art Dealers Association of America.
Directors: Kristin Heming, Carlo Bella, Alexandra Schwartz & Lisa Bradley.
Work shown: Contemporary, Modern and Old Master prints, and African art.
Artists represented: 20 male/10 female. **Ages:** 30-80.
Origins: Predominantly U.S. All of the artists are in museum collections.
Work by: Chuck Close; Jim Dine; Rembrandt; and Picasso – all prints.
Markets: Individual, corporate, and museum.
Collectors: MoMA, Metropolitan, Whitney, and National Gallery.
Annual exhibitions: 5 solo/5 group.
Advertising: *New York Times* and *ARTnews.*
Focus/Mission: To publish and distribute a mix of younger and established artists and offer for sale these editions in the context of the masters of printmaking from Dürer to Rembrandt, to Picasso and Matisse, to Jim Dine.

Selection process: 50% of the artists are selected from referrals, 50% through exhibitions. We are currently not accepting unsolicited artists' materials.

PACE/MACGILL

32 East 57 St., 9th floor, 10022.   **T:** (212) 759-7999.
F: (212) 759-8964.   **Year established:** 1983.
Owner: Peter MacGill.   **Open:** Tues.-Fri. 9:30-5:30, Sat. 10-6;
Summer: Mon.-Thurs. 9:30-5:30, Fri. 9:30-4.
Work shown: 20th Century photography.
Work by: Dieter Appelt; Richard Avedon; Harry Callahan; John Chamberlain; William Christenberry; Chuck Close; among others.

PACEWILDENSTEIN

32 East 57 St., 10022.   **T:** (212) 421-3292.
F: (212) 421-0835.   **Chairman**: Arne Glimcher.
Open: Tues.-Fri. 9:30-6, Sat. 10-5; Summer: Call for hours.
Year established: 1960. Member of Art Dealers Association of America.
Work shown: Modern and Contemporary art.
Work by: Alexander Calder; John Chamberlain; Chuck Close; George Condo; Jim Dine; Jean Dubuffet; Barbara Hepworth; Elizabeth Murray; among others.
Additional information: See Pace Wildenstein in Chelsea section.

PALEY

1 East 53 St., 10022.   **T:** (212) 355-4171.
F: (212) 431-6939.   **Open:** Mon.-Fri. 8-8, Sat 8-6.
Year established: 1993.   **Work shown:** All styles and media.
Annual exhibitions: 5-6 group.
Focus/Mission: To present artworks created by students of Studio in a School Association.

FRANKLIN PARRASCH

20 West 57 St., 10019.   **T:** (212) 246-5360.
F: (212) 246-5391.   **E:** franklin@franklinparrasch.com
W: www.franklinparraschgallery.com
Year established: 1986.   **Size:** 2,000 sq. ft.
Owner/Director: Franklin Parrasch.
Co-Director: Allison Stites.
Open: Tues.-Sat. 10-6. July and Aug. Tues.-Fri.10-6.
Work shown: Contemporary American sculpture, specializing in Westcoast ceramic sculpture.
Artists represented: 9. 60% male/40% female. **Ages:** 30-60's. All origins. All of the artists are in museum collections.
Work by: John Cederquist: furniture; Louis Mueller: furniture; Steven De Staebler: clay; Richard Marquis: glass; and Ken Price, ceramic art; among others.
Prices: $3,000-85,000.
Collectors: Philadelphia Museum, Metropolitan, American Craft Museum.
Annual exhibitions: 10 solo/ 3-4 group.
Advertising: *Art in America, American Ceramics* and *ARTnews*.
Selection process: Most artists are selected from referrals and exhibitions. We are currently not looking for new artists.

KATHARINA RICH PERLOW

41 East 57 St., 13th floor, 10022.   **T:** (212) 644-7171.
F: (212) 644-2519.   **Year established:** 1985.
W: www.galleryguideonlin.com/gallery/kperlow and www.artnet.com/perlowgallery
Open: Tues.-Sat. 10-6. July Mon.-Fri. 10-6. Aug. Mon.-Fri. 10-5:30.
Owner/Director: Katharina Rich Perlow.
Assistant to the Director: Jennifer Zazo.
Work shown: Varied styles and philosophies of painting and sculpture from Abstraction to Realism.
Work by: John Ferren: Modernist painting and sculpture; Lani Irwin: enigmatic Realist painting; Forrest Moses: Semi-Abstract landscape painting; Stephen Pace: Abstract and Expressionist painting; and John Winship: Figurative Realist painting; among others.
Focus/Mission: The gallery maintains active and ongoing relationships with museums, institutions, major corporations and private collectors who are serious and passionate about art.
Selection process: Artists may mail slides, photographs, and resumé with SASE.

PETERSBURG PRESS

444 West 20 St., Garden Entrance, 10011.
Mailing address: P.O. Box 2238, 10101.
T: (212) 206-7888.   **F:** (413) 254-7472.
E: petrsbrg@ix.netcom.com   **Open:** By appointment.
Year established: 1973.   **Director:** Tamie Swett.
Work shown: Contemporary and Modern graphics, work on paper, and painting by primarily American and European artists.
Work by: Frank Stella; David Hockney; Jasper Johns; Howard Hodgkin, and Duchamp; among others.

PHILLIPS DE PURY & LUXEMBOURG

3 West 57 St., 10019.   **T:** (212) 940-1200.
W: www.phillips-auctions.com   **Open:** Mon.-Fri. 9-5.
Year established: 1796.
Work shown at auction: Impressionist and Modern Art; Contemporary art; American art; antique and fine jewelry; 20th Century decorative arts; 20-21st Century design art and photography. Swiss art, European and Continental furniture.
Additional information: Phillips also offers a complete range of Trusts and Estates services. For a catalogue of exhibitions call (800) 825-2781.

REECE

24 West 57 St., Suite 304, 10019.   **T:** (212) 333-5830.
F: (212) 333-7366.   **E:** sireece@reecegalleries.com
W: www.reecegalleries.com   **Open:** Tues.-Sat. 10-5:30.
Year established: 1974.   **Size:** 2,000 sq. ft.
Owner/Director: Shirley Reece.
Work shown: Contemporary art in addition to stone sculpture from Zimbabwe.
Artists represented: 20. 50% male/female. Mid to late career artists from all origins. 75% of the artists are in museum collections.
Work by: Tsugio Hattori, painting; Sica, mixed media; Jian-Guo Xu, painting; and

Fred Otnes, mixed media; Armentia: paintings and sculpture; among others.
Prices: $1,000-50,000. **Annual exhibitions:** 7-8.
Advertising: *ARTnews* and *Gallery Guide.*
Focus/Mission: We are dealers and consultants specializing in corporate and private collections.
Selection process: 90% of the artists are selected from referrals and slides submitted to the gallery. Artists should mail 20 slides, biography, prices, and SASE. **Response time:** 6 weeks.
Requirements: Mid-career artists with Contemporary art.

REHS

5 East 57 St., 10022.   **T:** (212) 355-5710.
F: (212) 355-5742.   **E:** info@rehsgalleries.com
W: www.rehsgalleries.com   **Open:** Mon.-Fri. 10-5:30.
Year established: 1935.   **Owners:** Joseph Rehs and Howard Rehs.
Summer: June and July Mon.-Thurs. 10-5:30 and Aug. Tues.-Thurs. 10-5:30.
Work shown: 19th and early 20th Century European academic and Contemporary art.
Artists represented: 100 +
Work by: Daniel Ridgway Knight: painting; Edward Cortes: painting; Julien Dupre: painting; Fred Morgan: painting; and Barry Oretsky: painting; among others.
Advertising: *Architectural Digest, Antiques* and *Art and Antiques.*

RICHART DESIGN ET CHOCOLAT

7 East 55 St., 10022.   **T:** (212) 371-9369.
Open: Mon.-Fri. 10-7, Sat. 10-6.   **Owner:** Jennifer Park.
Work shown: Contemporary work by New York artists. Paintings, photography and drawings.
Prices: $1,000-2,500 (for artwork). **Annual exhibitions:** 6.
Selection process: Artists should mail slides and SASE. We exhibit positive themes only; no political themes.
Additional Information: Richart is a chocolate boutique with a modern art theme.

ROSENBERG + KAUFMAN PHOTOGRAPHY & WORK ON PAPER

30 W. 57 St., 6th floor, 10012.   **T:** (212) 757-7401.
F: (212) 431-1067.   **E:** rkart@earthlink.net
W: www.artnet.com   **Size:** 1,800 sq. ft.
Open: Tues.-Sat. 11-6 and by appointment. Aug. by appointment.
Year established: 1983.
Owners/Directors: Stephen Rosenberg: attorney; and Fran Kaufman: former TV executive.
Work shown: Contemporary American and European painting, drawing, work on paper, and 3-dimensional art.
Artists represented: 14. 90% of the artists are in museum collections.
Work by: Wayne Levin, photography; among others. **Annual exhibitions:** 9.
Advertising: *Art in America, Gallery Guide, ARTnews* and *The Art Newspaper.*
Focus/Mission: To exhibit contemporary art by mid-career and emerging artists. The emphasis is on Abstraction and Abstract Figuration, from Minimal to Expressive, with a select group of artists who have a unique perspective on the landscape.

Selection process: Artists should visit the gallery and view several exhibitions to acquaint themselves with the work the gallery represents. At this time the gallery is not taking on any new artists.

Additional information: The gallery's other location is in SoHo.

MICHAEL ROSENFELD

24 West 57 St., 10019. **T:** (212) 247-0082.
F: (212) 247-0402. **E:** info@michaelrosenfeldart.com
W: www.michaelrosenfeldart.com **Year established:** 1989.
Owner/Director: Michael Rosenfeld. **Co-Director:** Halley K. Harrisburg.
Open: Tues.-Sat. 10-6. July and Aug. Mon.-Fri. 10-6.
Work shown: This gallery specializes in 20th Century American art from 1910-1970. Exhibitions include early American Abstraction, Abstract Expressionism, Modernism, Realism, Social Realism, and Surrealism, and art by African-American artists.

MARY RYAN

24 West 57 St., 10019. **T:** (212) 397-0669.
F: (212) 397-0766.
Owner/Director: Mary Ryan. **Manager:** Catherine Ryan.
Open: Tues.-Sat. 10-5; Summer: Tues.-Fri. 10-5 and Mon. by appointment.
Work shown: British and American paintings, prints, and work on paper, from 1910 to Contemporary.
Work by: Exhibitions have included the work of Yvonne Jacquette; Michael Mazur; DeLoss McGraw; May Stevens; and Donald Sultan; among others.
Annual exhibitions: 8-10 mostly solo shows.

SAINT PETER'S CHURCH LIVING ROOM

619 Lexington Ave., 10022. **T:** (212) 935-2200.
W: www.saintpeters.org **Open:** Daily 9-7.
Size: 2,000 sq. ft.
Work shown: All styles and media.
Annual exhibitions: 15 solo/at least 2 group.
Advertising: *Gallery Guide.*
Focus/Mission: We are dedicated to the exhibition of art to enhance the human spirit. Exhibitions are shown in the interior and exterior spaces of the church. In addition, permanent installations of commissioned work, such as the Erol Beker Chapel of the Good Shepard, sculpted by Louise Nevelson and the Exterior Cross by Arnold Pomodoro, are keystones of the St. Peter's ministry.
Selection process: Artists should send up to 12 slides, biography, and SASE to Art and Architecture, St. Peter's Church, to the attention of Tanya Gresh, Chairperson of Art Exhibition Committee. The review committee meets 2 times each year. For more information visit the web site or call.

SUSAN SHEEHAN

20 West 57 St., 7th floor, 10019. **T:** (212) 888-4220.
F: (212) 489-4009. **E:** susan.sheehangallery@verizon.net
W: www.artnet.com **Open:** Tues.-Sat. 10-6.
Year established: 1985.
Owner: Susan Sheehan. Member of Art Dealers Association of America and

International Fine Print Dealers Association.
Work shown: 19th and 20th Century American & European prints, work on paper.
Work by: Hopper; Johns; Kelly; Marden; Rauschenberg; Stella; and Warhol; among others.

SPANIERMAN

45 East 58 St., 10022.
F: (212) 832-8114.
W: www.Spanierman.com
Director: Gavin Spanierman.

T: (212) 832-0208.
E: info@spanierman.com
Open: Mon.-Sat. 9:30-5:30.

Work shown: 19th and early 20th Century American art and some Contemporary art. Painting, sculpture, watercolors and drawing.
Work by: Metcalf; Parris; Prendergast; Twachtman; and Hassam; among others.
Selection process: We are currently not looking for new artists.

GERTRUDE STEIN

56 West 57 St., 3rd floor, 10019.
F: (212) 765-6178.
Size: 2,500 sq. ft.

T: (212) 535-0600.
Year established: 1963.

Open: Tues.-Sat. 10-5; August: Mon.- Fri. 12-5.
Work shown: Predominantly Modern Masters, some Contemporary Masters. Paintings, works on paper, and sculpture.

USB PAINEWEBBER

1285 Ave. of the Americas, 10019.
F: (212) 713-9739.
Year established: 1985.
Size: 4,000 sq. ft.

T: (212) 713-2885.
Open: Mon.-Fri. 8-6.
Director: Colin Thomson.

Work shown: All exhibitions are organized by New York area non-profit arts and cultural organizations.
Annual exhibitions: 4-5 group that run for about 3 months.
Focus/Mission: To enable nonprofit arts and cultural organizations to acquaint a mid-town audience with their collections and activities. Each year, four organizations are invited to exhibit, resulting in a program of variety and breadth.
Selection process: Call to inquire about current review policy.

VENEZUELAN CENTER

7 East 51 St., 10022.
F: (212) 644-7471.
Year established: 1985.

T: (212) 826-1683.
Open: Mon.-Fri. 9-4.

Annual exhibitions: 24/mostly solo.
Cultural Attaché/Curator: Carolina Salaverria.
Work shown: Contemporary art by Venezuelan and other South American artists. Primarily paintings, in addition to drawings, sculpture and photography.
Focus/Mission: To make Venezuelan artists known in the U.S. and to encourage and promote these artists. The Center also presents lectures and stage readings.
Selection process: Artists should mail slides and photographs and SASE.

JOAN T. WASHBURN

20 West 57 St., 8th floor, 10019.
F: (212) 397-4853.
E: jwashburn@earthlink.net
Size: 4,000 sq. ft.
T: (212) 397-6780.
W: www.artnet.com/jwashburn.html
Year established: 1971.

Owner/Director: Joan T. Washburn. Member of Art Dealers Association of America.
Open: Tues.-Sat. 10-6; June Mon.-Fri. 10-5:30; July and Aug. Tues.-Fri. 10-5:30.
Work shown: 19th and 20th Century paintings, drawings, sculpture, prints, and photographs.
Artists represented: 15 male/5 female, predominantly from the U.S.
Work by: Louise Nevelson: sculpture and drawings; James Brooks: paintings, work on paper; Jackson Pollack: paintings; Anne Ryan: collage; and Georgia O'Keefe: paintings; among others. Advertising: *Gallery Guide.*

JOAN WHALEN FINE ART

24 West 57 St., Suite 507, 10019.
F: (212) 397-6188.
W: www.artnet.com
Size: 2,000 sq. ft.
T: (212) 397-9700.
E: jwhalenfineart@worldnet.att.net
Open: Mon.-Sat. 10-6, Sun. by appointment.
Year established: 1997.

Owner/Director: Joan Whalen.
Work shown: 19th and 20th Century American Art and Contemporary Art. Oils, watercolors, prints, and drawings.
Work by: Theresa Bernstein; Isabel Bishop; Guy Wiggins; Ernest Lawson; and Frederick Childe Hassam; among others.
Selection process: Artists should mail slides, photographs, biography, resumé and SASE.

ZABRISKIE

41 East 57 St., 4th floor, 10019.
F: (212) 752-1224.
W: www.zabriskiegallery.com
Year established: 1955.
T: (212) 752-1223.
E: vzny@zabriskiegallery.com
Open: Tues.-Sat. 10-5:30.
President: Virginia M. Zabriskie.

Director: Julie Castellano.
Work shown: Modern and Contemporary American and European art; Vintage and Contemporary photography.
Work by: Abraham Walkowitz; William Zorach; Nicholas Nixon; Joan Fontcuberta; and Ben Vautier; among others.

UPTOWN

SIXTIES & ABOVE

MAKOR

"MAKOR is a place of rediscovery, meaning and inspiration – a place where arts, life, history and the spirit can connect. "

SIXTIES

ACADEMY GALLERY OF ART & SCIENCE
NY Academy of Sciences, 2 East 63 St., 10021. **T:** (212) 838-0230.
F: (212) 838-5226.   **E:** communications@nyas.org
W: www.nyas.org   **Open:** Mon.-Fri. 9-5.
Year established: 1817.   **Owner:** Non-profit organization.
Work shown: A wide range of styles and media. Exhibitions originate from the State University at Binghamton, NY, curated by Lynn Gamwell.
Annual exhibitions: 4-6.
Additional information: The Academy publishes *The Sciences* magazine.

AMERICAN FOLK ART MUSEUM
Eva and Morris Feld Gallery, 2 Lincoln Square, Columbus Ave., between 65 and 66 St., 10023.   **T:** (212) 595-9533.
F: (212) 977-8134.   **E:** info@folkartmuseum.org
W: www.folkartmuseum.org   **Admission:** Free.
Open: Mon. 11-6; Tues.-Sun. 11:30-7:30. **Year established:** 1961.
Owner: Non-profit museum.   **Director:** Gerard C. Wertkin.
Work shown: A permanent collection ranging from 18th Century to current quilts, weathervanes, folk paintings, whirligigs, painted tin ware, sculpture, and works by 20th Century Self-taught artists.
Annual exhibitions: Changing traveling exhibitions.
Focus/Mission: To preserve the rich and diverse cultural history of America through the presentation of exhibitions, educational programs, and publications of the highest quality.
Additional information: School and other groups may arrange tours. Call: (212) 595-9533. There is a museum book and gift shop at Columbus Ave. and 66 St. The museum publishes *FOLK ART* magazine. It also conducts lectures, Folk Art Explorers' Club trips, and creative educational workshops for children and adults.

AMERICAS SOCIETY

680 Park Ave., 10021.
F: (212) 249-5868
E: exhibitions@as-coa.org
Year established: 1967.
Work shown: Pre-Columbian to Contemporary art in all media.
Size: 1,800 sq. ft.
Caribbean, and Canada.

T: (212) 249-8950.
W: www.americas-society.org
Open: Tues.-Sun. 12-6.
Director, Visual Arts: Gabriel Perez.

Work by: Artists from the Americas, the
Annual exhibitions: 3-4.
Advertising: *Gallery Guide, Time Out, The New York Times, Art Nexus.*
Focus/Mission: To mount exhibitions from the Americas, from Pre-Columbian times to the present. To concentrate on scholarly exhibitions and publications that illuminate the important contributions of Latin Americans to the history of art.
Selection process: Artists from our geographic sphere of interest should submit a resumé, 15-20 slides, artist statement, and SASE. Response time: 4 weeks.

JACK ARNOLD FINE ART

5 East 67 St., 10021.
F: (212) 249-7332.
Owner/Director: Jack Arnold.

T: (212) 249-7218.
Open: By appointment Mon.-Fri. 10-5:30.
Work shown: Contemporary graphics and
paintings. Markets: Museums and galleries.
Work by: Alain Bonnefoit; Claude Gaveau; Bracha Guy; Claude Hemeret; France Hilon; among others.

ARSENAL

64 St. at Fifth Ave. (in Central Park), 3rd floor, 10021.
T: (212) 360-8163.
W: www.nyc.gov/parks.org

F: (212) 360-1329.
Open: Mon.-Fri. 9-5.
Owner: NYC Dept. of Parks and Recreation. Director: Adrian Sas.
Work shown: Varied styles and varied media of 2-d art.
Annual exhibitions: 8-10. Advertising: *New York, Time Out,* and *New Yorker.*
Focus/Mission: Non-profit, public service-oriented organization that offers exposure to artists who might not have a private gallery space.
Selection process: 90% are selected from slides sent to the gallery. Artists should call or visit the web site for current submission guidelines. Art inspired by our properties and parks are preferred, but we consider all proposals. Proposals should include a description of proposed exhibition (conceptual theme or curatorial statement), slides or photographs, resumé or description of organization, and SASE.

ART ADVISORY SERVICES

T: (212) 935-1272.
F: (212) 755-3924.
Open: By appointment.

W: www.artadvisoryservices.com

Owner/Director: Judith Selkowitz, accredited appraiser and a member of Appraisers Association of America. The firm provides advice on the acquisition of artwork for the corporate market and for private collectors.
Work shown: Contemporary artists and 19th and 20th Century masters. Paintings and work on paper.
Focus/Mission: To develop and advance aesthetically appropriate art programs that endure and retain value.

CHRISTIE'S

20 Rockefeller Plaza, 10020.   **T:** (212) 636 2000
W: www.christies.com
Year established: 1766 Christie's is a major auction house.
Work shown at auction: Antiquities, Asian and Islamic art, books and manuscripts, collectibles, fine art, furniture and decorative arts, jewelry and watches, motorcars, photographs and prints, wine and cigars.
Additional Information: Christie's offers appraisal and valuation services.

CORK

Avery Fischer Hall, Lincoln Center, Broadway at 65 St., Concourse level, 10023. Office: 70 Lincoln Center Plaza, 0023.
Open: 7 days 10am-10:30pm.   **Size:** 1,552 sq. ft.
Director of Community Relations: Jenneth Webster.
Work shown: Painting, drawing, photography, and sculpture.
Annual exhibitions: 26 group. Duration: 2 weeks.
Selection process: Artist organizations may approach the gallery anytime. Multi-cultural artists are particularly welcome. Groups must submit slides, documentation about the organizations, and letters of proof of involvement with community services. Exhibitors must provide sitters and hang the work themselves. Groups are not required to pay any exhibition fees for the use of the space. No artwork with frontal nudity or controversial subject matter is permitted.

CORNING GALLERY AT STEUBEN

667 Madison Ave., 10021.   **T:** (646) 497-3744.
W: www.corning.com   **Open:** Mon.-Fri. 10-7, Sat. 10-6.
Manager: Patricia Y. Marti.   **Size:** 2,500 sq. ft.
Work shown: Diverse media including glass.   **Annual exhibitions:** 4.
Fission/Mission: To provide the arts with a forum for dialogue. To contribute to the diverse cultural landscape of New York.

CAROL CRAVIN

T: (212) 734-2125.   **F:** (212) 734-2125
E: ccraven@vineyard.net   **W:** www.cravengallery.com
Open: By appointment.
Owner/Director: Carol Cravin, an art dealer in NYC since the early 1970's.
Work shown: Contemporary and American Modernist paintings, drawing and photography.
Additional information: Carol Cravn also offers comprehensive art advisory services for private and corporate collectors. Her other gallery is located in Martha's Vineyard, open May-Nov. T: (508) 693-3535.

DAVIS & LANGDALE CO.

231 East 60 St., 10022.   **T:** (212) 838-0333.
F: (212) 752-7764.   **Year established:** 1953.
Open: Tues.-Sat. 10-5; Summer: Mon.-Fri. 10-4.
Owners: Roy Davis and Cecily Langdale. **Director:** Michelle Martin.
Member of Art Dealers Association of America.
Work shown: Late 18th, 19th and early 20th Century British and American works on paper, and Contemporary art.

Work by: Aaron Shikler: painting; Robert M. Kulicke: painting; Harry Roseman: sculpture, drawing, and collage; Stuart Shils: oil painting and works on paper; and Albert York, painting; among others.
Annual exhibitions: 4-5.
Advertising: *The New York Times* and *Gallery Guide*.

KEITH DE LELLIS

47 East 68 St., 10021.　　　　　**T:** (212) 327-1482.
F: (212) 327-1492.　　　　　**E:** Defoto@earthlink.net
Open: Tues.-Sat. 10:30-5:30. Closed Sat. in July and Aug.
Owner/Director: Keith De Lellis.　**Background:** Private fine art photography dealer for more than 25 years.　**Member of AIPAD.**
Work shown: Modernism, journalism, fashion and industrial photography.
Markets: Individual, corporate, and museum. **Prices:** $750-7,500.
Artists represented: 35. All origins. 80% male/20% female. 90% are in museum collections.
Annual exhibitions: 4.
Advertising: *Photography in New York* and *Gallery Guide*.
Focus/Mission: Rediscovering of seminal 20th Century photographers.
Selection process: Artists should call for an appointment. We only look at vintage work from the 1860's - 1960's. **Response time:** Immediate.

LYNNE EPSTEIN

T: (212) 753-2408　　　　　**F:** (212) 249-3898
Open: By appointment.　　　　**Year established:** 1965.
Owner/Director: Lynne Epstein, MA Fine Art; Assistant Director, Picasso Arts. Member of Art Dealers Association of America.
Work shown: Impressionism and Modern European and American Masters. Painting, works on paper and small edition sculpture.
Work by: Picasso; Giacometti; Matisse; Miró; and Cezanne; among others.
Selection process: Lynne Epstein is always interested in reviewing new artists' work. Although she may not be able to represent them, she tries to steer them in the right direction to other appropriate galleries. Artists may call for information.

BARRY FRIEDMAN, LTD

32 East 67 St., 10021.　　　　　**T:** (212) 794-8950.
F: (212) 794-8889.　　　　　**W:** www.barryfriedmanltd.com
Open: Mon.-Fri. 10-6, Sat. 10-5.　**Size:** 4,000 sq. ft.
Owner/Director: Barry Friedman, 30 years presence in the world of historical works of the 20th Century.
Work shown: European decorative arts; avant-garde paintings from the 1920s and '30s; works on paper; sculpture; and vintage and contemporary photography. In the past two years, the Gallery has moved forward into to the field of contemporary decorative arts with exhibitions featuring studio glass, art furniture, ceramics and wood objects
Work by: Cristiano Bianchin: glass; Dale Chiluly: glass; Laura de Santillana: glass; Bennett Bean: ceramics; and Pierre Bayle ceramics; among others.

GALERIE LE PROVENCE

42 East 60 St. 10022.
E: artprovence@aol.com
Open: Mon. - Sat. 10-6, Sun. 10-5.
Owner/ Director: Ange Bova.
Artists represented: 6-7.

T: 212-588-1772.
F:(212) 588-1774.
Size: 1800sq. ft.
Work shown: Impressionist, oil on canvas.
Work by: Betty Wittwe, impressionist
paintings; Michele Vezinter, impressionist paintings.
Prices: $4,000- $15,000.
Advertising: *Avenue.*
Selection Process: Call for information.

GALLERI ORREFORS & KOSTA BODA

685 Madison Ave., 10021.
F: (212) 752-3705.
Year established: 1985.
Owner: Orrefors Kosta Boda, Inc.

T: (212) 752-1095.
Open: Mon.-Sat. 10-6.
Size: 1,600 sq. ft.
Director: Eric Otero.

Work shown: Fine crystal glass by Swedish glass artists and designers.
Artists represented: 17. Ages: 34-65.
Work by: Bertil Vallien; Ulrica Hydman Vallien; Kjell Engman; and Erika Lagerbielke; among others.
Collectors: Metropolitan Museum, Bausch/Lomb, Corning Museum, and Heller Gallery. Prices: $20-35,000.
Advertising: *American Craft, Glass,* and *ARTnews.*
Focus/Mission: To exhibit the new designs every year that each designer creates for the tabletop market. The gallery carries a varied collection of unique glass pieces from all 17 designers.
Selection process: All artists are exclusive employees of Orrefors Kosta Boda.

GALLERY AT LINCOLN CENTER

136 West 65 St., concourse level, Lincoln Center for the Performing Arts, 10023.
T: (212) 580-4673.   W: www.metguild.org
Open: Mon.-Sat. 10-8; Summer: July-August Mon.-Sat. 10-6.
Director: Curtis Redhead.
Work shown: Specialize in memorabilia paintings, photographs, drawings, prints and sculpture, all related to the performing arts scheduled at Lincoln Center for the Performing Arts, in addition to the Lincoln Center Print and Poster Collection.
Prices: $30 and above.
Work by: Howard Hodgkin; William Bailey; Ben Schonzeit; Judith Murray; and Helen Frankenthaler; among others.
Annual exhibitions: 8 or more.
Selection process: Artists whose work relates to that of the gallery may mail slides with SASE. Response time: 1 month.

GALLERY AT MAKOR

35 West 67 St., 10023.
F: (212) 601-1060.
Open: Mon.-Thurs. 2-10, Sun. 12-9.
Contact person: Ken Sherman.

T: (212) 601-1000.
W: www.makor.org
Year established: 1999.

Owner: Makor, a non-profit arts and cultural organization.
Work shown: Contemporary art in all media by international artists with a focus on Jewish artists.   Advertising: *Time Out* and *Village Voice.*   *continued*

Focus/Mission: MAKOR is a place of rediscovery, meaning and inspiration – a place where arts, life, history and the spirit can connect.
Selection process: Guest curators organize the exhibitions. We are currently not accepting submissions.
Additional information: MAKOR presents exhibitions, live music, literary events, theater and film. There is a café-lounge, restaurant and music café.

GROLIER CLUB

47 East 60 St., 10022. **T:** (212) 838-6690.
F: (212) 838-2445. **W:** www.grolierclub.org
Open: Mon.-Sat. 10-5. Closed in August.
Year established: 1884. **Size:** 2,400 sq. ft.
Owner: Non-profit membership club. **Director:** Eric Holzenberg.
Work shown: Books and Book Art. **Annual exhibitions:** 4.
Focus/Mission: The promotion of the Book Arts.
Additional information: The Club has 700 members worldwide.

LILLIAN HEIDENBERG

45 East 66 St., 10021. **T:** (212) 628-6110.
F: (212) 628-4958. **W:** www.heidenbergfineart.com
Open: By appointment. **Year established:** 1976.
Owner/Director: Lillian Heidenberg. Member of Art Dealers Assoc. of America.
Work shown: Modern and Contemporary art, in addition to the secondary market, paintings, sculpture and prints.
Work by: Henry Moore: sculpture and painting; Lynn Chadwick: sculpture; and Yrjo Edelmann: painting; among others.
Selection process: We rarely look at new artists' materials.

HOORN-ASHBY

766 Madison Ave., 2nd floor, 10021. **T:** (212) 628-3199.
F: (212) 861-8162. **E:** hoornashby@aol.com
Open: Mon.-Sat. 10-6; Summer: Call for hours. Closed in Aug.
Year established: 1991. **Size:** 2,500 sq. ft.
Owner: Mary-Claire Barton. **Background:** Professor at Parsons.
Assistant Director: Alex Hulse.
Work shown: Contemporary Realism paintings in oil, tempera and watercolor; also etchings, drawings, and monotypes.
Work by: Donald Jurney: oil painting; Janet Rickus: oil painting; David Rohn: watercolor; Polly McCaffrey: oil; and Joan Griswold: oil; among others.
Prices: $2,000-50,000. **Annual exhibitions:** 6-7 solo/5-6 group.
Focus/Mission: The gallery has long-term relationships with its artists. We represent good value, integrity, serious work, and respect for clients and collectors.
Selection process: We are taking on few, if any, new artists in the foreseeable future. Artists should mail slides, biography, current prices and SASE.
Response time: 1 month.
Requirements: Artists should have a mastery of their medium, awareness of art history, professionalism, integrity, and a cohesive body of work.

VIVIAN HORAN FINE ART

35 East 67 St., 2nd floor, 10021. T: (212) 517-9410.
F: (212) 772-6107. E: horan@nyct.net.
Open: Mon.-Sat. 10-6.
President: Vivian Horan, an art dealer for more than 25 years.
Work shown: 20th Century painting, sculpture, photography, and drawing.
Secondary market only.

JUDITH HUGHES DAY / SARAH WOODS

10 West 66 St., 11 G, 10023.
Mailing Address: P. O. Box 231364, Ansonia Station, 10023.
T: (212) 721 3053. F: (212) 877 9455.
E: JHDArtAsia@aol.com Open: By appointment.
Owners/Directors: Judith Hughes Day and Sarah Woods.
Work shown: Vietnamese contemporary art.
Work by: Quang Em Do; Quoc Viet Le; Trung Nguyen; Cam Thuong Phan; and
Luu Hau Tran; among others.

HUNTER COLLEGE: BERTHA AND KARL LEUBSDORF,

SW corner of 68 St. and Lexington Ave., 10021. T: (212) 772-499
F: (212) 772-4554. W: www.hunter.cuny.edu/artgalleries
Curator: Tracy Adler. Work shown: Contemporary art in all media.
Open: Sept.-June Tues.-Sat. 1-6. Closed July and August.
Work by: All exhibitions are curated by members of the art department faculty.
Each semester ends with student art exhibitions.
Selection process: Artists should mail slides, biography and SASE.

PAT KERY FINE ARTS

T: (212) 826-3735. F: (212) 980-5857.
E: patkery@worldnet.att.net Open: By appointment.
Owner/Director: Pat Kery, author of 3 books including *Art Deco Graphics.*
Work shown: Impressionist Modern and Contemporary Masters, and
Contemporary photography.
Work by: Dubuffet, Francis, Picasso, Degas, Dufy, Leger, Toulouse-Lautrec,
Matisse, Miró, Oldenburg, Stella, Cecilia, Lichtenstein, Sultan, and Wesselmann.

LA GALERIE AT FIAF

French Institute Alliance Francais, 22 East 60 St., 10022.
T: (212) 355-6100. F: (212) 935-4119.
E: jchambord@fiaf.com W: www.fiaf.org
Director: Jacqueline Chambord.
Work shown: Primarily photography, also paintings, with a French connection.
Selection process: Artists should visit the gallery and contact Jacqueline by
email if their work is appropriate.

BRUCE R. LEWIN

150 East 69 St., 10021. T: (212) 517-7869.
FAX: (212) 628-8957. E: gallery @brucerlewin.com
W: www.brucerlewin.com Open: By appointment only.
Year established: 1992. Owner/Director: Bruce R. Lewin.

continued

Work shown: Photorealist and Figurative painting, drawing, sculpture, and Pop and Pin-up Art.
Work by: Andy Warhol: screen prints; Trova: stainless steel and bronze sculpture; Robert Chapman: charcoal on paper and oil on canvas; Robert Cottingham: all media; and Mel Ramos: oil on canvas; among others.
Prices: $500-1,000,000.
Collectors: MoMA, Metropolitan, Guggenheim, and Whitney.
Advertising: *ARTnews* and *Gallery Guide*.
Selection process: Artists should mail slides and SASE.
Response time: 2 weeks. Artists must have talent and originality.

OBLIQUE

210 East 60 St., 10022.   **T:** (212) 421-8338.
F: (212) 421-8111.   **E:** info@obliquegallery.com
W: www.obliquegallery.com   **Open:** Mon.-Fri. 10-5.
Year established: 1998.
Owners: Joel and Jeanne Leff; Backgrounds: Wall Street.
Work shown: An eclectic mix of museum quality decorative objects and furniture from the Han Dynesty to French Art Deco and some Contemporary art.
Artist represented: The sole rights to Luc Fournal, photographer.

SCHOLTEN JAPANESE ART

63 East 66 St., 10021.   **T:** (212) 585-0474.
F: (212) 585-0475.   **E:** info@scholten-japanese-art.com
W: www.scholten-japanese-art.com
Open: Tues.-Sat. 11-5 by appointment.   **Year established:** 2000.
President: Rene Scholten.   **Director:** Katherine Martin.
Size: Three floors. This is the largest gallery in New York to specialize in Japanese art.
Work shown: A variety of Japanese works of art, including: lacquer, inro, netsuke, screens, hanging scrolls, woodblock prints, and other fine works of art.
Focus/Mission: To promote education and to actively contribute to the Japanese art field.
Additional information: SJA will organize lecture series and seminars, and offer its facilities to individuals and organizations in the Japanese art community.

ANITA SHAPOLSKY

152 East 65 St., patio entrance, 10021. **T:** (212) 452-1094.
F: (212) 452-1096.   **E:** anitashap@aol.com
W: www.galleryguideonline.com/gallery/shapo and www.artincontext. org/new_york/anita_shaplosky_gallery/ and www.asartfoundation.netfirms.com
Open: Wed.-Sat. 11-6.   **Year established:** 1982.
Owner/Director: Anita Shapolsky.
Work shown: Abstract Expressionism and art in that tradition. Painting, sculpture, and works on paper.
Artists represented: 25. 60% male/ 40% female. **Origins:** North America, South America, Europe, and Asia. 50% of artists are in museum collections.
Work by: Ernest Briggs: paintings (second generation Abstract Expressionist, New York School); Clement Meadmore: sculpture; Erik van der Grijn: paintings and prints (third generation Abstract Expressionist); and Michael Loew: painting; among others.

Prices: $500-30,000.   **Annual exhibitions:** 5 group/solo.

Advertising: *ARTnews, Gallery Guide* and *Art and Auction*.

Focus/Mission: We seek to exhibit work by under-known artists who work in the Abstract Expressionism tradition.

Selection process: 80% of the artists are selected from professional referrals, and 20% from materials sent to the gallery. Artists should mail slides, biography, and SASE. We review artists materials in May and October.

Response time: 2 months.

Requirements: Abstract work only; artists must have a New York exhibition history. No emerging artists. Artists are expected to pay for their framing.

THE SPANISH INSTITUTE

684 Park Ave., 10021.   **T:** (212) 628-0420.

F: (212) 734-4177.   **W:** www.spanishinstitute.org

Open: Mon.-Fri. 11-6, Sat. 11-5.   **Year established:** 1954.

President: Inmaculada de Hadsburgo.

Work shown: All styles and media by Spanish artists and/or of the art of Spain.

Annual exhibitions: 3 or more.

Focus/Mission: The Spanish Institute is dedicated to increasing awareness of Spain's culture and history.

Selection process: Artists should contact the Spanish Institute Gallery for current policy. Shows are scheduled at least 1 year in advance.

THROCKMORTON FINE ART

153 East 61 St., 10021.   **T:** (212) 223-1059.

F: (212) 223-1937.   **W:** www.artnet.com/throckmorton.html

Open: Tues.-Sat. 11-5 and by appointment.

Year established: 1980.   **Size:** 2,200 sq. ft.

Owner: Spencer Throckmorton, Art History, University of VA.

Director: Kraige Block.

Work shown: Modern and Contemporary photography, Latin American drawings and paintings and Pre-Colombian art.

Work by: Marta Maria Perez-Bravo: photography; Tina Modotti: photography; Francisco Toledo: paintings and mixed media; Bastienne Schmidt: photography; Manuel Alvarez Bravo: photography; and Edward Weston: photography; and the Estate of Lola Alvarez Bravo: photography; among others.

Markets: Individual and corporate.

Collectors: Metropolitan, MoMA, Citibank, and J.P. Morgan Collection.

Prices: $500-100,000.   **Annual exhibitions:** 5 solo.

Advertising: *Latin American Art, Photography in New York*, and *ARTNews*.

Focus/Mission: To promote Latin American Art and Culture. The gallery's inventory includes museum quality works. We are committed to showing works by established as well as emerging artists. The gallery is unusual in that it emphasizes the contextual where one can find ancient artifacts juxtaposed with Contemporary paintings and photographs.

Selection process: Most of the artists are selected from referrals. If the work is applicable, artists should mail slides and resumé to Kraige Block.

Response time: 2 weeks. There may be some exhibition expenses.

Additional information: We offer a full range of curatorial and scholarly services. We believe in the importance of connoisseurship and of educating the collector.

JOANNE TURNEY STUDIO 2

809 Lexington Ave., 10021. **T:** (212) 333-6089.
Open: By appointment. **Year established:** 1999.
Owner: Joanne Turney, artist.
Work by: Joanne Turney: mixed media Abstract paintings and works on paper.
Markets: Individual, corporate and museum. **Prices:** $400-4,000.
Collectors: International Resources Corporation; Hyatt Hotel; Washington Hospital Center; TROA Collection (museum); and Pillsbury; among others.
Focus/Mission: To create art that expresses the harmony and beauty that emanates from beneath the surface of life.

ISLAND WEISS

201 East 69 St., Penthouse M, 10021. **T:** (212) 861-4608.
F: (212) 861-0093. **E:** iwgallery@aol.com
Open: By appointment. **Owner:** Island Weiss.
Work shown: 19th Century American and European Contemporary works. Primarily paintings and work on paper.
Work by: Martin Johnson Heade; A. T. Britcher; Richard E. Miller; Andrew Wyeth; and Degas; among others.
Additional information: Weiss also owns galleries in Los Angeles, CA.

WILDENSTEIN

19 East 64 St., 10021. **T:** (212) 879-0500.
F: (212) 517-4715. **W:** www.wildenstein.com
Open: Mon.-Fri. 10-5.
Work shown: Predominantly Old and Modern Masters; some Contemporary art.
Additional information: See other locations in Chelsea and in Midtown.

WINWOOD

1079 Third Ave., 10021. **T:** (212) 355-2508.
F: (212) 355-0176. **W:** www.winwood.baweb.com
Open: Mon.-Fri. 11-7 and Sat. 11-6.
Work shown: Modern and contemporary oil paintings, pastels and watercolors by young talents from America, Russia, Spain, Israel, China and other countries.

RICHARD YORK

21 East 65 St., 10021. **T:** (212) 772-9155.
F: (212) 288-0410. **E:** info@ryorkgal.com
W: www.artnet.com **Open:** Mon.-Fri. 10-5:30, Sat. 10-5.
Year established: 1981. **Owner:** Richard York.
Member of Art Dealers Association of America.
Work shown: American Art 1750-1950.

ZWIRNER & WIRTH

32 East 69 St., 10021. **T:** (212) 517-8677.
E: Kristine@zwirnerandwirth.com **W:** zwirnerandwirth.com
Open: Tues.-Sat. 10-6. **Year established:** 2000.
Owners: David Zwirner and Iwan Wirth.
Work shown: Modern and Contemporary masters.
Work by: Bruce Nauman; Dan Flavin; Ori Kawara; Gerard Richter; among others.

WHERE TO FIND IT

Contemporary Realism at Hoorn-Asbhy, Pop and Pin-Up at Bruce R. Lewin, Latin American at Throckmorton, and 5,000 years of art at the Metropolitan Museum.

ACQUAVELLA

18 East 79 St., 10021.   T: (212) 734-6300.
F: (212) 794-9394.   Open: Mon.-Fri. 10-5.
Owner: William R. Acquavella.   Director: Duncan MacGuigan.
Member of Art Dealers Association of America.
Work shown: 19th and 20th Century Master paintings, drawings and sculpture.
We represent: Lucian Freud: painting.
Collectors: Metropolitan, MoMA, Tate, and Hirsshorn.
Advertising: *The New York Times, Artforum,* and *Arts & Auction.*
Selection process: Artists should not approach the gallery; we handle secondary market art only.

ADELSON

The Mark Hotel, 25 East 77 St., 3rd floor, 10021.
T: (212) 439-6800.   F: (212) 439-6870.
E: info@adelsongalleries.com   W: www.adelsongalleries.com
Open: Mon.-Fri. 9:30-5:30, Sat. 10-5 during special exhibitions.
Year established: 1969.   President: Warren Adelson.
Work by: Kenneth Draper: painting; Terry Frost: painting; Andrew Stevovich: painting; Jim Ritchie: sculpture; and Peter Reginato: sculpture; among others.

AMERICAN ILLUSTRATORS

18 East 77 St., 10021.   T: (212) 744-5190.
F: (212) 744-0128.   E: art@americanillustrators.com
W: www.americanillustators.com   Open: Mon.-Fri. 12-5.
Owner/Director: Judy Goffman Cutler.
Work shown: Illustrations from 1880-1960's.
Work by: Maxfield Parrish; N.C.Wyeth; Norman Rockwell; J.C. Howard; Chandler Christy; among others.

ASH FINE ART LLC

51 East 78 St., Suite 1A, 10021.   T: (212) 734-0100.
F: (212) 734-8840.   E: lorinda@ashfineart.com
Open: By appointment.   Directors: Lorinda Ash and Maya Nussbaum.
Work shown: Specializing in Post-war American paintings, sculpture and works on paper.
Additional information: We provide art advisory services by appointment.

ASIA SOCIETY AND MUSEUM

725 Park Ave., 10021.
W: www.asiasociety.org
Year established: 1956.
President: Nicholas Platt.
T: (212) 288-6400.
Open: Tues.- Sun. 11-6, Fri. 11-9.
Owner: Non-profit cultural institution.
Annual exhibitions: 6.
Director of Cultural Programs: Vishakha Desai.
Work shown: Asian sculpture, fabric, photography, paintings, baskets, accessories, in various styles from Ancient to Contemporary.
Additional information: The Museum presents performances and other events. T: (212) 517-ASIA. It has a gift store and café. Membership is available.

ADAM BAUMGOLD

74 East 79 St., 10021.
F: (212) 288-1261.
E: abaumgold@aol.com
Year established: 1985.
T: (212) 861-7338.
W: www.adambaumgoldgallery.com
Open: Tues.-Sat 11-5.
Size: 700 sq. ft.
Owner/Director: Adam Baumgold, educated in Art history and art collector.
Work shown: Contemporary and 20th Century art in all media.
Artists represented: 12. **Work by:** Saul Steinberg; Seth Michael Forman; David Wojnarowicz; Jessica Gandolf; and Andras Borocz; among others.
Annual exhibitions: 6 solo/2 group.
Advertising: *Gallery Guide* and *Art in America*.
Focus/Mission: To exhibit emerging and established artists together.
Selection process: Artists are selected as a result of referrals, slides it receives, exhibitions and publications. Artists should mail 6 or more slides, biography and SASE. No calls, please. **Response time:** 1 month.

BONNI BENRUBI

52 East 76 St., 10021.
F: (212) 288-7815.
W: www.bonnibenrubi.com
T: (212) 517-3766.
E: benrubi@aol.com
Owner: Bonni Benrubi.
Work shown: Photography. **Open:** Tues.-Sat. 11-6; Summer: Mon.-Fri. 11-5:30.
Work by: Abelardo Morell; Louis Stettner; Jack Spencer; Robert Parke Harrison; and Tom Baril; among others.
Selection process: Artists should drop off portfolio the first Thursday of every month, and can pick it up the next day, or send slides with SASE.

CLAUDE BERNARD

900 Park Ave., 10021.
F: (212) 737-2290.
Year established: 1970.
T: (212) 988-2050.
Open: By appointment.
Owner/Director: Michel Soskine.
Work shown: 20th Century and Contemporary art.
Work by: Balthus; Baghosian; Blake; Giacometti; Morales; and Wyeth.

BERRY-HILL

11 East 70 St., 10021.
F: (212) 744-2838.
W: www.berry-hill.com
T: (212) 744-2300.
E: reception@berry-hill.com
Year established: 1934.
Open: Mon.-Fri. 9:30-5:30, Sat 10-5; Summer: Mon.-Fri. 9:30-5:30.
Member of Art Dealers Association of America.
Directors: James Berry Hill and Frederick D. Hill.

Work shown: 18th-20th Century American and European paintings and sculpture, 19th Century China Trade Paintings, and Contemporary paintings and sculpture. **Work by:** Judith Belzer; Varujan Boghosian; Bunny Harvey; Doug Trump; Esteban Vicente; and Michael Zansky; among others.

LORI BOOKSTEIN FINE ART

50 East 78 St., Suite 2A, 10021.   **T:** (212) 439-9605.
F: (212) 439-9698.   **W:** www.artnet.com
Open: Tues.-Sat. 10:30-5:30. July by appointment. Closed in August.
Year established: 1997.   **Size:** 1,500 sq. ft.
Owner: Lori Bookstein, former Director of Salander-O'Reilly.
Director: Lauren Bakoian.
Work shown: American Modernist, 2nd generation New York School, and Contemporary art by artists primarily from the U.S.
Work by: Estate of Anne Tabachnick; Paul Resika: works on paper; the estate of Aristodimos Kaldis; Alfred Mauer; and Jan Muller; among others.
Annual exhibitions: 6-7.   **Advertising:** *Gallery Guide.*

DENISE CADE

1045 Madison Ave., 10021.   **T:** (212) 734-3670.
W: www.artincontext.org   **Owner:** Denise Cade.
Open: Tues.-Sat. 10-5:30; Summer: Tues.-Fri. 11-5.
Work shown: Paintings, drawings, and sculpture.
Work by: Paul Rotterdam: painting and drawing; Bruce Edelstein: sculpture; Jean-Pierre Pincemin: painting and prints; Charles Belle: painting; and Lester Johnson: paintings; among others. **Artists represented:** 12.
Collectors: MoMA, Guggenheim, Metropolitan, Estee Lauder Collection.
Annual exhibitions: 3 or 5 solo/1or 2 group. **Advertising:** *Gallery Guide.*

C & M ARTS

45 East 78 St., 10021.   **T:** (212) 861-0020.
F: (212) 861-7858.   **W:** www.c-m-arts.com
Open: Tues.-Sat. 10-5:30; Summer: Mon.-Fri. 10-5.
Year established: 1993.   **Owner:** Robert Mnuchin.
Director: Jennifer Vorbach.
Work shown: Abstract Expressionism and 20th Century Masters. Paintings, sculpture, and works on paper.
Work by: De Kooning; Cornell; Matisse; and Twombly; among others.

LEO CASTELLI

59 East 79 St., 10021.   **T:** (212) 249-4470.
F: (212) 249-5220.   **E:** info@castelligallery.com
W: www.castelligallery.com   **President/Owner:** Barbara Castelli.
Director: Diana Turco.
Open: Tues.-Sat. 10-6; Summer: Mon.-Fri. 10-5.
Year established: 1957. Member of Art Dealers Association of America.
Work shown: Contemporary art in all media.
Artists represented: 40, primarily U.S., some international.
Work by: Jasper Johns; Robert Morris; Lawrence Weiner; Ed Ruscha; and Andy Warhol; among others.   **Annual exhibitions:** 4-5.
Advertising: *The New York Times* and *Artforum and Art in America.*

CDS

76 East 79 St., 10021.   **T:** (212) 772-9555.
F: (212) 772-9542.   **E:** cdsgallery@aol.com
Open: Tues.-Sat. 10-5:30. July: Mon.-Fri. 10-5:30. Closed in August.
Year established: 1981, Member of Art Dealers Association of America.
Director: Clara Diament Sujo.
Work shown: Contemporary art of the Americas, Europe and Australia.
Work by: Hedda Sterne; J. Torres-Garcia; John Walker; Melvin Edwards; and Adja Yunkers; among others.

CITIBANK

171 East 72 St., 10021.   **T:** (212) 535-6314.
Open: Mon.-Fri. 9-5, Sat. 10-2.   **Contact:** Anthony S. Arbucci, Manager.
Year established: The exhibition program was established in 2000.
Work shown: Two-dimensional art in all media by contemporary artists.
Focus/Mission: Based on Citibank's belief in getting involved in the community. The gallery's purpose is to offer artists exposure and to bring art to bank customers.   **Annual exhibitions:** 6-8.
Selection process: Artists should contact Anthony S. Arbucci.

CHINA BRILLIANCE

155 West 72 St., #703, 10023.   **T:** (646) 295-5667.
E:michellehill@nyc.rr.com   **Open:** Wed.-Sat. 2-6.
Owner/Director: Michelle Hill, Artist, MA from Columbia.
Work shown: Contemporary art in 2-D by emerging artists.
Work by: Eric Ginsburg; and Michelle Hill; among others.
Prices: $75-2,000.
Focus/Mission: To treat emerging artists fairly and give them an opportunity to exhibit their work.
Selection process: Artists should send slides, resumé, and SASE.
Requirements: Artist should have a consistent body of work.

COLLECTION DOBE FINE ARTS/BECK & EGGELING

43 East 78 St., 10021.   **T:** (212) 327-1850.
F: (212) 327-1861.   **E:** ArtDobe@aol.com
W: www.dobefineart.com   **Open:** Tues.-Sat. 11-5 and by appointment.
Year established: 1997.   **Owner:** Ralph J. Dosch, art historian.
Work shown: Classical, Modern, Impressionist and Contemporary art.
Work by: Monet; Renoir; Chagall; Tapies; Eduardo Chilleda and Herbert Beck; among others.   **Advertising:** *Gallery Guide.*
Additional information: The gallery's other location is in Dusseldorf, Germany.

EKSTROM & EKSTROM

417 East 75 St., 10021.   **T:** (212) 988-8857.
F: (212) 744-4944.   **E:** cordieks@aol.com
Open: By appointment.   **President:** Nicolas H. Ekstrom.
Year established: Originally in 1959. It was temporarily inactive until 1999.
Work shown: Modern and Contemporary art. Primarily Dada and Surrealism.
Work by: Duchamp; ManRay; Ernst; Arp; and Dubuffet; among others.
Advertising: *Gallery Guide* and *Etnat Donnée* and *The New York Times.*

EZAIR

905 Madison Ave., Mezzanine, 10021. **T:** (212) 628-2224.
W: www.ezairgallery.com **Open:** Tues.-Sat. 12-6.
Year established: 1995. **Director:** Mariana Bego.
Work shown: Contemporary paintings and sculpture in varied styles and media.
Work by: Bego: energizing art; Mason: virtual art; Nuzum: regional art; Gallin: sculpture in relief; and Bromilow: Australian wood sculptures; among others.
Annual exhibitions: 8.
Advertising: *Gallery Guide*; *Art in America.*

DAVID FINDLAY

984 Madison Ave., 10021. **T:** (212) 249-2909.
F: (212) 249-2912. **E:** dfindlayga@aol.com
W: www.davidfindlaygalleries.com **Year established:** 1870.
Open: Mon.-Sat. 10-5. July and Aug. Mon.-Fri. 10-5.
Work shown: Contemporary color oriented Figurative Representational paintings influenced by the Impressionists, Expressionists, and the Fauves; lithographs by gallery artists, bronze sculptures; and 19th and 20th Century French paintings.
Work by: Guy Bardone: still life and landscape paintings; Rene Genis: still life and landscape paintings; Pierre Lesieur: interior and landscape paintings; and Roger Muhl: rooftop, landscape, and still life paintings; among others.
Annual exhibitions: 6 solo/3-4 group.
Collectors: MoMA, Nelson Gallery of Art, Brooklyn Museum and Metropolitan.
Selection process: We are currently not looking at new artists' materials, however, in the future we may be interested.
Additional information: We have represented most of our Contemporary artists for over 30 years and followed the careers of this group of artists.

ANITA FRIEDMAN FINE ARTS

980 Madison Ave., 10021. **T:** (212) 472-1527.
F: (212) 517-2174. **W:** www.artnet.com
Open: Mon.-Fri. 10-5 and by appointment. Closed in August.
Year established: 1985. **Owner/President:** Anita Friedman.
Work shown: The focus is on secondary market Modern Masters, Contemporary paintings, work on paper and photography.
Annual exhibitions: 4 group.
Selection process: We are currently not looking at new artists' works.

GAGOSIAN

980 Madison Ave., 10021. **T:** (212) 744-2313.
F: (212) 772-7962. **W:** www.gagosian.com
Open: Tues.-Sat. 10-6; Summer: Tues.-Fri. 10-6.
Work shown: Contemporary and Modern art in all media.
Size: Over 8,000 sq. ft.
Work by: Francesco Clemente: painting; David Salle: painting and sculpture; Philip Taaffe: painting; and Mark di Suvero: sculpture.
Advertising: *Artforum, Atelier, Art in America* and *ARTnews.*
Selection process: Artists should not submit materials. We approach artists.

GALERIE LE PROVENCE

962 Madison Ave, 10021.
E: artprovence@aol.com
Open: Mon. - Sat. 10-6, Sun. 10-5.
Owner/ Director: Ange Bova.
Prices: $4,000- $15,000.
Selection Process: Call for information.

T: (212) 794-1340.
F:(212) 588-1774.
Size: 400sq. ft.
Work shown: Impressionist, oil on canvas.
Advertising: *Avenue.*

GALERIE RIENZO

41 East 78 St., 10021.
F: (212) 988-1539.

T: (212) 288-2226.
W: www.gallerierienzo.com

Open: Tues.-Sat. 11-5; Summer: Tues.-Fri. 11-3.
Owner: Robert Rienzo, B.A. Art, minor in Business.
Year established: 1980.
Work shown: Impressionists, Post-Impressionists and Modern French paintings and works on paper. Prices: $5,000-1,000,000.
Artists represented: 18 male/2 female.
Work by: Bernard Buffet (Rienzo is the artist's New York representative / expert); Paul Aixpiri; J.P. Cassigneul; Dufy; and Jean Jansem; among others.
Annual exhibitions: 3 solo/ 3 group.
Advertising: *The New York Times* and *Gallery Guide.*
Focus/Mission: To show master works –top 10% of each artist's work.

GALLERY SCHLESINGER

24 East 73 St., 2nd floor, 10021.
F: (212) 472-6519.

T: (212) 734-3600.
Year established: 1980.

Open: Tues.-Fri.11-5, Sat.12-4; Summer: Call for hours.
Size: 400 sq. ft.
Director: Stephen L. Schlesinger.
Work shown: American and European 20th Century painting, drawing, and sculpture.
Work by: Hannelore Baron; Jean-Michel Basquiat; Ray Johnson; William Kentridge; Pablo Picasso; and Paul Klee; among others. The gallery also represents the Estate of Fritz Bultman: drawings, paintings, collage, and sculpture. Prices: $200-200,000.
Collectors: MoMA, Metropolitan, Whitney, and Guggenheim.
Mission: To show works of art inspired by something other than the market place.
Annual exhibitions: 4, plus evolving exhibitions.

GALLERY 71

974 Lexington Ave., 10021.
E: gallery71@aol.com
Open: Mon.-Sat. 10-7.

T: (212) 744-7779.
W: www.gallery71.com
Year established: 1994.

Director: Alfred Gonzalez, Former Director, Newmark Gallery.
Work shown: Contemporary art specializing in NYC themes. Paintings, sculpture, watercolors, pastels, lithographs, etchings, aquatints, woodblock prints, mezzotints, and other prints.
Artists represented: 25.
Work by: Frederick Mershimer: mezzotints; Marion Welch: still lifes in watercolor, New York cityscapes, and landscapes; Lynn Shaler: Paris cityscapes and interiors in etchings and aquatints; Don Hong Oai: photography; and Harold Altman: lithographs; among others.

Annual exhibitions: Continual group exhibitions of gallery artists.
Prices: $100-10,000.
Selection process: Artists should submit slides and SASE.
Response time: 1 week.
Additional information: Gallery 71 offers custom framing services.

HILDE GERST

Carlyle Hotel, 987 Madison Ave., 10021. **T:** (212) 288-3400.
F: (212) 288-7878.   **Open:** Mon.-Sat. 11-5.
Year established: 1956.   **Size:** 800 sq. ft.
Owner/Director: Hilde Gerst, background as a collector.
Work shown: Impressionist and Post Impressionist, primarily Master paintings.
Also sculpture and Master lithographs.
Work by: Vlaminck; Lebasque; Renoir; Loiseau; and Picasso; among others.
Advertising: *Gallery Guide.*
Focus/Mission: To encourage visitors to ask questions and keep informed about
the art they have already acquired.
Selection process: Artists should call first to find out about the current slide
reviewing procedures.

JOHN GIBSON

205 East 78 Street, 10021.   **T:** (212) 925-1192.
F: (212) 925-1274.   **Open:** By appointment only.
Year established: 1961.   **Owner/Director:** John Gibson.
Assistant Director: David Gibson.
Work shown: Contemporary European and American art in all media.
Artists represented: 20.
Work by: William Beckley: photography; Mac Adams: photography; Eve Andree
Laramee: mixed media installation; Samm Kunce: mixed media installation; and
Thom Merrick: mixed media installation; among others.

JAMES GRAHAM & SONS

1014 Madison Ave., 10021.   **T:** (212) 535-5767.
F: (212) 794-2454.   **W:** www.artnet.com
Open: Tues.-Sat. 9:30-5:30; Summer: Mon.-Fri. 9:30-5:30.
Year established: 1857.   **Size:** 3,000 sq. ft.
Member of Art Dealers Association of America.
Work shown: 19th and early 20th Century American painting, 19th and 20th
Century American and European sculpture, Contemporary art in all media, and
Contemporary British ceramics.
Artists represented: 4 male/5 female (not including early American and
European artists). Ages: 45-65.   **Origins:** U.S. and Great Britain.
75% of the artists are in museum collections.
Work by: Aric Obrosey; Stephen Hannock; David Mann; Hal Hirshorn; and
Andrew Ehrenworth; among others.
Collectors: Metropolitan, MoMA, Denver Art Museum, National Portrait Gallery,
Smithsonian Institution.
Annual exhibitions: 5 solo/5 group.
Advertising: *Antiques, ARTnews, Art in America, The New York Times,* and *The
Maine Antiques Digest.*   *continued*

Markets: Private, corporate, and museum.
Selection process: Artists are selected as a result of referrals only.
Requirements: Artists with professional reputation, primarily representational art work.

RICHARD GRAY

1018 Madison Ave., 4th floor, 10021. **T:** (212) 472-8787.
F: (212) 472-2552.   **W:** www.richardgraygallery.com
E: info@richardgraygallery.com   **Size:** 2,000 sq. ft.
Open: Mon.-Sat. 10-5:30.   **Year established:** 1963.
President: Richard Gray.   **Director:** Andrew Fabricant.
Member of Art Dealers Association of America.
Work shown: Secondary market. Modern and Contemporary masters.
Work by: Roy Lichtenstein; Sam Francis; David Hockney; Andy Warhol and Willem DeKooning; among others. **Advertising:** *Art in America.*

HARRIET GRIFFIN FINE ARTS

32 East 76 St., 10021.   **T:** (212) 737-6116.
F: (212) 472-3079.   **Open:** By appointment.
Work shown: Modern European masters including Arp; Calder; Klee; Kandinsky; Marini; Morandi; Picasso; among others.

HIRSCHL & ADLER

21 East 70 St., 10021.   **T:** (212) 535-8810.
F: (212) 772-7237.   **W:** www.hirschlandadler.com
Open: Tues.-Fri. 9:30-5:15, Sat 9:30-4:45; Summer: Mon-Fri. 9:30-4:45.
Year established: 1981.   **Size:** 2 floors of exhibitions.
President: Stuart Feld. Member of Art Dealers Association of America.
Work shown: Contemporary paintings, sculpture, photography, work on paper, and Conceptual art.
Focus/Mission: American and European paintings, watercolors, drawings, and sculpture from the 18th - early 20th Centuries; American prints of all periods; and American decorative arts from 1810 -1910. Its Contemporary arm, Hirschl & Adler Modern, shows American and European art from the Post-War period.
Work by: Bill Traylor; John Moore; Fairfield Porter; Christopher Wilmarth; and Piero Manzoni; among others.   **Annual exhibitions:** 10.
Selection process: Artists are selected from referrals only.

STELLAN HOLM

17 East 71 St., 3rd floor, 10021.   **T:** (212) 734-8270.
F: (212) 734-8269.   **E:** shinc@dti.net
Open: Mon.-Fri. 10-6. July and August by appointment.
Work shown: Works by major Contemporary artists.

HOMER

939 Madison Ave., 10028.   **T:** (212) 744-7705.
F: (212) 744-7359.   **Open:** Mon.-Sat. 10-6.
Year established: 1999.   **Size:** 3,200 sq. ft.
Owner: Richard Mishaan, architect, furniture and interior designer.
Work shown: Furniture designs and art in all media by international artists.

HUBERT

1046 Madison Ave., 10021.
F: (212) 794-3889.
W: www.hubertgallery.com
Size: 120 sq. ft.
Director: Kathleen Guzman.
T: (212) 628-2922.
E: info@hubertgallery.com
Year established: 1989.
Owner: Greg Hubert.
Work shown: Modernist work on paper.
Open: Tues.-Sat. 10-6; Summer: Mon.-Fri. 9-5.
Artists represented: 3 male/2 female. Ages: 30-55. All origins. Most of the artists are in museum collections. **Prices:** $850-5,000.
Collectors: Whitney, High Museum, Chase-Manhattan Bank, Coca-Cola.
Annual exhibitions: 4 group.
Focus/Mission: To offer the finest Modernist work on paper for the best price and quality.
Selection process: 25% of the artists are selected from referrals, 25% from slides sent to the gallery; and 50% from exhibitions. Artists should send 12 slides and SASE. Artists should approach the gallery in writing in January and August only. **Response time:** 1 month.

LINDA HYMAN FINE ARTS

172 West 79 St., #17F, 10024.
F: (212) 721-3227.
Year established: 1981.
T: (212) 787-0452.
Open: By appointment.
Owner: Linda Hyman. Member of Art Dealers Association of America.
Work shown: 20th Century art with an emphasis on American Modernism.

EVAN JANIS FINE ART

70 East 79 St., 10021.
F: (212) 639-1502.
Owner/Director: Evan Janis.
T: (212) 639-1501.
E: evjan@aol.com
Open: By appointment.
Work shown: Specializing in 20th Century Masters, Abstract, Expressionist and Contemporary art.
Work by: Picasso; Avery; Pollock; de Kooning; Segal; among others.

JO-AN FINE ART

247 East 77 St., 10021.
F: (212) 717-9116.
W: www.jo-an.com
Summer: By appointment.
T: (212) 717-9111.
E: Joanpictur@aol.com
Open: Tues.-Sat. 10-5:30.
Year established: 1998.
Owner/Director: Anne Costello, private art dealer for 16 years.
Work shown: 20th Century paintings and fine prints by old and new Masters.
Work by: Raphael Soyer; Frank Vincent Dumond; Terence Coyle; Theresa Bernstein; and Robert Philip; among others. **Advertising:** *Gallery Guide.*

JANE KAHAN

922 Madison Ave., 2nd floor, 10021. **T:** (212) 744-1490.
F: (212) 744-1598.
W: www.janekahan.com
Open: Tues.-Sat. 10-6; Summer: Mon.-Fri. 11-5
Year established: 1973.
Owner: Jane Kahan.
Director: Charles Mathes.

continued

Work shown: 19th and 20th Century European and American Modern Masters. Paintings, prints, ceramics, sculpture, and tapestries.
Artists represented: 2 French artists.
Work by: Istvan Sondorfi: Contemporary Realist/Surrealist; and Etienne: Contemporary sculptor. **Prices:** $1,000-200,000.
Advertising: *Gallery Guide* and *ARTnews*.
Selection process: We are currently not looking for new artists.

KNOEDLER & COMPANY

19 East 70 St., 10021.   **T:** (212) 794-0550.
F: (212) 772-6932.
Open: Tues.-Fri. 9:30-5:30, Sat. 10-5:30; Summer: Mon.-Fri. 9:30-5.
Director: Ann Freedman, Member of Art Dealers Association of America.
Work shown: Contemporary Abstract art in all media.
Work by: Frank Stella: paintings, metal reliefs, sculpture, works on paper and prints; David Smith: sculpture, paintings, works on paper; Helen Frankenthaler: paintings and works on paper; Donald Sultan: paintings, works on paper, sculpture, and prints; among others. **Prices:** $10,000 and above.
Annual exhibitions: 9-10.
Advertising: *The New York Times, Art in America* and *ARTnews*.
Selection process: Most artists are selected from referrals. Many of the artists have been represented for 30 years. The gallery is not looking for new artists.

KOUROS

23 East 73 St., 10021.   **T:** (212) 288-5888.
F: (212) 794-9397.   **W:** www.kourosgallery.com
Open: Tues.-Sat. 10-6; Summer: Mon.-Fri. 11-6.
Year established: 1980.   **Size:** 3 floors.
Owner/Director: Angelo Camillos.
Work shown: 20th Century Contemporary sculpture and painting; and Modern Masters.
Artists represented: 30. 50% male/female. Ages: 20's-90's. All origins. 70% of the artists are in museum collections.
Work by: Paul Manes: painting; Melinda Stickney-Gibson: painting; Reuben Nakian: sculpture; Stamos: painting; Lin Emery; Bruno Romeda; Dimitri Hadzi; and Biala; among others.
Collectors: Metropolitan, Guggenheim, and Whitney museums.
Annual exhibitions: 14. **Advertising:** *ARTnews* and *The New York Observer.*
Focus/Mission: To exhibit non-figurative and Contemporary work as well as Impressionist, Modern Masters, and Latin American art. Its sculpture center in Connecticut is designed to exhibit monumental sculpture of gallery artists and emerging sculptors.
Selection process: We are currently not accepting any artists' materials.

LAWRENCE MARKEY

42 East 76 St., 10021.   **T:** (212) 517-9892.
F: (212) 517-9894.   **E:** lawrencemarkey@earthlink.net
W: www.lawrencemarkey.com   **Open:** Tues. - Sat. 10-5, and by appointment.
Year established: 1990.   **Owner/Director:** Lawrence Markey.

Work shown: Contemporary painting, sculpture and works on paper.
Artists represented: American and European.
Work by: Suzan Frecon: paintings and works on paper; Joel Fisher: sculpture and works on paper; Fred Sanback: sculpture and works on paper; and Richard Tuttle: sculpture and works on paper; and Mel Bochner: works on paper; among others.

MADISON ART PARTNERS

16 East 71 St., 10021.   **T:** (212) 628-3304.
F: (212) 628-3624.   **Open:** Mon.-Fri. 9:30-5:30 & by appointment.
Work shown: Dealing in 19th and 20th Century Impressionist, Post-Impressionist, Modern and Contemporary Masters.

MAGIDSON FINE ART

41 East 78 St., 10021.   **T:** (212) 288-0666.
F: (212) 288-6050.   **E:** magidson@ultinet.net
W: www.magidson.com   **Open:** By appointment.
Director: Melton Magidson.   **Work shown:** Contemporary and Modern art.
Work by: Richard Carter; Eva Cellini; Juan Kelly; Annie Leibovitz; and Paul Pascarella; among others.
Additional information: The gallery has another gallery in Aspen, Colorado.

MANHATTAN ARTS INTERNATIONAL

Mailing address: 200 East 72 St., Suite 26L, 10021.   **T:** (212) 472-1660.
E: gallery@ManhattanArts.com
W: www.ManhattanArts.com
Open: By appointment only.
Owner: Manhattan Arts International is an artist resource company.
Director: Renée Phillips, curator and public speaker. Member of International Association of Art Critics.
Year established: The company in 1983; the gallery in 2002.
Work shown: Contemporary art in all media by emerging U.S. artists.
Focus/Mission: To provide exposure and career guidance to artists who have not had solo exhibitions in commercial galleries in NYC.
Selection process: Artists are selected from 3-4 annual juried competitions, from workshops, and from artists' referrals. Artists should visit the web site for details.

MARY-ANNE MARTIN FINE ART

23 East 73 St., 10021.   **T:** (212) 288-2213.
F: (212) 861-7656.   **E:** mail@mamfa.com
W: www.mamfa.com   **Year established:** 1982.
Open: Mon.-Fri. 11-6; Summer: Mon.-Fri. 10-6.
Owner: Mary-Anne Martin.
Director: Sofia Lacayo.
Member of Art Dealers Association of America.
Work shown: Focus on Modern art from Mexico and Latin America.
Work by: Diego Rivera; Rufina Tamayo; Roberto Matta; Gunther Gerzso; Alfredo Castaneda; and Elena Climent; among others.

MARYMOUNT MANHATTAN COLLEGE

21 East 71 St., 10021.　　　　　T: (212) 517-0692.
F: (212) 517-0541.　　　　　　　W: www.marymount.mmm.edu
Size: 1,600 sq. ft.　　　　　　　Open: Mon.-Sun. 9-9. Closed July and Aug.
Year established: 1983.　　　　Annual exhibitions: 8 group.
Director: Millie Burns, Assistant Professor of Art, Marymount Manhattan College.
Work shown: Primarily two-dimensional art in all styles and media.
Focus/Mission: To show the work of emerging artists who are not receiving enough exposure in commercial venues.
Selection process: Artists are selected from slides. A panel of judges meets in March. Submissions are accepted in Jan. and Feb. Artists should submit up to 20 slides with an artist's statement, resumé, and SASE.

MC GRATH

9 East 77 St., 10021.　　　　　T: (212) 737-7396.
F: (212) 737-2767.　　　　　　　E: info@mcgrathgalleries.com
W: www.mcgrathgalleries.com　　Open: Mon.-Fri. 10-5.
Owners / Directors: Eugenia Korrossy, trained at the Courtault Institue of Art in London; and Julia Coleman has spent 10 years at Sotheby's New York.
Focus/Mission: To provide emerging artists an opportunity to shown within the usually limited gallery space in the Upper East side of New York.
Selection process: The gallery is always open to new work. Artists should send CD's, printed mages or slides, 1 page resumé, contact details and SASE. Please do not call the gallery directly, we shall contact you.

MITCHELL-INNES & NASH

1018 Madison Ave., 5th floor, 10021. T: (212) 744-7400.
F: (212) 744-7401.　　　　　　　W: www.miandn.com
E: info@miandn.com　　　　　　Year established: 1996.
Open: Tues.-Sat. 10-5; Summer: Mon.-Fri. 10-5.
Owners: Lucy Mitchell-Innes and David Nash, former Directors at Sotheby's.
Directors: Adrain Turner and Robert Grossman.
Work shown: Impressionist, Modern and Contemporary Master works.
Work by: Willem DeKooning; Tony Smith; Jack Tworkov; and Roy Lichtenstein; among others.
Advertising: *Art News, Art in America, Artforum* and *Gallery Guide.*

ACHIM MOELLER FINE ART

167 East 73 St., 10021.　　　　T: (212) 988-4500.
F: (212) 988-5400.　　　　　　　W: www.moellerart.com
E: info@moellerart.com
Open: Mon.-Sat. 10-6; Summer: Mon.-Fri. 10-6.
Year established: Achim Moeller Ltd., London 1972-85; Achim Moeller Fine Art, New York 1983. Member of Art Dealers Association of America.
President/CEO: Achim Moeller.
Work shown: Impressionism to Modern and Contemporary Art. Paintings, drawings and sculpture.
Work by: Brancusi; Cezanne; Duchamp; Klee; and Picasso; among others.
Additional information: Lyonel Feininger and Mark Tobey catalogues raisonné in preparation. Upon request, Moeller provides written opinion on the authenticity of works attributed to Lyonel Feininger and Mark Tobey.

ARTISTS' PRAYERS ARE ANSWERED

*Among the many religious institutions that exhibit contemporary artists'
work include the Cathedral of St. John the Divine, St. Peter's Church,
Jewish Institute of Religion, Synagogue for the Arts,
and Union Theological Seminary.*

DONALD MORRIS

32 East 76 St., 10021. **T:** (212) 570-1567.
F: (212) 517-6479. **Open:** By appointment.
Year established: 1958. Member of Art Dealers Association of America.
Owners/Directors: Donald, Florence, and Steven Morris.
Work shown: 20th Century European and American art, traditional African art.
Paintings, sculpture, and works on paper.
Work by: Avery; Dubuffet; Matisse; Cornell; and Miró; among others.
Focus/Mission: Presentation and sale of museum quality works of art.
Selection process: We are not looking for new artists.

MARK MURRAY FINE PAINTINGS

980 Madison Ave., 10021. **T:** (212) 585-2380.
F: (212) 585-2383. **E:** markmur@aol.com
W: www.markmurraypaintings.com **Open:** Mon.-Fri. 11-6, Sat. by appointment.
Year established: 1997. **Owner/Director:** Mark Murray.
Work shown: European and American paintings from the 19th and early 20th
Centuries. Landscapes, still life, genre, Orientalist, sporting and marine subjects.
Work by: Bridgman; Corot; Cropsey; Cucuel; and Rico y Ortega; among others.
Advertising: *Gallery Guide.*

NEW-YORK HISTORICAL SOCIETY

2 West 77 St. and Central Park West, 10024. **T:** (212) 873-3400.
W: www.nyhistory.org **Open:** Tues.-Sun. 10-5.
Admission: $5 general; $3 seniors and students.
Work shown: All media. Permanent collection includes paintings from the
Hudson River School; Tiffany Glass; American Photography; and watercolors by
John James Audubon; among other works of art.
Annual exhibitions: 4-6.
Additional information: The Society contains more than half a million books, 2
million maps, manuscripts, and other documents; and thousands of works of art.

NEW YORK SCHOOL OF INTERIOR DESIGN

170 East 70 St., 10021. **T:** (212) 472-1500.
F: (212) 472-3800. **W:** nysid.edu **Open:** Tues.-Sat. 10-5.
President: Inge Heckel. **Dean:** Scott Ageloff.
Year established: Chartered in 1916; established in this location in 1994.
Work shown: Art and design in all media.
Additional information: The school has two galleries: The main gallery at 161
East 69 St. and the Sherrill Whiton Gallery, 170 East 70 St.

NORTH STAR

3 East 76 St., Suite 2B, 10021.   **T:** (212) 794-4277.
F: (212) 794-5264.   **E:** gregg470@aol.com
W: www.northstargalleries.com   **Open:** By appointment.
Owner/Director: Gregg Dierich.
Work shown: Antique, folk, Contemporary and Maritime art. Paintings, limited edition prints, vintage photographs and other collectibles related to the sea.
Work by: James Bard; Anton Otto Fischer; Daniel W. Huntington; and Warren E. Rollins; among others.
Focus/Mission: To offer the romance of the world's waterways and history in art and collectibles.
Additional information: The gallery also offers in-house viewing for corporate clients. The gallery is also happy to advise first time buyers.

OWEN

19 East 75 St., 10021.   **T:** (212) 879-2415.
F: (212) 879-2799.   **E:** info@owengallery.com
W: www.owengallery.com   **Open:** Tues.-Sat. 10-5.
Year established: 1986.   **Owner/Director:** Michael Owen.
Work shown: Paintings by important American artists, 1880-1940.
Work by: George Bellows; William Bradford; Emil Carlsen; William Glackens; Robert Henri; among others.   **Advertising:** *Gallery Guide.*

MARTHA PARRISH & JAMES REINISH, INC.

25 East 73 St., 2nd floor, 10021.   **T:** (212) 734-7332.
F: (212) 734-7303.   **E:** parrein@aol.com
Open: By appointment Mon.-Fri. 9:30-5:30.
Owners: Martha Parrish and James Reinish.
Work by: Milton Avery; Thomas Hart Benton; Georgia O'Keeffe; Fairfield Porter; and John Singer Sargent among others.
Advertising: *Gallery Guide.*

GERALD PETERS

24 East 78 St., 10021.   **T:** (212) 628-9760.
F: (212) 628-9635.   **W:** www.gpgallery.com
Open: Mon.-Sat. 10-5; Summer: Mon.-Fri. 10-5.
Size: 6,000 sq. ft.   **Annual exhibitions:** 3-4.
Year established: 1992 in NY, 1975 in Santa Fe.
Owner: Gerald Peters.
Directors: Reagan Upshaw, Lily Downing Burke, Gerry Wunderlich and Alice Levi.
Work shown: The focus is on late 19th and 20th Century painting and sculpture, from the Hudson River School to Modernism, in addition to European Modern Masters. The gallery also shows Contemporary art in its two other U.S. locations.
Work by: Albert Bierstadt; Robert Henri; John Singer Sargent; Georgia O'Keefe; and Marsden Hartley; among others.
Additional information: Other galleries located in Santa Fe, NM, and Dallas, TX.

PAST LIVES

Marian MacKinney (Portraits Inc.), was an anthropologist, William Secord is the founder of the Dog Museum in St. Louis, and James Curtis (An American Space), was a Senior Cataloguer at Sotheby's.

PORTRAITS, INC.

985 Park Ave., 10021.
F: (212) 988-3755.
W: wwwportraitsinc.com
Size: 1,800 sq. ft.

T: (212) 879-5560.
E: info@portraitsinc.com
Year established: 1942.

Open: Mon.-Fri. 10-5, Sat. by appointment; Summer: Mon.-Fri. 10-3.
Owner/Director: Marian MacKinney, anthropologist, antique dealer, and opera singer. Associate Director: Leslie Bridgman.
Work shown: Contemporary Realist Portraits in oil, pastel, drawings, and sculpture. Also landscapes, animals, and other subjects by commission.
Artists represented: 175.
Work by: Aaron Shikler; William Draper; Nelson Shanks; Jacob Collins; and Daniel Greene; among others.
Markets: Corporate and individual. Prices: $2,000-250,000.
Collectors: Metropolitan, The White House, N.Y.U., NY Court of Appeals.
Advertising: *Town and Country* and *The New Yorker.*
Focus/Mission: To promote portraiture as fine art. To assist clients in the selection of the most appropriate artists for their unique projects.
Selection process: 90% of the artists are selected from portfolios submitted to the gallery. Artists should call and ask for the gallery's portfolio procedure form. The Portfolio Review Board meets twice each year. Artists must have established their own styles and have the ability to collaborate with clients.

PRAXIS INTERNATIONAL

25 East 73 St., #4, 10021.
F: (212) 772-0949.
E: ny@praxis-art.com
Size: 1,500 sq. ft.

T: (212) 772-9478.
W: www.praxis-art.com
Year established: 1987.

Open: Tues.-Sat. 11-6; Summer: Tues.-Fri. 11-6.
Owner/Director: Miguel Kehayoglu, background in business.
Work shown: Contemporary Latin American paintings and works on paper.
Artists represented: 30. Mostly Latin American. 15% of the artists are in museum collections.
Work by: Ignacio Iturria; Mario Perez; Ana Fabry; Eduardo Esquivel; and Fernando Allievi – all paintings; among others.
Markets: Individual and corporate. Prices: $500-30,000.
Annual exhibitions: 4-5 solo/2 group.
Advertising: *ARTnews, Gallery Guide, Artforum,* and *Art in America.*
Focus/Mission: To promote the awareness of Latin American art and Latin American artists.
Selection process: The artists are selected by Miguel Kehayoglu of which 30% are selected from juried competitions and exhibitions. Artists may send 8-10 slides and SASE. Response time: 3-5 weeks.

WHAT IS CONTEMPORARY?

For the purpose of this book, we define Contemporary as art created after World War II. That embraces a broad range of styles and every visual thing including Classic Realsim, Abstract Digital, New Media, Outsider, Conceptual, Self-Taught, Site-Specific, Latin-American, Russian, Vintage, Video, Minimal and Pop... and more..

JOSEPH RICKARDS

1045 Madison Ave., 2nd floor, 10021. **T:** (212) 924-0858.
F: (212) 255-2115.   **E:** RickardsNY@aol.com
W: www.artincontext.org   **Open:** Tues.-Sat. 11-5.
Year established: 1997.   **Owner/Director:** Joseph Rickards.
Work shown: Contemporary art in all media.
Artists represented: 12, international, mostly American.
Work by: Lester Johnson: paintings and works on paper; Robert Jessup: paintings; Paul Jenkins: paintings; Kara Hammond: paintings and drawings; and Alan Davie: paintings and works on paper; among others.
Annual exhibitions: 6-8.
Advertising*: ARTnews, The New York Times and Art in America.*

MICHELLE ROSENFELD

16 East 79 St.,10021.   **T:** (212) 734-0900.
 F: (201) 327-1794.   **Open:** By appointment.
Directors: Michelle and Herbert Rosenfeld.
Work shown: Contemporary and Modern Masters and Impressionist paintings, sculpture, and drawings.
Work by: Chagall; Leger; and Picasso. Occasionally the gallery will show works by Arman, Chun, Lichtenstein, and Rivers.

SALANDER - O'REILLY

20 East 79 St., 10021.   **T:** (212) 879-6606.
F: (212) 744-0655.   **W:** www.salander.com
E: info@salander.com   **Year established:** 1975.
Size: 6,000 sq. ft.   **Owner:** Lawrence Salander.
Director: Leigh A. Morse.
Work shown: All styles and all media.
Open: Mon.-Sat. 9:30-5:30. Closed July 22-Aug 16, 2002.
Artists represented: 38; all origins.
Work by: Gustave Courbet; Stuart Davis; Robert De Niro Sr.; Elie Nadelman; Stone Roberts; and Michael Steiner; among others.
Prices: $1,000-3,000,000.
Annual exhibitions: 9 solo/11 group.
Advertising: *The New York Times* and *New York Observer.*
Focus/Mission: To exhibit and sell art from all periods.
Selection process: All of the artists are selected from referrals.

WILLIAM SECORD

52 East 76 St., 10021.
F: (212) 288-1938.
W: www.dogpainting.com
appointment.

T: (212) 249-0075.
E: wsecord@dogpainting.com
Open: Mon.-Sat. 10-5. August by
Year established: 1990.

President: William Secord, founder and former director of the Dog Museum, currently in St. Louis, MO, originally in New York; author of *Dog Painting 1840-1940, Dog Painting: The European Breed* and *A Breed Apart: The Collection of the American Kennel Club and Dog Museum.*
Work shown: The gallery specializes in fine 19th and early 20th Century animal paintings with dog paintings as its specialty.
Work by: Sir Edwin Landseer; Maud Earl; Bert Cobb; Marguerite Kirmse; and Christine Merrill; among others.
Advertising: *Gallery Guide.*

SHEPHERD & DEROM

58 East 79 St., 10021.
F: (212) 772-1314.
Year established: 1966.

T: (212) 861-4050.
E: sheperdny@aol.com
Owner/Director: Robert Kashey.

Assistant Director: David Wojciechowski.
Open: Tues.-Sat. 10-6; Summer: Mon.-Fri. 10-6
Work shown: 19th and 20th Century European paintings, drawings and sculpture. The Shepherd Gallery is the New York representative for Derom Gallery, in Brussels.
Owner/Director of Derom Gallery: Patrick Derom.
Work shown: Classical 20th Century Modern, Symbolism through Surrealism.
Work by: Jerome; Klinger; Meunier; Rops; and Magritte; among others.
Annual exhibitions: 4, with fully illustrated published catalogues.
Advertising: *ARTnews* and *Gallery Guide.*

SKARSTEDT FINE ARTS

1018 Madison Ave., 3rd floor, 10021. **T:** (212) 737-2060.
F: (212) 737-4171.   E: info@skarstedt.com
Open: Tues.-Fri. 10-6, Sat. 10-5:30; July, Tues.-Fri. 10-5. Closed in August.
Year established: 1995.
Owner/Director: Per Skarstedt, gallery owner in Sweden.
Work shown: Post 80's Contemporary art.
Work by: Cindy Sherman; Richard Prince; Christopher Wool; Rosemarie Trockel; Keith Haring; and Mike Kelly; among others.

SOLOMON & CO.

959 Madison Ave., 10021.
Year established: 1970.

T: (212) 737-8200.
Directors: Gerald Solomon, Sally Solomon.

Open: Mon.-Sat. 10:30-5:30; Summer: Tues.-Fri. 10-30-5.
Member of Art Dealers Association of America.
Work shown: Modern European and American Post-war Abstract Expressionism. Paintings, watercolors and sculpture.
Work by: Calder; de Kooning; Kandinsky; Botero; and Dubuffet; among others.

SOTHEBY'S

1334 York Ave., 10021.   T: (212) 606-7000.
W: www.sothebys.com
Year established: 1744. Sotheby's is the world's premier auction house.
Work shown at auction: Fine Art and Antiques. Paintings; jewelry; furniture; decorative arts; Asian and Tribal arts; prints; photographs; and more.
Advertising: *The New York Times.*
Additional information: To purchase illustrated catalogues call (800) 444-3709 or the numbers above. Sotheby's Institute of Fine Art offers the American Arts Course, a nine-month accredited program. There is a café on the 10th floor. Bid is a restaurant currently in the lobby.

SOUFER

1015 Madison Ave., 10021.   T: (212) 628-3225.
F: (212) 628-3752.   **Year established:** 1977.
Director: Mahboubeh Soufer.
Open: Tues.-Sat 10-5; Summer: Mon- Fri 10-5.
Work shown: French and European Post-Impressionism, European Naïve, and some German Expressionism.   Paintings and sculpture.
Work by: Samuel Bak: Contemporary paintings and works on paper; Camille Bombois: primitive paintings; George Grosz: watercolors and inks; Raoul Dufy: paintings and works on paper; Ossip Zadkine: bronze sculpture; and Ernst Barlach: woodcut prints, and bronze sculpture; among others.

SUITE 106 (AT THE MILBURN HOTEL)

242 West 76 St., 10023.   T: (212) 362-1006 ext 106.
F: (212) 721-5476.   E: info@suite106.com
W: www.suite106.com   **Open:** Wed.–Sat. 11-6.
Work shown: Video, photography, and other technologically-inflected practices.
Work by: Cordy Ryman; Michael Dee; Nicholas & Thomas de Monchaux; among others.

HOLLIS TAGGART

48 East 73 St., 10021.   T: (212) 628-4000.
F: (212) 717-4119.   E: HollisTaggart@HollisTaggert.com
W: www.HollisTaggart.com   **Year established:** 1994.
Open: Mon.-Sat. 10-5. Mid June-Sept. 1 Mon.-Fri. 10-5.
President: Hollis Taggert.
Director: Vivian Bullaudy.
Assistant Director: Debra Pesci.
Work shown: 19th and 20th Century American paintings including Impressionism, Hudson River School, Ashcan, American Modernism and Contemporary Realism.
Work by: Alfred Maurer; Arthur B. Karles; Frederick Carl Frieseke; Manierre Dawson; and John Singer Seargent; among others.
Additional Information: The gallery was located in Georgetown, DC before moving to this location.

JAMES FRANCIS TREZZA

39 East 78 St., Ste. 603, 10021.　**T:** (212) 327-2218.
F: (212) 327-2161.　**E:** jamestrezza@trezza.com
W: www.trezza.com　**Open:** Tues.-Sat. 11-5.
Work shown: 19th and 20th Century paintings, sculpture, work on paper. Academic, Barbizon, Impressionism, Post Impressionism, Modern and 20th Century photography.
Work by: Picasso; Rodin; Giacometti; Klimt; and Janet Sternburg; among others.

TRI COLOUR

69 West 71 St., Suite 1L, 10023.　**T:** (212) 580-4914.
W: www.tricolour.com　**E:** info@Tricolour.com
Open: By appointment.　**Year established:** 1997.
Owner/Director: Cassandra Dooley, founder and director of the Bass Manor Museum, in Malta, NY; (518) 581-8045.
Work shown: Contemporary painting, sculpture, and photography.
Work by: Truman Egleson's 70's work, in addition to his current abstract Luminiscence series; Robert Birbeck; Vera De Rivales; Joy Manor; and Leah Roff.

UBU

16 East 78 St., 10021.　**T:** (212) 794-4444.
F: (212) 794-4289.　**Owners:** Jack Banning and Adam J. Boxer.
 Year established: 1994.
Open: Tues.-Sat. 11-6.　Closed Sat. in July.　Closed in August.
Work shown: 20th Century Avant-garde, and innovative Contemporary art and photography, collage, drawings, books and sculpture.
Work by: Hans Bellmer; Laszlo Moholy-Nagy; Pierre Molinier; Yoko Ono; and Jindrich Styrsky; among others. Mostly European artists.
Annual exhibitions: 6.
Focus/Mission: To highlight the interrelationship among the media in contemporary art.
Selection process: We are currently not interested in reviewing artists' materials.

DIANE UPRIGHT FINE ART

188 East 76 St., 10021.　**T:** (212) 734-3072.
F: (212) 517-7055.　**E:** dufinearts@nyc.rr.com
Open: By appointment.　**Owner:** Diane Upright.
Work shown: Contemporary American and European Masters. Exclusive representative for the estate of Morris Louis.
Advertising: *Gallery Guide.*

URSUS PRINTS

981 Madison Ave., 10021.　**T:** (212) 772-8787.
F: (212) 737-9306.　**E:** ursus@ ursusbooks.com
W: www.ursusbooks.com　**Year established:** 1972.
Director: Peter Kraus.　**Assistant Director:** Evelyn L. Kraus.
Open: Mon.-Fri. 10-6, Sat. 11-5; July and August: Mon.-Fri. 10-6.
Work shown: Contemporary botanical art, rare and antique books, Modern illustrated books, and fine antique Master prints. The gallery also carries in print and out of print art reference books.　　　*continued*

Work by: Robert Rauschenberg; Marc Chagall; Pablo Picasso; and Jim Dine; among others. **Prices:** $50-$150,000. Major credit cards are accepted. **Focus/Mission:** We offer the best quality we can find in the best condition available. The antique prints are as close to the orginal quality. The gallery provides genuine works only. The integrity of the object is very important to us.

MICHAEL WERNER

4 East 77 St., 10021.   **T:** (212) 988-1623.
F: (212) 988-1774.   **E:** info@michaelwerner.net
Year established: 1989.   **Owner:** Michael Werner.
Director: Gordon VeneKlasen.
Open: Mon.-Sat. 10-6; Summer: Mon.-Fri. 10-6.
Work shown: All styles and media by predominantly German artists.
Work by: Georg Baselitz; Markus Lupertz; Jorg Immendorff; James Lee Byars; and Per Kirkeby – all media; among others.
Annual exhibitions: 3-4 solo/2 or more group.
Advertising: *ARTnews, Gallery Guide*, and *Art in America*.
Focus/Mission: To show Modern and Contemporary European and American paintings, sculpture and drawings, specializing in German Contemporary art.

WHITNEY MUSEUM OF AMERICAN ART

945 Madison Ave., at 75 St., 10021. **T:** (212) 570-3676.
Director: Maxwell Anderson.   **Year established:** 1966.
Open: Tues.-Thurs. 11- 6, Fri. 1-9, Sat. and Sun. 11-6.
Admission: $10 adults. $8 seniors and students with ID. Free for members and children under 12. Admission is "pay as you wish" Fri. 6-9.
Work shown: Exhibitions of 20th Century American painting, sculpture, drawing, photography, prints, film, and video, in addition to education programs.
Annual exhibitions: 8-10.
Selection process: The Museum rarely looks at unsolicited artists' materials. For information about a portfolio review call (212) 570-3600.
Additional information: A café and a gift shop are on the premises.

D. WIGMORE FINE ART

22 East 76 St., 10021.   **T:** (212) 794-2128.
W: www.dwigmore.com   **Year established:** 1980.
Owner/Director: Deedee Wigmore.
Open: Mon.-Sat. 9:30-5:30; Summer: Mon.-Fri. 9:30-5:30.
Work shown: American art: Hudson River School; Impressionism; Modernism and American Scene of the 1930s and 1940s.
Work by: John Steuart Curry; Adolf Dehn; Doris Lee; Reginald Marsh; and Isaac Soyer; among others.
Annual exhibitions: 6.   **Advertising:** *Gallery Guide*.

WINSTON WACHTER MAYER FINE ART

39 East 78 St., 10021.   **T:** (212) 327-2526.
F: (212) 327-2529.   **E:** nygallery@winstonwachter.com
W: www.winstonwachter.com   **Year established:** 1996.
Open: Tues.-Sat. 10-6; Summer: Mon.-Fri. 10-6.
Owners: Stacey Winston, Christine Wachter and Elizabeth Mayer.

Backgrounds: 12-15 years gallery experience.

Work shown: Realistic, landscape, abstract painting; photography; and work on paper.

Markets: Individual, corporate, and museum.

Prices: $1,000-10,000.   **Artists represented:** 15.

Work by: Jeff Joyce: Contemporary landscape paintings that have been influenced by 19th Century literature and Hudson River School painting; Anne Siemes: painting; Sherry Kerlin: paintings and drawings; Tony Scherman: paintings; and Seton Smith: photography; among others.

Annual exhibitions: 6 solo/2 group.

Advertising: *Gallery Guide, Artforum*, and *Art in America*.

Focus/Mission: Winston Wachter Mayer sees its role as arts educators through our exhibitions, lectures, art tours and personal relationship with the art community.

Selection process: We are currently not looking for new artists.

Additional information: We are involved with exhibitions and art consulting and are the organizers of the Chelsea Art Walk. Also, we run art tours through galleries, artists' studios and other art venues.

EIGHTIES AND ABOVE

EL MUSEO DEL BARRIO

"This is the only visual arts institution in NYC dedicated to preserving and interpreting the artistic heritage of Latinos and Latin Americans. It also serves as a vital educational forum where artistic expression reflects the issues and concerns of a changing society."

MARION ALEXANDER

167 East 87 St., 10128.   **T:** (212) 427-4333.
E: malexandergallery@aol.com   **W:** www.artnet.com
Year established: 1991.

Owner/Director: Marion Alexander.

Open: Mon., Wed., Sat. 11-6, Tues., Thurs., Fri. 11-5, Sun. 12-5; Summer: Tues.-Sat. 11-5.

Work shown: Oils on canvas 1930's-1960s; 20th Century original prints; 20th Century African-American originals and prints.

Work by: Norman Lewis; Frederick Serger; William Tolliver; Scott Duce; and Sam Gilliam.

Annual exhibitions: 4.   **Advertising:** *Gallery Guide.*

Additional information: The gallery offers custom framing from hard exotic woods.

PEG ALSTON FINE ARTS

407 Central Park West, Suite 1-C, 10025. **T:** (212) 663-8333.
F: (212) 663-9663. **E:** pegalston@aol.com
Open: By appointment. **Year established:** 1972.
Director: Peg Alston.
Work shown: Early and Contemporary African-American Art.

AMERICAN-EUROPEAN ART ASSOCIATES, INC.

1100 Madison Ave., Suite 6A, 10028. **T:** (212) 517-4010.
F: (212) 439-9114. **E:** art@aeaainc.com
W: www.aeaainc.com **Open:** Tues.-Sat. 10-5.
Year established: 1986. **Owner/Director:** Arnold Katzen.
Work shown: 19th and 20th Century Masters and Contemporary paintings, drawings and sculpture.
Work by: Sibille Rath: painting; Michel Haas: works on paper; D.A.R.M. (group of four artists): painting; Dan Ascher: photography; and Dieter Appelt: photography; among others.
Annual exhibitions: 6. **Advertising:** *Gallery Guide, Flash Art* and *Artforum.*

AN AMERICAN SPACE

1305 Madison Ave., 2nd floor, 10128. **T:** (212) 426-2879.
E: anamspace@aol.com **Year established:** 1999.
W: www.artnet.com\anamericanspacegallery.html
Open: Wed.-Sat. 11-6 and by appointment. Closed in August.
Owner/Director: James Curtis. Background: Senior Cataloguer in Sotheby's Print Department.
Work shown: 19th and 20th Century and Contemporary American photography.
Work by: Alfred Stieglitz; Margaret Bourke-White; Lewis Hine; Robert Frank; and Eadweard Muybridge; among others.
Annual exhibitions: 6-7. **Advertising:** *Photography in New York.*

ART GALLERY - INTERNATIONAL AGENCY FOR MINORITY ARTIST AFFAIRS

163 West 125 Street, Adam Clayton Powell, Jr. State Office Building, 2nd floor, 10027. **T:** (212) 749-5298.
W: www.Ha m.cc **Open:** Mon.-Fri. 12-3.
Year estab hed: 1972. **Director/Curator:** Gregory Mills.
**Work show Contemporary art in all styles and media by semi-professional artists to em ging artists.
Annual exhi itions: 6-10 plus permanent collection.
Selection process: The Curatorial Committee meets regularly to select work for shows. Applications are accepted throughout the year. Artists should call and request the application guidelines. **Requirements:** Artists must be residents of NY state for two years prior to applying to exhibit. Artists who are residents of the Greater Harlem community are strongly encouraged to apply. Artists may apply individually or on behalf of a group of artists. Collaboration projects are strongly encouraged.
Additional information: The organization does not take a commission from artists on sales. There are no membership requirements or exhibition fees for artists.

BARD GRADUATE CENTER FOR STUDIES IN THE DECORATIVE ARTS

18 West 86 St., 10024. T: (212) 501-3000.
F: (212) 501-3099. Open: Tues.-Sun. 11-5, Thurs. 11-8.
Year established: 1993. Director: Susan Weber Soros.
Work shown: Decorative arts from all periods. Most exhibitions have focused on art from the 18th, 19th, and 20th Centuries.

BARON/BOISANTÉ

300 East 85 St., #2702, 10028. T: (212) 288-0448.
F: (212) 288-0921 Open: By appointment.
Year established: 1988. Size: 1,000 sq. ft.
Owners/Directors: Mark Baron and Elise Boisanté, publishers of prints and multiples.
Work shown: Drawings, sculpture, paintings and prints in all media.
Artists exhibited: Predominantly American, also European. 95% of the artists are in museum collections.
Work by: Jennifer Bolande: photography, and found object sculpture; Donald Baechler: paintings and bronze; Not Vital: bronze and hydrocal; Michael Byron: paintings and works on paper; and Sandrine Guerin: photography; among others.
Collectors: Metropolitan, MoMa, Whitney, and Guggenheim.
Advertising: *Gallery Guide* and *Artforum*.
Selection process: Artists should visit the gallery. If there is an opportunity to look at their slides they will.

VIVIANE BREGMAN FINE ART

1010 Fifth Ave., 10128. T: (212) 988-8655.
F: (212) 772-0411. E: vbfineart@hotmail.com
W: www.artnet.com Open: By appointment.
Owner/Director: Viviane Bregman, private dealer and corporate art consultant. Member of Appraisers Association of America.
Work shown: Impressionist, Modern and Contemporary painting, work on paper, and prints. Work by: Helen Frankenthaler; Adolph Gottlieb; Eric Fischl; Ellsworth Kelly; Frank Stella; among others.

CASA LINDA

300 East 95 St., 10128. T: (212) 860-8016.
F: (212) 860-4811. Open: Sun. 12-6, Mon.-Wed. 10-6, Thurs.-Sat. 10-7.
Work shown: International artists and artisans with an emphasis on Latin artists. Paintings, sculpture, ceramics, pottery, wood and stone carvings, wall plaques, hand made accessories and unique gifts.

THE CATHEDRAL CHURCH OF ST. JOHN THE DIVINE

1047 Amsterdam Ave., 10025. T: (212) 316-7485.
W: www.stjohndivine.org Open: Daily 8-6.
Director: Reverend Canon Jay Wegman.
Work shown: Painting, Drawings, Photography, Sculpture, Video Art and Craft. Themes relating to the concerns of the Cathedral are prevalent.
Annual exhibitions: 6-8 solo and group.
Selection process: Solo and group shows are considered. Artists and organizations should submit slides, proposals, biography and/or other documentation. Exhibitors must provide their own gallery sitters.

CHILDREN'S MUSEUM OF MANHATTAN

212 West 83 St., 10024.   **T:** (212) 721-1234.
Open: Wed.-Sun. 10-5.
Admission: $5 adults and children, $2.50 for seniors, free for children under one.
Work shown: Interactive exhibitions for children of all ages, including an imaginative exploration space for babies and toddlers devoted to language and the Body Odyssey exhibit and interactive media center for early elementary school children.

COOK FINE ART

1063 Madison Ave., 10028.   **T:** (212) 737-3550.
F: (212) 737-3440.   **E:** artabazus@cookfineart.net
Open: Tues.-Fri. 10-6, Sat. 12-5, and by appointment.
Work shown: Drawings, pastels and watercolors by Manet, Renoir, Miro, and others. Also 19th Century painting and sculpture; 19th Century, Modern and Contemporary Photography.
Work by: Nan Golden; Sarah Jones; Sally Mann; Cindy Sherman; and Nikki Sl Lee; among others.

CZECH CENTER NEW YORK

1109 Madison Avenue, 10028.   **T:** (212) 288-0830.
F: (212) 288-0971.   **W:** www.czechcenter.com
E: nycenter@czech.cz.   **Open:** Tues.-Fri. 9-5, Thurs. 9-8.
Year established: 1995.   **Director:** Peter Polednak.
Work shown: Czech artists or art that is related to the Czech Republic.
Annual exhibitions: 6; mostly solo shows.
Selection process: Artists should mail slides, resumé and SASE.

WILLIAM DOYLE

175 East 87 St., 10128.   **T:** (212) 427-2730.
F: (212) 369-0892.   **E:** info@doylegalleries.com
W: www.doylenewyork.com   **Chairman:** Kathleen M. Doyle.
Work shown at auction: This American-owned auction house specializes in American and British estates. Fine art, jewelry, furniture, books, prints and other collecting categories.   **Advertising:** *The New York Times.*
Additional information: William Doyle Galleries offers personalized appraisal and auction services. Free walk-in appraisals are offered on Tues. 9:30-11:30 am. Consignments are accepted for future auctions. For more information or to schedule an appointment for another time, call (212) 427-4141 or email info@doylenewyork.com

THE ELKON

18 East 81 St., 10028.   **T:** (212) 535-3940.
F: (212) 737-8479.   **E:** elkongallery@earthlink.net
Open: Mon.-Fri. 9:30-5:30.   **Year established:** 1961.
Member of the Art Dealers Association of America.
Owner/Director: Dorothea McKenna Elkon.
Work shown: 20th Century Modern and Contemporary masters.
Work by: Botero; Ernst; Matisse; Miró; Picasso; among others.

EL MUSEO DEL BARRIO

1230 Fifth Ave., 10029. **T:** (212) 831-7272.
F: (212) 831-7927. **W:** www.elmuseo.org
Open: Wed.- Sun. 11-5. **Year established:** 1970.
Work shown: Art by Latino and Latin American artists.
Focus/Mission: The only visual arts institution in NYC dedicated to preserving and interpreting the artistic heritage of Latinos and Latin Americans. It is a vital educational forum where artistic expression reflects the issues and concerns of a changing society. Through exhibitions, publications, symposia, lectures, concerts, festivals, and special interpretive educational programs, it serves to contextualize and disseminate the Latino and Latin American cultural heritage.
A programmatic mix pursues a healthy balance between past and present. It preserves and interprets culturally important historical materials, yet also offers a network of support to Latino and Latin American artists who transform that heritage into vital, contemporary works.
Selection process: The review board meets quarterly. Latino and Latin American artists may send slides and resumé to the Curatorial Department.

EL TALLER BORICUA,

Julia de Burgos Latino Cultural Center,
1680 Lexington Ave., 10029. **T:** (212) 831-4333.
F: (212) 831-6274 **E:** tallerboricua@yahoo.com
W: tallerboricua.org **Open:** Tues.-Sat. 12-6, Thurs. 1-7.
Year established: 1971. **Owner:** Puerto Rican Workshop, Inc.
Executive Director: Fernando Salicrup. **Artistic Director:** Marcos Dimas.
Work shown: All styles and media. **Size:** 4 galleries totaling 3,000 sq. ft.
Artists exhibited: All origins. 25% of the artists are in museum collections.
Annual exhibitions: 12 solo/2 group.
Focus/Mission: We exhibit young, emerging and mid-career artists.
Selection process: 90% of the artists are selected from slides submitted. Artists should submit 10 slides, resumé or biography and SASE for consideration.
Response time: Months.
Requirements: Good work. There are no exhibition fees however the artist will incur any costs above our budgetary limit.
Additional information: The Workshop has an Artist Residency Program in addition to an Arts and Culture Enrichment Program in the public schools. Every Thursday from 7-midnight, El Taller Boricua holds a poetry and music improvisational session called "Julia's Jam," where musicians and poets from Manhattan showcase their talents. Their current collector's portfolio is available for collectors. It is called the Alma Portfolio and includes 7 original graphic renderings accompanied by 7 poems of the Nuyorican Experience.

LESLIE FEELY FINE ART

1000 Park Ave., 10028. **T:** (212) 737-4989.
F: (212) 628-7294. **W:** www.artnet.com
Open: By appointment. **Owner/Director:** Leslie Feely.
Work shown: 19th, 20th and Contemporary Masters. Paintings, works on paper, sculpture, and prints.
Work by: Richard Diebenkorn; Roy Lichtenstein; Frank Stella; Howard Hodgkin; and David Hockney; among others.

GALLERY AT THE MARMARA-MANHATTAN

301 East 94 St., 10128.　**T:** (212) 427-3100.
F: (212) 348-7363.　**Open:** Daily 11-7.
E: info@marmara-manhattan.com　**W:** www.marmara-manhattan.com
Year established: 2000.　**Size:** 1,000 sq. ft.
Owner: Marmara-Manhattan Hotel. **Curator:** Zishan Ugurlu.
Work shown: Contemporary art in all media by local and international artists.
Collectors: Moscow Museum of Modern Art, among others.
Work by: Exhibitions have included Peter D. Hristoff; Dimiter Hristoff; Peter Hristoff; Serdar Arat; and Elena Milonas; among others.
Advertising: *Gallery Guide.*　**Annual exhibitions:** 4-5.
Focus/Mission: To promote local and international artists.
Selection process: Artists may mail their portfolio and resume to Zishan Ugurlu.
Response time: 2 weeks.

GALLERY SPACE AT RUSS BERRIE

1150 St. Nicholas Ave., near 168 St., 10032. (See West Harlem Art Fund.)

GALLERY X

23 West 129th St. (between Lenox Ave., also known as Malcolm X Boulevard, and Fifth Ave.), 10027.　**T:** (212) 534-7044.
Open: Wed.-Sun. 12-5.　**Year established:** 1998.
Owner/Director: Gülsün Erbil, artist; MA in Fine Art from Mimar Sinan University, Istanbul. Former gallery owner in Istanbul and London.
Work shown: Contemporary paintings, drawings, prints, sculptures, installations and performance art. All media.　**Annual exhibitions:** 12.
Work by: Fred Mitchell: American Abstract Expressionist; Jia Min: Chinese-Canadian artist whose abstractions are based on subliminal imagery; Fredo: African-American Minimalist artist; Larry Gomez: art that explores the immediacy of drawing in paint; and Gülsün Erbil: a Sufi, whose art is related to metaphysical realities; among others.
Focus/Mission: Gallery X is a contemporary art space committed to exhibiting the works of emerging artists of exemplary talent. It also coordinates scholarly discussions and gallery talks by internationally recognized art critics, artists, and art historians.
Selection process: Artists should call for an appointment to bring presentation materials. Ms. Erbil will visit the artist's studio if interested in the work.

JANOS GAT

1100 Madison Ave., 10028.　**T:** (212) 327-0441.
F: (212) 327-0442.　**W:** www.janosgatgallery.com
Open: Tues.-Sat. 11-6.　**Year established:** 1993.
Owner/Director: Janos Gat. poet, writer, rock music composer.
Work shown: Classic Hungarian art and Contemporary American art. Painting, photography and sculpture.
Focus/Mission: The gallery shows non-mainstream, but important and influential, European Modernists such as Istvan Farkas and the members of the Viennese Actionism; American artists working in a similar vein, such as Knox Martin, and Boris Lurie, and the No! art movement. Also shows Ann Wilson Carol Ross.
Selection process: We are currently not accepting unsolicited materials.

GLASS ART

315 Central Park West, #8W, 10024.   **T:** (212) 787-4704.
F: (212) 799-3204.   **Open:** Mon.-Sat. 1-6.
Year established: 1959.   **Owner/Director:** Wendy D. Glass.
Work shown: American Works on Paper, European Graphics, and Japanese woodblock prints.
Work by: Max Weber: woodcuts and drawings; Raphael Soyer: watercolors, drawings and lithographs; Chaim Gross: watercolors and drawings; Benny Andrews: collage and drawings; and Haim Mendelson: intaglio collage; among others.
Collectors: C.B.S. and Dr. Nathan M. Davis.
Focus/Mission: To show high quality work.
Additional information: Wendy Glass is also an art appraiser.

GOETHE INSTITUT NEW YORK/GERMAN CULTURAL CENTER

1014 Fifth Ave., 10028.   **T:** (212) 439-8700.
F: (212) 439-8705.   **E:** program@goethe-newyork.org.
W: www.goethe.org   **Director:** Dr. Stephan Nobbe.
Program Director: Irmtraut Hubatsch.
Open: Mon., Wed. and Fri. 10-5. Tues., Thurs. 10-7; Summer: Call for hours.
Work shown: Conceptual, Sculpture, Installation, and Photography by primarily German artists. All media.
Work by: Ute Juerss: video installation; Eran Schaerf: installation; Abisag Tullmann: photography; and Neo Rauch: painting; among others.
Annual exhibitions: 8-10.   **Advertising:** *Gallery Guide* and *Artforum*.
Focus/Mission: Goethe Institut New York/German Cultural Center is the New York branch of the Goethe-Institut, a worldwide organization founded in 1951 to promote a wider knowledge of the German language abroad and to foster cultural cooperation with other countries. The gallery aims at presenting contemporary artists from Germany chosen by German and American curators.
Selection process: Artists are generally selected by an advisory board of German curators or by referral. Artists should submit a written proposal and resumé with slides or prints anytime with SASE. Artists should be German nationals.

SOLOMON R. GUGGENHEIM MUSEUM

1071 Fifth Ave., 10128.   **T:** (212) 423-3500.
W: www.guggenheim.org   **Open:** Sun.-Wed. 9-6, Fri.-Sat. 9-8.
Year established: 1959.   **Director:** Thomas Krens.
Admission: $15 adults, $12 members, seniors and students, free for children under 12.
Work shown: Modern and Contemporary painting, sculpture, drawings, photography, video and multi-media installations.
Additional information: The museum presents gallery talks and other special events. A Museum café is on the premises. The building was designed by Frank Lloyd Wright.

PETER HAMMAR

69 West 107 St., 10025.
E: peterhammar@aol.com
Open: By appointment.
Size: 2,000 sq. ft. studio/showroom.
Work by: Peter Hammar: paintings and work on paper.
Markets: Individual, corporate and museum.
Collectors: Private and corporate collections.
Additional information: Peter Hammar is represented by Samson Fine Art in New York; Boston Corporate Art, Boston; and Elizabeth Edwards Fine Art, Palm Desert and Laguna Beach, California.

T: (212) 727-1119.
W: www.peterhammar.com
Owner: Peter Hammar, artist.

HISPANIC SOCIETY OF AMERICA

Entrance on Broadway between 115 and 156 St., 10032. Mailing address: 613 West 155 St., 10032.
E: info@hispanicsociety.org
Open: Tues.-Sat. 10-4:30, Sun. 1-4.
Admission: Free, group visits by appointment only.
Year established: 1904, by Archer Milton Huntington.
Work shown: The permanent collection includes masterpieces by El Greco, Velazquez; Goya; and Sorolla; among others.
Focus/Mission: The Hispanic Society of America was established as a free museum and reference library for the study of the arts and culture of the Iberian Peninsula and of Latin America. It contains approximately 300,000 books. In addition to functioning as a library and to mounting permanent museum displays, the Hispanic Society organizes temporary exhibitions, serves as a resource for the education of school children, and collaborates with other cultural institutions to host symposia. For group visits call (212) 926-2234 x 254.

T: (212) 926-2234.
W: www.hispanicsociety.org

IRENA HOCHMAN

1100 Madison Ave., 10028.
F: (212) 772-2222.
Open: By appointment.
Owner: Irena Hochman, MA in art history.
Work shown: 20th Century and Contemporary American and European Art. All media.
Work by: Sonia Delaunay; Tamara de Lempicka; Damien Hirst; Donald Judd; Tadeusz Myslowski; and Andy Warhol; among others.
Collectors: MoMA, Tate, National Museum, Warsaw.
Advertising: *Gallery Guide*.

T: (212) 772-2227.
E: ny@irenahochmen.com
Size: 1,000 sq. ft.

INTERCHURCH CENTER (LOBBY and TREASURE ROOM)

475 Riverside Dr. at 120 St., 10115. (Across the street from Columbia University.)
T: (212) 870-2933.
Open: Mon.-Fri. 9-5.
Owner: Not-for-profit agency building. Director/Curator: Dorothy Cochron.
Work shown: All styles and media. Artists exhibited: All ages. All origins.
Annual exhibitions: 20 exhibitions in two gallery spaces.
Advertising: *Gallery Guide* and *The Record* of Columbia University.

F: (212) 870-2440.
Year established: 1959.

Focus/Mission: Interchurch Center Galleries primarily serve as an educational means of exposing artists' work to the public.

Selection process: Artists of color are encouraged to approach. All artists are selected from slides submitted. Artists should write to Dorothy Cochron, Room 253, for guidelines and an application form. An exhibit panel reviews proposals 5 times a year. Decisions are made 2 years in advance.

Requirements: Artists must have work with vision and focus; an artist's statement is required.

Additional information: There are occasional lunchtime lectures presented by the exhibiting artists.

THE JEWISH MUSEUM

1109 Fifth Ave., 10128. **T:** (212) 423-3200.
Year established: 1904. **Director:** Joan Rosenbaum.
Open: Sun., 10-5:45, Mon., Tues., Wed., 11-5:45, Thurs. 11-8, Fri. 11-3.
Admission: $8 adults, $5 children, $5.50 for students and seniors. Thurs. 5-8, pay what you wish.
Work shown: Jewish archeology, fine arts, ethnography, video, and changing exhibitions on Jewish culture.
Annual exhibitions: 6-8.
Focus/Mission: The Jewish Museum is devoted to the collection, preservation, interpretation, and dissemination of art and artifacts relating to the Jewish experience, from ancient times to the present throughout the world. While each of the programs, exhibitions, collections, educational activities and publications are related specifically to aspects of Jewish culture – religious, historical, artistic, ethnographic or philosophical – each is also related to broad humanist or aesthetic concerns. "Culture and Continuity: The Jewish Journey" is an on-going centerpiece exhibition of the Museum on the Jewish experience which conveys the essence of Jewish identity – the basic ideas, values and culture developed over 4,000 years. It showcases 28,000 works of art, antiquities, ceremonial objects and electronic media materials.
Additional information: Café Weissman is a kosher café on the premises with live music in the summer months.

LOBBY GALLERY AT AUDUBON

3960 Broadway, entrance on 166 St., 10032. See West Harlem Art Fund.

MACY

Columbia University Teachers College, 525 West 120 St., 4th floor, Macy Hall, 10027. **T:** (212) 678-3681.
E: macygallery@columbia.edu **Open:** Mon.-Fri. 11-5.
Year established: 1894. **Size:** 1,377 sq. ft.
Director: Anthony Mbogho.
Owner: Columbia University Teacher's College.
Work shown: Mostly graduate student works and faculty. Sometimes the work features artists outside the college, which include multi-cultural shows.
Selection process: A jury selects the work. Individual artists and artist groups may send slides, biography and SASE. 20% commission is taken on sales.
Response time: 2 weeks.
Additional information: We encourage group visits. Call to make arrangements.

CHERYL MCGINNIS GALLERY/A CONTEMPORARY SALON

215 West 88 St., Suite 8C, 10024. **T:** (212) 579-8485.
F: (212) 579-4426. **E:** cmggallery@aol.com
Open: By appointment. **Year established:** 1997.
Owner/Director: Cheryl McGinnis, former director at Z Gallery in SoHo. She is currently actively involved with Art in General, the Bronx Museum of the Arts and ArtTable.
Work shown: Asian and Second Generation Feminist artists.
Artists represented: 10. **Origins:** Asia and North America.
Work by: Tomei Arai; Emma Enos; Stephanie Hightower; Zhang Hongtu; and Mary Ting; among others.
Annual exhibitions: 6.
Advertising: *Gallery Guide.*
Focus/Mission: The art is exhibited in an intimate, pre-war space in which the artists discuss their work with viewers. This conversation and exploration into the artist's world leads to a deeper understanding and appreciation of Contemporary art. Follow up visits to the artists' studios are then arranged.
Selection process: Artists should call for current procedure.
Additional information: Call for information about gallery and artist studio tours. Catalogues are available.

METROPOLITAN MUSEUM OF ART

1000 Fifth Ave., 10028. **T:** (212) 879-5500. Info: (212) 535-7710.
Open: Sun., Tues.-Thurs. 9:30-5:15, Fri.-Sat. 9:30-8:45.
Admission: Suggested donation $10.
Director: Philippe de Montebello.
Work shown: 5,000 years of art, historical to 20th Century, from Egypt, Rome, Asia, Africa, Europe and the Americas.
Additional information: The museum houses five restaurants, bars and cafes. Ask for a "Dining Guide" at the museum's information desk. Self-guided audio tours in English and other languages are available for a fee. The museum also sponsors many films, lectures, gallery talks, concerts, and other special programs. Call (212) 879-5500 for information on gallery and museum tours. Memberships are available which includes free admission and a discount in the museums' gift shops and a subscription to the museum's magazine.

MUSEUM OF THE CITY OF NEW YORK

1220 Fifth Ave., at 103 St., 10029. **T:** (212) 534-1672.
W: www.mcny.org **Open:** Wed.-Sat. 10-5; Sun. 12-5.
Year established: 1923. **Director:** Robert R. MacDonald.
Admission: $7 suggested contribution; $4 seniors and students; $12 families.
Deputy Director of Curatorial Affairs: Deborah Waters.
Deputy Director of Institutional Advancement: Patricia Ogden.
Work shown: All exhibitions seek to preserve the history of New York City. Work is dated from the time the island was discovered to contemporary, in all media.
Annual exhibitions: 10.
Additional information: The museum presents educational programs, group tours, and walking tours. Call for information.

NATIONAL ACADEMY MUSEUM AND SCHOOL OF FINE ARTS,

1083 Fifth Ave., 10128.   **T:** (212) 369-4880.
W: www.nationalacademy.org   **Open:** Wed.-Sun. 12-5, Fri. 10-6.
Admission: $8 adults; $4.50 students, children 6-16 and seniors; free to
Academy "Friends" and children under 6 years old. $4 with Channel 13, New
York Times or Transmedia card.
Year established: 1826. This museum, fine-arts school and artists association
was modeled after the Royal Academy in London.
Director: Dr. Annette Blaugrund.   **Annual exhibitions:** 9-12.
Work shown: Special exhibitions of drawings, paintings, sculpture, and
architecture. Permanent collection of 19th and 20th Century American art.
Selection process: Artists should call for membership application guidelines.
Additional information: There are workshops and classes for artists. A
bookstore is located in the lobby. The National Academy Museum holds a juried
competition / exhibition in even numbered years.

PROJECT

427 West 126 St.,10027.   **T:** (212) 662-8610.
F: (212) 662-2800.   **Open:** Wed.-Sun. 12-6.
E:mail@elproyecto.com.   **W:** www. elproyecto. com
Year established:1998
Owners: ChristianHaye, critic, writer for *Frieze,* and curator, and Jenny Liu,
lawyer, writer for *Frieze,* previously worked at 303 Gallery.
Focus/Mission: To bring art that hasn't been shown in traditional venues and to
integrate it into art publications in addition to the museum consciousness.
Work shown: Emerging artists.   **Annual exhibitions:** 7.
Work by: Paul Pfeiffer: video, photography, sculpture and installation; Julie
Mehretu: painting, printmaking and drawing; Soja Kim: installation and video art;
Daniel J. Martinez: sculpture and photography; and Kori Newkirk: multimedia;
among others.
Selection process: Artists should send slides and SASE.
Response time: 6 months.

SAMSON FINE ARTS

1150 Fifth Ave., 10128.   **T:** (212) 369-6677.
F: (212) 426-5223.   **W:** www.samsonfinearts.com
E: mgyenes@aol.com   **Open:** By appointment.
Year established: 1992.   **Director:** Maeve Gyenes.
Work shown: Contemporary painting, photography, work on paper and sculpture.
Work by: Fernand Fonssagrives; David Gordon; Liam Roberts; Jill Moser; Robert
Valdes; among others.   **Annual exhibitions:** 4.

SCHOMBURG CENTER FOR RESEARCH IN BLACK CULTURE

A branch of New York Public Library, corner of Malcolm X Blvd. and 135 St.
T: (212) 491-2200.   **Director:** Howard Dodson.
Year established: 1925.
Open: Mon.-Wed. 12-8, Thurs.-Sat. 10-6, Sun. 1-5.
Work shown: Prints, photographs, art and artifacts in addition to oral histories of
the enduring African traditions, the civil rights movements, and a wide variety of
topics associated with the African-American experience in this country.

SOUND SCULPTURE STUDIO

205 West 80th St., Storefront B2, 10024. **T:** 212-769-4940.
F: 212-769-4940. **E:** jazzwithsculpture@hotmail.com
Open: By appointment. **Year established:** 2001.
Owner: Roberta Berman, artist.
Size: 130 sq.ft. plus small outdoor vestibule.
Work by: Roberta Berman: Sound Sculptures and drawings; in collaboration with David Pleasant: 2DeePercussion drum-line, and *The Sonic Art Garden* improvisational festivals-Inside and Outside. The artist also invites other artists to show their work in the studio or to participate in musical events.
Artists shown: Kathe Frantz, painter; Pam Noftsinger, printmaker; William Pleasant, video poet. Musicians who have performed: David Pleasant, percussionist; Miles Griffith, vocalist; Kid Lucky, vocal-electronica.
Selection process: Most suitable for someone who needs wall space or floor space to exhibit for a short time, and by appointment only. Artists should visit and deliver slides, color Xeroxes, photographs, resume, and other materials for consideration.
Fees: Artists should be prepared to pay exhibition and promotion expenses and gallery-sit for their show.

ALLAN STONE

113 East 90 St., 10128. **T:** (212) 987-4997.
F: (212) 987-1655. **W:** www.allanstonegallery.com
Year established: 1960. **Owner:** Allan Stone.
Director: Claudia Stone.
Open: Tues.-Fri. 10-6, Sat 10-5; Closed in August.
Work shown: Contemporary American Art with a focus on emerging art, while maintaining a tradition of expertise in the New York School of Abstract Expressionism including Willem de Kooning; Franz Kline; Archile Gorky; John Graham; and Joseph Cornell. Painting, drawing, work on paper, collage, and construction.

STUDIO GALLERY 88

205 West 88 St., #1D, 10024. **T:** (212) 579-4654.
W: www.artincontext.org **Year established:** 1997.
Open: Fri., Sat. and Sun., 1-5 and by appointment; Summer: By appointment.
Owner: Barbara Beck, artist and teacher, BA in Studio Art.
Work shown: Contemporary art in all media. Paintings, drawings, sculpture, photography, works on paper and ceramics.
Prices: $100 and up.
Work by: Barbara Beck; Judith Shawn; Victor Laredo; Esti Dunow; and Bill Engel; among others.
Annual exhibitions: 4. **Advertising:** *Westsider* and *West Side Spirit.*
Focus/Mission: To show under-represented artists who are very talented and somewhat overlooked.
Selection process: Artists are selected from slides sent to the gallery in addition to professional referrals. Artists may mail slides, photographs, resumé and SASE or may call to make an appointment. She is very interested in looking at work.
Additional information: There are six artists working in this space.

THE STUDIO MUSEUM IN HARLEM
144 West 125 St., 10027.   **T:** (212) 864-4500.
W: www.studiomuseuminharlem.org **Open:** Mon.-Fri. 10-6.
Size: 60,000 sq. ft.   **Year established:** 1968.
Director: Lowery Stokes Sims.
Deputy Director for Exhibitions and Programs: Thelma Golden.
Work shown: Changing exhibitions and permanent collection of African-American, African, Caribbean art, and Artists-in-Residence. Its collections include over 1,500 objects and are divided into three broad categories: 19th and 20th Century African-American art; 20th Century Caribbean and African art; and traditional African art and artifacts.
Work by: Exhibitions have included Emma Amos; Benny Andrews; Romare Bearden; Elizabeth Catlett; Jacob Lawrence; and Faith Ringgold; among others.
Focus/Mission: The collection, documentation, preservation, and interpretation of the art and artifacts of Black America and the African Diaspora.
Selection process: Contact Curatorial Department. Artists should send materials and SASE. There is also an Artist-in-Residence program. Call or write for details.

SUGAR HILL ART CENTER
Broadway & 151 St., 10031.   **T:** (212) 491-5890.
F: (212) 283-6522.   **E:** SugarhillAC@yahoo.com
Open: Tues.-Sat. 11-5:30.   **Year established:** 2001.
Owner: Donald Weiss.   **Director:** Marylyn Rosenberg.
Size: 4 galleries.
Work by: Danny Simmons: painting; and Fred Mitchell: painting; among others.
Focus: Mission: To show high quality painting and sculpture with an African-American presence.
Selection process: Artists should mail slides, photographs, resumé and SASE.
Additional information: The gallery has a roof sculpture garden.

SUMMA
527 Amsterdam Ave., 10024.   **T:** (212) 787-8533.
F: (212) 875-0035.   **Directors:** Sal Cigna and Donald Pandina.
Open: Tues., Wed., Fri. 11-7, Thurs. 11-8, Sat. 10-6:30, Sun. 12-5. July and August closed Sun. and Mon.
Work shown: Contemporary painting, pastels, watercolors and graphics.
Work by: Jim Buckles; Roy Fairchild; Kaiko Moti; and Frederick Mershimer; among others.

UNION THEOLOGICAL SEMINARY
3041 Broadway, 10027.   **T:** (212) 280-1523.
W: www.uts.columbia.edu   **Director of Worship:** Troy Messenger.
Work shown: Contemporary, religious paintings, sculpture and liturgical art. The Worship Office of Union Theological seeks to integrate the arts and events-of-gathering in a single space – James Memorial Chapel.
Annual exhibitions: 6 solo, from September through May.
Focus/Mission: We open our doors in the hope that artists who might not be granted exhibition space elsewhere will have the opportunity to be heard.
Selection process: Artists should mail a portfolio containing slides/photographs, resumé and a one-page exhibition proposal to the attention of Troy Messenger.

UPTOWN

1194 Madison Ave., 10128.   T: (212) 722-3677.
F: (212) 410-2097.   E: swilliams@uptowngallerynyc.com
W: www.uptowngallerynyc.com   Size: 600 sq. ft.
Year established: 1972.   Owner/President: Steven Williams.
Open: Mon.-Sat. 10-6; Summer: After July 4, Mon.-Fri. 10-6.
Work shown: Contemporary American Realism by Contemporary Masters from North America. All media.
Artists represented: 26. 45% male/55% female. 38% are in museum collections.
Work by: Michael H. Lewis: turpentine oil wash paintings that depict luminous Maine landscapes/seascapes; Barbara Edidin: complex still-life drawings in colored pencils; Hely Lima: detailed and witty 3-d mixed media constructions, and historical works based on NYC tenement buildings; Jon R. Friedman: detailed landscape paintings that evoke contemplation and a sense of place; and Bascove: three areas of interest including the figurative, the still-life, and the Bridge series; among others.
Prices: $500-100,000.
Markets: Individual, corporate, and museum.
Annual exhibitions: 4 solo/ 3 group.
Advertising: *The New York Times* and *Gallery Guide.*
Focus/Mission: To represent and nurture a small, personally selected group of talented, artistically-powerful, unique artists with a strong vision of personal creativity working in all media under the umbrella category of Realism.
Selection process: 15% of the artists are selected from professional referrals; 25% of the artists are selected from materials sent to gallery; 60% of the artists are selected from art seen in exhibitions and artists studios. Artists should mail slides, biography, photos, resumé, prices, and SASE.
Response time: 2-4 months.
Requirements: Artist must have an established career and market. Artists are expected to incur fees for framing, transportation of their art to the gallery, and advertising for shared show expenses.

ELFI VON KANTZOW

1148 Fifth Ave., 10128.   T/F: (212) 348-0133.
Open: By appointment.
Owner/Director: Elfi Von Kantzow, private art dealer and independent curator who has curated exhibitions in New York of Contemporary Scandinavia artists and Scandinavian related subjects, many of which were presented at the Scandinavian Society.
Work by: Exhibitions have featured Siri Berg; Bjorn Runquist; and Marianne Falk; among others.

MIRIAM & IRA D. WALLACH

826 Schermerhorn Hall, Columbia University, 10027. T: (212) 854-7288.
F: (212) 854-7329.   W: www.columbia.edu/cu/wallach
Year established: 1986.   Director: Sarah Elliston Weiner.
Annual exhibitions: 4.
Open: Wed.-Sat. 1-5. Thurs. 1-8; Summer: Closed.

Focus/Mission: To contribute to Columbia's long-standing tradition of historical, critical, and creative engagement in the visual arts. Operating under the auspices of the Department of Art History and Archeology, the gallery presents exhibitions and related programming that complement the mission of the university.
Selection process: We do not accept unsolicited materials from artists. Curatorial proposals are accepted for projects directly and indirectly related to the fields of instruction at the university. Guidelines may be acquired by telephone or by email.

PHYLLIS WEIL & COMPANY

1065 Park Ave., Suite 9A, 10128.   **T:** (212) 369-0255.
F: (212) 831-0745.   **E:** weilart@aol.com
W: www.weilart.com   **Open:** By appointment.
Year established: 1977.   **Size:** 1,500 sq. ft.
President /Director: Phyllis Weil. Background: Collector.
Work shown: Contemporary Art. Painting, sculpture and photography.
Work by: Scott Duce: painting, oil and wax on board; Knut Marion: painting; Beth Ames Swartz: paintings; and Sharon Loper: bronze sculpture; among others.
Markets: Individual, corporate and museum. **Prices:** $1,200-25,000.
Focus/Mission: Being a private dealer allows Weil to nurture and assist her artists as their careers succeed. The gallery's artists exhibit in the U.S. and Europe.

WEST HARLEM ART FUND

Administrative Office: 530 West 143 St., 10031. **T:** (212) 690-0867.
E: sbaileymcc@aol.com   **W:** www.westharlemartfund.org
Open: Daily 9-9.   **Year established:** 1998.
Owner: The West Harlem Art Fund is a cultural arts and preservation organization with two gallery locations: Lobby Gallery at Audubon, 3960 Broadway at 166 St., and Gallery Space at Russ Berrie, 1150 St. Nicholas Ave., near 168 St., 10032.
Director: Savona Bailey-McCailen, liberal arts degree with a concentration in Black Studies, curator, and public speaker.
Work shown: Urban contemporary African and Latino art in all media including painting, mixed media, photography, work on paper, sculpture, and Outsider Art.
Work by: Exhibitions have featured James C. Best, Jr.; Rudy Gutierrez; Douglas Quackenbush; Soraya Marcano; and Clymenza Hawkins; among others.
Annual exhibitions: 4-5 at each location.
Focus/Mission: To clean up community parks for children and senior citizens and to also bring "Arts in the Park." WHAF understands that through arts and culture in open, public spaces, area residents can reclaim individual neighborhoods, share its beauty and preserve their history with others.
Selection process: Artists should call first to obtain written guidelines. Then they may mail slides or laser copies of their work, artist's statement, resumé, and SASE.
Additional information: The organization organizes private studio tours and other opportunities to meet the artists directly. It also presents concerts and other events including an annual outdoor art exhibition in May with musical entertainment.

WEST SIDE ARTS COALITION

Broadway Mall Community Center, on the center island at 96th and Broadway.
Mailing address: West Side Arts Coalition, Box 527, Cathedral Station, 10025.

T: (212) 316-6024.

E: wsany@aol.com

W: www.wsacny.com

Owner: A non-profit organization.

Size: 360 sq. ft. *org*

President: Peter Reyes.

Open: Wed. 6-8, Sat. and Sun. 12-6. Closed July and Aug.

Work shown: All styles and media.

Artists represented: 150 visual artists, 40 photographers. 50% male/female. All ages. All origins.

Focus/Mission: This is a non-profit space concerned with helping as many artists as possible. Quality and professionalism are stressed. The Coalition encompasses both visual and performing arts.

Annual exhibitions: 12 group shows in this space. The West Side Arts Coalition also organizes shows at Cork Gallery, Lincoln Center and other alternative spaces. The group also exhibits internationally.

Advertising: *Gallery & Studio.*

Collectors: Texaco Corporation; International World Company, Montreal Canada, Iberian Airlines; and Henri Pouget, Paris, France.

Selection process: Artists join without being juried, however, some exhibitions are juried individually. Annual membership fee is $40 per year with a one-time registration fee of $10. Exhibiting artists contribute very nominal fees toward exhibition expenses for only those shows in which they participate.

Additional information: The organization publishes a periodical newsletter, which highlights members' exhibitions and contains other art-related activities and opportunities. It is distributed to its members. Artists who are interested in membership should visit the gallery, call or send an email to the West Side Arts Coalition.

THE OUTER BOROUGHS

BROOKLYN
BRONX
QUEENS
STATEN ISLAND

THE PARLOR
"To make the ownership of fine art more accessible to all by displaying the work in an environment similar to the viewers' homes."

BROOKLYN

AJ FINE ARTS
6208 Mill Lane, 11234.
F: (718) 241-4389.
Open: By appointment.
Owner: Mark Schachner.
Annual exhibitions: 6.
T: (718) 531-7830.
W: www.nymuseum.com
Year established: 1980.
Director: Wayne Paris.

Work shown: Contemporary painting, graphics, and sculpture jewelry.
Work by: Will Barnet; Marc Chagall; Erte; Roy Lichtenstein; and Tom Wesselmann; among others.

ARENA@FEED
313 Clinton St., 11231.
T: (646) 734-2261.
E: arenagal@thing.net
Open: Sat. and Sun. 12-6 and by appointment.
Directors: Barry Hylton, Lisa Schroeder and Renée Ricardo.
Work shown: Contemporary art in all media by emerging artists.
Artists represented: 15.

continued

Work by: Cotter Luppi; Rande Darke; Rachel Harrison; Malcolm Hill; and Frank Webster; among others.
Selection process: The gallery is not interested in receiving submissions.

BROOKLYN COLLEGE
City University of New York, 2900 Bedford Ave 11210.   **T:** (718) 951-5882.
E: adoyle@brooklyn.cuny.edu   **Director/Curator:** Maria Catalano Rand.
Work shown: The gallery features exhibitions of Brooklyn community artists and international exhibitions, with one annual exhibition of women artists and one annual exhibition of minority artists. They will have MFA thesis exhibitions.
Focus/Mission: To educate the college and community about the multi-ethnic population that surrounds the college.
Selection process: Artists should send slides to the attention of Maria Catalano Rand, Art Dept. of Brooklyn College, 2900 Bedford Ave, Brooklyn, NY 11210-2889. They will be reviewed by a committee.

BELANTHI
142 Court St., 11201.   **T:** (718) 855-2769.
Open: Mon.-Sat. Call for hours.   **Size:** 2,400 sq. ft.
Year established: 1978.   **Owner/Director:** Paulette Hios.
Work shown: Contemporary art in all styles and media.
Prices: $100-25,000.
Artists represented: 20 or more. All ages. All origins.
Work by: John Arruda: paintings; Liz Holly: paintings; Jean Kroeber: sculpture; Philip Martin: paintings; and Mark Esper: paintings and sculpture; among others.
Collectors: Honolulu Academy of Arts and Boston Museum of Fine Arts.
Annual exhibitions: 8-10 solo/continuous group.
Focus/Mission: The gallery is dedicated to everything that is creative in man and nature – plants, the arts, music, poetry readings and recitals.
Selection process: Artists are selected from slides. The Director likes to see a cross-section of the artist's work that reflects strong craftsmanship and has something to say. Artists should visit the gallery, call, or mail 25-40 slides with SASE. **Response time:** 1 month.

BELLWETHER
335 Grand St., 11222.   **T:** (718) 387-3701.
W: www.bellwethergallery.com   **Year established:** 1999.
Size: 2,000 sq.ft.   **Director:** Rebecca Smith, artist. MFA,Yale.
Open: Fri.-Mon. 12-6 and by appointment.
Work shown: Work by emerging artists in all media.
Annual exhibitions: 14 solo/2 group. **Prices:** $200-2,000.
Work by: Exhibitions have featured Sarah Bedford: painting; Alison Smith: conceptual sculpture; Susan Black: video; Marc Swanson: sculpture and installation; and Matt Ducklo: photography; among others.
Focus/Mission: To be a peer-run space for emerging artists. The exhibitions are directed and curated in that manner with an advisory panel.
Selection process: Artists should mail slides or photographs with resumé and SASE.
Additional information: We have a flat file featuring works on paper by 50 emerging artists associated with the gallery.

BROOKLYN BOTANIC GARDEN STEINHARDT CONSERVATORY

1000 Washington Ave., 11225.   **T:** (718) 623-7200.
F: (718) 622-7839.   **W:** www.bbg.org
Year established: 1988.   **President:** Judith D. Zuk.
Open: April-September: Tues.-Fri. 10-5:30; October-March: Tues.-Fri. 10-4:30.
Admission: Adults 16-over $3. Adults 65-over: $1.50. Students with ID $1.50. Children under 16, frequent visitor pass holders, members, school groups free.
Work shown: Contemporary art on the subject of nature or work that has been influenced by the Brooklyn Botanic Garden.
Selection process: Contact Trish Lindemann, (718) 623-7227, for current policy.

BROOKLYN CHILDREN'S MUSEUM

145 Brooklyn Ave., 11213.   **T:** (718) 735-4400.
F: (718) 604-7442.   **E:** www.brooklynkids.org
Admission: Suggested donation $4. **Year established:** 1899.
Open: Wed.-Fri. 2-5, Sat., Sun. 10-5. Call for summer and holiday hours.
Focus/Mission: To actively engage children in educational and entertaining experiences through innovation and excellence in exhibitions, programs, and use of its collections.
Additional information: Call for group reservations.

BROOKLYN FIRE PROOF

101 Richardson St., 11211.   **T:** (718) 302-4702.
E: brooklynfire.proof@verizon.net   **W:** www.brooklynfire.proof.com
Open: By appointment.   **Year established:** 1999.
Size: 4,000 sq. ft.
Owner/Director: Burr Dodd, artist with background in financial investments.
Work shown: Wide range of Contemporary art in all media by primarily emerging artists in addition to established artists.
Prices: $100-10,000.   **Annual exhibitions:** 4-5.
Focus/Mission: To help motivate and facilitate the pursuit of human creativity in our complex environment. This artistic enterprise provides studio space, a darkroom, and future library with art fellowship / grant information.
Selection process: Artists are encouraged to visit. Please do not send slides.
Requirements: Artists are selected for their commitment to artistic expression, with special attention given to original and emotional content.

BROOKLYN MUSEUM OF ART

200 Eastern Parkway, 11238.   **T:** (718) 638-5000.
E: information@brookynmuseum.org   **W:** www.brooklynmuseum.org
Year established: 1823.   **Director:** Arnold L. Lehman.
Annual exhibitions: 20.   **Size:** 450,000 sq. ft.
Open: Wed.-Fri. 10-5, Sat. and Sun. 11-6. The first Sat. of every month the museum is open from 11-11.
Admission: Suggested donations: $6 adults; $3 students/seniors; free for members and children under 12.
Focus/Mission: As the second largest art museum in NYC, it possesses a permanent collection that represents almost every culture and includes more than 1 ½ million objects, from ancient Egyptian masterpieces to Contemporary art.

continued

Selection process: Artists should contact the appropriate department to find out the requirements for obtaining exhibitions.

Additional information: The museum presents a range of programs for adults and children including movies, lectures, and performances.

BROOKLYN PUBLIC LIBRARY

Grand Army Plaza, 11238.　　**T:** (718) 230-2122.
W: www.brooklynpubliclibrary.org　**Year established:** 1998.
Open: Mon.-Thurs. 9-8, Fri. and Sat. 9-6, Sun. 1-5.
Work shown: Contemporary art.
Focus/Mission: A forum for the great variety of artwork from this region. To bring into focus the dialogue between the written word in books and its visual expression in artwork.
Annual exhibitions: 20, within the many exhibition and display spaces.
Selection process: Artists should mail slides/photographs and resumé to the attention of: Florence Neil, Willendorf Division, Brooklyn Public Library, Grand Army Plaza, Brooklyn, NY 11238.

BROOKLYN PUBLIC LIBRARY, CARIBBEAN, LITERARY and CULTURAL CENTER FLATBUSH GALLERY

22 Linden Blvd., 11226.　　**T:** (718) 230-2122.
Year established: 1897.　　**Work shown:** Contemporary Art by Caribbean and Caribbean-American artists. All media.
Annual exhibitions: 4-6.
Selection process: Artists should mail slides and photographs, resumé and other materials to the Attention of: Manager for the Caribbean Literary and Culture Center, Brooklyn Public Library, 22 Linden Blvd., Brooklyn, NY 11226.

BRUSHSTROKES FINE ART

4612 Thirteenth Ave., 11219.　　**T:** (718) 972-0682.
F: (718) 972-3642.
Open: Sun-Mon., Wed., Thurs. 11:30-6:30, Fri. 11-1:30, Tues. by appointment.
Work shown: Oil paintings and lithographs on Jewish themes.
Work by: Elena Flerova; Itshak Holtz; Zvi Mainovitzer; Anton Rosenberg; and Yossi Rosenstein; among others.

CAVE

58 Grand St., 11211.　　**T:** (718) 388-6780.
Director: Shige Moriya　　**Open:** Fri.-Sun. 1-6 and by appointment.
Year established: 1996. An experimental performance and exhibition space.
Owners: Shige Moriya and Naoki Iwakawa.
Work shown: Contemporary art in all media.
Artists represented: 5.　　**Annual exhibitions:** 9.
Work by: Zana Wimmer; Naoki Iwakawa; Michael Krynski; Ür; and Rodney Dickson; among others.
Focus/Mission: An alternative space devoted to experimentation in visual and performance art. It responds to the ways technology and modern conveniences tend to pull us away from our creativity, blocking avenues of spiritual expression. In this space artists are able to influence one another through experiencing each other's individual expressions, deepening their personal practices and creativity.

Selection process: Artists should mail slides, artist's statement, and SASE. Shige Moriya will call to arrange an appointment. **Response time:** 1 month.

CH'I: AN ART SPACE

184 Kent Ave., #511, 11211. **T:** (718) 302-3689.
E: tracy@qianartspace.com **W:** www.qianartspace.com
Size: 500 sq. ft. **Open:** Wed.-Fri. 6-9 and Sat.-Mon. 12-8.
Year established: 2000. **Director:** Tracy Causey-Jeffery.
Background: Degrees in Asian Art and Art History, former Director of Finer Side Gallery, Maryland and Washington, DC
Work shown: Painting, photography, sculpture and mixed media by emerging and mid-career artists. **Artists represented:** 17. All origins.
Annual exhibitions: 10. **Prices:** $1,000-20,000.
Work by: Yoshio Itagaki: photography/computer-generated; Liu Jian: acrylic on canvas; Sy Gresser: hand carved stone; Michel Demanche: paintings/print works/ constructions; and Scott Cawood: sculpture; among others.
Focus/Mission: The name Ch'i comes from the ancient Taoist concept of life energy, vital energy or life's breath. The Director believes art, especially by currently living artists, is a vital part of our daily environment and culture. Her desire is to showcase artists and connect them with collectors so that the clients gain some ch'i for their own personal environments and the artists are enabled to continue to create and so strengthen our cultural energy.
Selection process: We review artists' materials on an on-going basis. We prefer the artist become familiar with the styles of the gallery before submitting materials. Artists should send slides, resumé, and SASE or send digital images via email.
Additional Information: Receptions are usually held the 2nd Fri. each month.

DUMBO ARTS CENTER

30 Washington St., 11201 **T:** (718) 624-3772.
E: mail@dumboartscenter.org **W:** www.dumboartscenter.org
Open: Th.- Mon. 12-6. **Year established:** 1997
Size: 3,000 sq. ft. **Director:** Joy Glidden.
Work shown: Emerging artists. 40% of the artists are from Brooklyn.
Annual exhibitions: 5.
Focus/mission: To preserve and enrich the identity of DUMBO as an artists community. To promote the work of emerging artists, collaborating with other organizations and maintain an artists' slide file.
Selection process: Artists should send slides and resume, or deliver to 70 Washington St. #505, 11201.
Additional Information: The organization presents an annual Fall arts festival, Winter auction, lectures and artwalks.

EYEWASH

143 North 7 St., 4th floor, 11211. **T:** (718) 387-2714.
W: www.eyewash.cc **Open:** Sat. and Sun. 1-6.
Year established: 1998. **Owner:** Larry Walczak.
Directors: Larry Walczak and Annie Herron.
Work shown: Contemporary art in all media with an emphasis on painting and installation.
Annual exhibitions: 5-6. *continued*

Work by: Jeannne Tremel; Sante Scardillo; Robin Michals; Thomas Broadbent; and Angela Wyman; among others.
Focus/Mission: This is a migratory gallery with an emphasis on experimental exhibitions and public art projects.
Selection process: We have an open viewing process. We look at submissions throughout the year. Artists should mail slides or photographs, resumé and SASE.
Response time: 2 ½ months.

FIGUREWORKS

168 North 6 St., 11211.　　　　　**T:** (718) 486-7021.
W: www.figureworks.com　　　　**Open:** Fri.-Mon. 1-6 and by appointment.
Size: 600 sq. ft.　　　　　　　**Year established:** 2000.
Owner/Director: Randall Harris, BFA from the University of Southern Maine.
Work shown: Contemporary Figurative art in all media.
Prices: $100-800.　　　　　　**Artists represented:** 10-20.
Work by: Arlene Morris: pastel; Randall Harris: oil pastel; Barry Steely: rapidograph drawings; George Alvarez: murals; and Paul Hollingsworth: floor cloths; among others.
Focus/Mission: To show fine art of the human form.
Annual exhibitions: 6 solo/2 group.
Selection process: Artists should mail photographs (preferred) or slides with resumé and SASE. **Response time:** 2-3 weeks.

FISH TANK

93 North 6 St., 11211.　　　　　**T:** (718) 387-4320.
W: www.fishtankgallery.net　　　**Year established:** 2000.
Director: Hilario Nuno.　　　　　**Creative Director:** Amadeo Penalver.
Open: Fri.-Mon. 12-6 and by appointment.
Work shown: Experimental Contemporary art with an emphasis on painting.
Artists represented: 6.　　　　**Annual exhibitions:** 9.
Work by: William Norton; Amadeo Penalver; Pan Xing Lei; Fernando Renes; and Peter Drake.
Focus/Mission: To support the medium of painting and all the action around painting. We believe in experimental with a strong academic background. Our exhibitions represent different philosophic visions.
Selection process: Painters may send slides and/or photographs, résumé, and SASE.

FLIPSIDE

84 Withers St., 3rd floor, 11211.　**T:** (718) 389-7108.
W: www.flipsideart.com　　　　**Open:** Sun. 1-6 and by appointment.
Year established: 1997.
Owners/Directors: Caroline Cox and Tim Spelios, both artists.
Work shown: Very eclectic range of art by emerging and established artists including video, painting, photography, installation, sculpture, and work on paper.
Annual exhibitions: 5.
Focus/Mission: To provide an exhibition space for the exchange of diverse ideas and ways of working.
Selection process: The gallery usually views slides during the summer. Artists should call for details.

FOUR WALLS PROJECTS

138 Bayard St., 11222.   **T:** (718) 388-3169.
Open: By appointment.   **Year established:** 1991.
Owner: Mike Ballou, artist, who studied with Siah Armajani.
Work shown: Collaborative and interdisciplinary.
Focus/Mission: To set up a condition for the exchange of different ideas.
Selection process: We don't look at slides. We prefer to meet with the artist to discuss the projects. Artists should call for additional information.

FRONT ROOM

147 Roebling St., 11211.   **T:** (718) 782-2556.
Open: Sat. - Mon. 1-6 and by appt.   **E:** soapboxnyc@cs.com
W: www.frontroom.org   **Year established:** 1999.
Director: Daniel Aycock.   **Annual exhibitions:** 10
Work shown: All media, especially video and installation
Selection process: Send slides or email or drop by gallery.

GALAPAGOS ART SPACE

70 North 6 St., 11211.   **T:** (718) 782-5188.
W: www.galapagosartspace.com/gallery.html
Open: Daily 6 pm-2 am.
Owner/Director: Robert Elmes. This is an art and performance space.
Work shown: Contemporary art. Exhibitions have featured Katherine Zuckerman: paintings; among others.
Selection process: Artists should contact Robert Elmes or John Wyszniewski.

GALE GATES ET AL.

37 Main St., 11201.   **T:** (718) 522-4596.
F: (718) 522-0082.   **E:** info@galegates.org
W: www.galegatese.org   **Open:** Wed.- Sat. 12-6 and by appointment.
Year established: 1995 in Manhattan, 1997 in this location.
Owner: A non-profit organization, performance and art space.
Artistic Director: Michael Counts.   **Annual exhibitions:** 4-6.
Work shown: All styles and media. Painting, sculpture, video and installation.
Focus/Mission: To support the work of emerging curators and emerging artists.
Selection process: Emerging curators select artists. Artists should send slides, resumé and biography, with SASE to the attention of the Visual Arts Program. They will be considered for the permanent slide file.

GOLIATH

117 Dobbin St., 11222.   **T:** (718) 389-0369.
E: goliath777@earthlink.net   **W:** www.goliath777.com
Year established: 1998.   **Owners/Directors:** Erik Guzman and
Mayumi Hayashi, artists and graduates of the School of Visual Arts.
Open: Sat. and Sun. 1-6 and by appointment.
Artists represented: 50+. All origins.
Work shown: Contemporary art in all media.
Work by: Dean Brown; James Cullinane; Thomas Lail; Karen Mirza; and Arimichi Iwasawa.

continued

Focus/Mission: Goliath has been established as a place external to existing models in which art is usually shown. A place, open for a variety of viewpoints which exist outside the establishment, often too complex and uncertain for direct means or definite proclamations. **Annual exhibitions:** 4.
Selection process: Artists should mail slides, resumé and SASE or may send images via email. Directors will try to visit artist's studio. **Response time:** 1 year.
Additional information: The gallery presents artists' talks and performances. There is no gallery commission taken on sales.

HOLLAND TUNNEL

61 South 3 St., 11211.　　　　　　**T/F:** (718) 384-5738.
E:hollandtunnel@hotmail.com　　**W:** www.hollandtunnel.com
Year established: 1997　　　　　**Owner/Director:** Pauline Lethen.
Open: Sat. and Sun. 1-5 and by appointment.
Work shown: Contemporary art by international artists in all media.
Artists represented: Susan Daboll: photography; Larry Webb; Bix Lye; and Jacques Roch; among others.　　**Annual exhibitions:** 10
Additional Information: The gallery maintains a flat file.

PRISKA JUSCHKA FINE ART

212 Berry St., 11211.　　　　　　**T/F:** (718) 384-5738.
E: gallery@priskajuschkafineart.com **W:** www.priskajuschkafineart.com
Year established: 2001　　　　　**Owner:** Priska C. Juschka.
Open: Wed.–Fri. 12-6pm, Sat. and Sun. 1-6pm, Mon. by appointment.
Work shown: Contemporary art in all media.
Artists represented: Ernesto Pujol.　**Prices:** $800 - $4,000

KENTLER INTERNATIONAL DRAWING SPACE

353 Van Brunt St., 11231.　　　　**T/F:** (718) 875-2098.
E: info@kentlergallery.org　　　**W:** www.kentlergallery.org
Year established: 1990.　　　　　**Open:** Fri.-Sun., 1-5 By appointment.
Size: 300 sq. ft.
Owner: Non-profit organization.
Director: Florence A. Neal, artist.
Work shown: Drawings and work on paper.
Prices: $100-6,000.
Annual exhibitions: 8 solo/2 group.
Markets: Individual, corporate, and museum.
Advertising: *Brooklyn Bridge* and *Waterfront Week*.
Selection process: 40% of the artists are selected from professional referrals, 30% from slides sent to the gallery, and 30% from art seen in exhibitions and artists studios. Artists, collaborators, and curators are invited to send a proposal description, slides, resumé and SASE. Artists should visit the gallery. Shows and events are scheduled a year in advance.
Response time: 2 months. Slides will be kept on file for viewing in the Kentler gallery unless otherwise requested return with SASE.
Requirements: Artists are responsible for the installation, reception, gallery sitting, and preparation of the gallery for the next show.
Additional Information: The gallery maintains a flat file and a slide file.

KINGSBOROUGH COMMUNITY COLLEGE

City University of New York, 2001 Oriental Blvd., 11235. **T:** (718) 368-5449.
F: (718) 368-4872.   **Open:** Mon.-Thurs. 10-4, Fri.10-2.
Year established: 1970.   **Director:** Peter Malone.
Size: 2,500 sq. ft.   **Work shown:** Contemporary art in all media.
Work by: Exhibiting artists have included Robert Arneson; Deborah Brown; Fred Scruton; Lois Dodd; among others. **Annual exhibitions:** 5.
Focus/Mission: To present to the college community and to the community at large, historical and contemporary art exhibitions reflecting outstanding achievement in fine art, graphic design, illustration, and design.
Selection process: Artists are selected by invitation, although we review slides, but we cannot guarantee the return of unsolicited materials.

DAVID LINKER

159 India St., Apt. 1, 11222.   **T:** (718) 349-2823.
E: dlinkebn@erols.com.   **W:** www.davidlinker.com.
Open: By appointment.   **Year established:** 1996.
Owner/Director: David Linker, Ebeniste antique furniture restorer. Trained in France and Holland 1967-1981.
Markets: Individual, corporate and museum.   **Prices:** $1,000 and above.
Work by: Jules Franck Mondoloni: sculpture and painting.
Advertising: *Gallery Guide, Art in America* and www.artnet.com.

LONG ISLAND UNIVERSITY GALLERIES: SALENA and RESNICK

One University Plaza, 11201.   **T:** (718) 488-1198.
F: (718) 488-1372.   **W:** www.liu.edu/bfastu
E: nancy.grove@liu.edu   **Open:** Mon.-Fri. 9-6, Sat.and Sun. 10-5.
Year established: 1986.   **Owner:** Long Island University.
Director: Bob Barry.   **Assistant Director:** Liz Rudey
Gallery Manager: Nancy Grove.   **Work shown:** All styles and media.
Annual exhibitions: 12.   **Advertising:** *Gallery Guide.*
Focus/Mission: To give emerging artists exhibition space in a university. Diversity of art work is important in this educational setting.
Selection process: Artists should submit their slides and other materials, with SASE. **Response time:** 1 month.
Additional information: The Annual Outdoor Sculpture Exhibition is curated by a well-known New York curator.

METAPHOR CONTEMPORARY ART

70 Washington St., Suite 1113, 11201. **T:**(646) 321-2370.
Open: Fri.-Sun. 12-6.   **E:** contact@metaphorcontemporaryart.com
W: metaphorcontemporaryart.com   **Year established:** 2001.
Owners/Directors: Julian Jackson and Rene Lynch, artists.
Work shown: Contemporary art in all media.
Annual exhibitions: 8-9.
Work by: Tricia Wright: painting; Holly Sears: painting; Jim Osman: sculpture; Janet Pihlblad: sculpture; and Madelon Galland: sculpture and prints.
Selection process: Artists may send slides and/or photographs and resumé with SASE.

MICRO MUSEUM

123 Smith St., 11201.
F: (718) 855-1208.
W: www.micromuseum.com

T: (718) 797-3116.
E:executive@micromuseum.com
Open: Daily by appointment.

Year established: 1995. It was incorporated as Promote Art Works, Inc., as an established art center in the early 1980s. **Director:** Kathleen Laziza.
Work shown: Interactive, kinetic sculpture and media art.
Annual exhibitions: 1group/monthly events. The artists' programs in painting, video, dance, sculpture, music, computer and environment produce leading-edge interdisciplinary works that apply creativity to contemporary technology.
Advertising: *ARTnews* and *Gallery Guide.*
Focus/Mission: To be a creative laboratory to support emerging and established artists working in different disciplines, in their artistic and economic growth, in exhibitions, public access television and their web site. To unite artists with the residential community and young people through participation in festivals, after-school programs and gallery talks. Our model youth program, SEED/ROOT has provided job training and placement through other local community institutions.
Selection process: Artists should inquire by phone.

MOMENTA ART

72 Berry St., 11211.
W: www.momentaart.org
Owner: Not-for-profit corporation.

T: (718) 218-8058.
Open: Fri.-Mon. 12-6.
Director: Eric Heist.

Assistant Director: Michael Waugh.
Year established: 1986 in PA, 1993 in NYC.
Work shown: All styles and all media of emerging artists, with an emphasis on, but not exclusive to, installation. **Annual exhibitions:** 7.
Focus/Mission: To increase the public's awareness of emerging artists' work, under-represented in the traditional exhibition forum, through highly focused presentations.
Selection process: Artists should send up to 20 slides with resumé and SASE.
Additional information: Artists are each given separate project rooms, allowing them the distinct opportunity to present a substantial body of work, focusing attention on their specific ideas. The culturally diverse Williamsburg community is considered an integral part of the exhibition process in that much of the work exhibited is created in this vibrant, creative community and many of the issues address concerns of the community at large.

MONK

301 Bedford Ave., 11211.
E: valessa@monkgallery.com
Year established: 1997.

T: (718) 782-2458.
W: www.monkgallery.com
Artists represented: 30.

Owner/Director: Valessa Monk, MA in Sculpture, graduated from Pratt Institute.
Open: Sat. and Sun. 12-6 and by appointment.
Work shown: Contemporary art in all media by artists from all origins.
Work by: The Astroturf Group: installation; Edward Manovich: drawing and painting; Liz and Val: installation; Christian Puopoll: painting and sculpture; Brenda Bradley: installation. **Annual exhibitions:** 7.
Selection process: Artists may mail slides and/or photographs or a video with resumé and SASE. They may also call to make an appointment.

Response time: 1 month.

Additional information: The gallery organizes performance and multi-media events outside the gallery.

JESSICA MURRAY PROJECTS

210 North 6 St., 11211.　　　　**T:** (718)384-9606.

E: jessicabmurray@hotmail.com　**Open:** Fri.- Sun., 12-6 and by appointment.

Year established: 2001.　　　　**Size:** 1200 sq. ft.

Owner/Director: Jessica Murray, curator.

Work shown: Emerging international artists in all media.

Work by: Franco Mondidn-Ruiz: sculpture and installation; Scott Teplin: drawings and books; Chris Doyle: public artworks, video, and work on paper; Alejandro Diaz: painting; Susan Daboll: photography.

Annual exhibitions: 8.　　　　**Prices:** $200 - $10,000.

Focus/Mission: To show the best of emerging art in all media in solo and curated exhibitions.

Additional Information: The gallery has small drawing room presentations, publications and other activities.

PARKER'S BOX

193 Grand St., 11211.　　　　**T:** (718) 388-2882.

E: parkersbox@hotmail.com　**W:**www.parkers.com

Year established: 2000.　　　**Open:** Fri.-Mon. 1-7 and by appointment.

Director: Alun Williams, artist, trained at Goldsmith College in London.

Work shown: Art that deals with the problematics of painting and sculpture through all media including painting, sculpture, photography, video and installation. Artists from Europe in context with artists from New York.

Work by: Joshua Stern: photography; Stefan Sehler: painting; Maggie Kleinpeter: painting; Janine Lariviere: photography; and Caroline McCarthy: sculpture and installation; among others.　　　**Annual exhibitions:** 5.

Selection process: Artists should mail slides and/or photographs, resumé and artist's statement with SASE by mail or may send digital files via email.

Additional information: Parker's Box has strong links with exhibition spaces and curatorial projects internationally including organizations that they have founded such as an international residency exhibition program in Marseilles. Several artists that exhibit in the gallery have come from these programs.

THE PARLOR

305 Vanderbilt Avenue, 11205.　**T:** (718)-789-2545

E: kthayek@aol.com　　　　**W:** www.parlorgallery.com

Owner: Kathleen Hayek, artist　**Open:** Tues. -Sun. by appointment

Year established: 1998.　　　**Annual exhibitions:** 2-6

Work shown: Primarily works on paper by local artists.

Focus/Mission: To make the ownership of fine art more accessible to all by displaying the work in an environment similar to the viewers' homes. To inspire artists to work cooperatively by hosting solo and small exhibits of local fine artists, thereby developing a thriving arts community of artists and art collectors.

Additional Information: The gallery also functions as a meeting place for the South Of the Navy Yard Artists (SONYA), and is a regular participant in SONYA's Open Studio Tour each May and October.

PIEROGI

177 North 9 St., 11211.
W: www.pierogi2000.com
Year established: 1994.
Work shown: Original art in all media. **Annual exhibitions:** 9-10.
T: (718) 599-2144.
Open: Fri.-Mon. 12-6 and by appointment.
Owner/Director: Joe Amrhein, artist.
Work by: Phyllis Baldino; Steven Charles; Jane Fine; Robert Lazzarini; and Mark Lombardi; among others.
Focus/Mission: To exhibit the work of emerging artists, both local and international, with a focus on solo shows. To feature the ever-expanding flat files which contain original works by over 600 artists.
Selection: Artists should mail slides and/or photographs, resumé and artist's statement with SASE.

ROEBLING HALL

390 Wythe Ave., 11211.
E: info@brooklynart.com
T: (718) 599-5352.
W: www.brooklynart.com
Open: Fri.-Mon. 12-6 and by appointment.
Year established: 1998. Formerly named Salon 75.
Owners/Directors: Joel Beck, painter; and Christian Viveros-Faune, art critic.
Work by: Kenn Bass; Sabastiaan Bremer; Heidi Cody; Sheila Moss; and David Opkyke; among others.

ROME ARTS

103 Havemeyer St., 11211.
Year established: 2000.
T: (718) 388-2009.
Owner/Director: Daniel Carello.
Open: Sat. and Sun. 12-6 and by appointment.
Work shown: Current practices developing in the visual arts.
Work by: Andrea Corson: sculpture; Lee Quinones: painting; Millie Benson: painting; Pedro Gomez: painting and sculpture; and Colin Keefe: sculpture.
Selection process: Artists should send slides and/or photographs, resumé, and SASE.

ROTUNDA

33 Clinton St., 11201.
F: (718) 488-0609.
T: (718) 875-4047.
W: www.brooklynx.org
Open: Tues.-Fri. 12-5, Sat. 11-4. Summer: Mon.-Thurs. 9-5, Fri. 9-2.
Year established: 1981.
Size: 600 sq. ft.
Owner: Non-profit exhibition space, project of the BRIC, (Brooklyn Information and Culture) formerly Fund for the Borough of Brooklyn.
Director: Janet Riker.
Associate Director: Meredith McNeal.
Work shown: Contemporary art, computer-generated art, video, sound installation, paintings, sculpture and photography.
Work by: Exhibitions have featured Judy Pfaff: sculpture/installation; Maria Elena Gonzalez: installation; Susan Leopold: installation; and Juan Sanchez: painting; among others.
Annual exhibitions: 5. Advertising: *Gallery Guide, Art in America, ARTnews*.
Focus/Mission: To exhibit the diversity of contemporary art in the borough.
Selection process: Artists who have a Brooklyn residence or studio should send slides with cover letter, resumé, and a slide registry application, which can be found on their website.

RUBELLE and NORMAN SCHAFLER, PRATT INSTITUTE

200 Willoughby Ave., Chemistry Building, 11205. **T:** (718) 636-3517.
W: www.pratt.edu/exhibitions   **Year established:** 1985.
Size: 2,300 sq. ft.   **Owner:** Pratt Institute.
Acting Director of Exhibitions: Nick Battis
Open: Mon.-Fri. 9-5; June-Aug. Mon.-Fri. 9-4.
Work shown: Contemporary art in all media.
Annual exhibitions: 9.   **Advertising:** *Gallery Guide.*
Focus/Mission: To present group exhibitions on issues of interest in contemporary fine arts, design, and architecture.
Selection process: Beginning in September, 2002, the gallery will shift its primary focus to artwork by Pratt students and faculty.
Additional Info: The gallery presents lectures. Programming changes will be made in September. Call for information.

HOWARD SCHICKLER

45 Main St., Studio 402, 11201.   **T:** (212) 431-6363.
E: info@schickler.com   **W:** schicklerart.com
Open: Tues.-Fri. 10-5:30 and by appointment.
Year established: 1975.   **Owner/Director:** Howard Schickler.
The gallery was originally located in SoHo.
Work shown: European avant-garde art, photography, and rare books.
19th and 20th Century astronomy and space exploration photography.
Work by: Photography by Edwin E. Aldrin; William Anders; Herb Greene; Graham Nash; and Richard Pare; among others.

SIDESHOW

319 Bedford Ave., 11211.   **T:**(718) 486-8180.
E: sideshowgallery@aol.com   **Open:** Fri.-Mon. 12-6 and by appt.
Year established: 1997.   **Owner/Director:** Richard Timperio.
Work shown: Contemporary art in all media including installations, sculpture, paintings, photography and works on paper.
Work by: Chris Martin: painting; Michael Talley and Elizabeth Cohen: video installation; Jill Corson: photography; TODT: installation; and Don Christensen: painting. **Annual exhibitions:** 10.
Selection process: Artists should send slides and/or photographs, resumé, and SASE. **Response time:** 1-2 months.
Additional information: The gallery also presents readings and music series.

65 HOPE ST. CERAMIC ART

65 Hope St., 11211.   **T:** (718) 963-2028.
E: hopestreetceramics@yahoo.com**W:** www.tigerblue.com/65hope
Year established: 2000.   **Open:** Sat. and Sun. 12-6 and by appt.
Director: Rina Pellig. This is a cooperative gallery.
Work shown: Ceramic and sculpture.
Artist members: 10.   **Annual exhibitions:** 10.
Work by: Meg Levine; Katrina Jeffries; Rina Pellig; Kathleen Moroney: and Laura Hammond.
Additional information: There is a ceramics studio on the premises.

STUDIO FACCHETTI

195 Grand St., 11211

E: studiofacchetti@mac.com

Open: Wed.-Mon. 11-7.

T: (718) 486-9331.

W: www.studiofacchetti.com

Year established: 2000.

Owner/Director: Bruno Facchetti. **Annual exhibitions:** 10.

Work shown: Contemporary art in all media.

Work by: Auguste Garufe: sculpture and painting; Fernando Molero: painting; Ralph Hassard: painting; Anthony Cafrit: sculpture; and Patcie Lerochereuil: sculpture, drawings, installation, and other media.

Selection process: Artists should mail slides and/or photographs, resumé, and SASE.

SKYLIGHT

At the Center for Art and Culture of Bedford Stuyvesant

1368 Fulton St., 3rd floor, 11216.   **T:** (718) 636-6948.

W: www.restorationplaza.org or www.nyc-arts.org

Open: Tues.-Fri. 11-7, Sat. 11-5.   **Admission:** $2 suggested donation.

Director: Eric Pryor.   **Size:** 2,000 sq. ft.

Work shown: Predominantly painting, photography, drawing and sculpture; sometimes crafts, video, and performance by established and emerging artists of African descent.

Work by: James "Jimmy" Green: painting; Chief Komalafe: sculpture; Jewel Golden: painting.

Annual exhibitions: 12 solo and group.

Focus/Mission: To present, promote, and preserve the multi-cultural legacy related to the Bedford Stuyvesant community. Program Vision: To be the cultural link between Bedford Stuyvesant Restoration Corp. and the community, through provision of exceptional arts education, exhibition, literary and Artist-in-Residence program.

Selection process: Artists should approach the gallery anytime by submitting proposals with slides, documentation about their work, resumé and/or biography, and budget. Art organizations may also apply as a group.

Additional information: The gallery was designed by architect I.M. Pei. It also houses the Abra-Ka-Zebra gift shop.

SUMMA

152 Montague St., 11201.   **T:** (718) 875-1647.

Year established: 1968.   **Directors:** Donald Pandina and Sal Cigna.

Open: Tues., Wed., Fri., Sat. 10-6:30, Thurs. 10-8, Sun. 12-5.

Work shown: Contemporary paintings, pastels, watercolors, and graphics.

Work by: Jim Buckles; Roy Fairchild; Kaiko Moti; and Frederick Mershimer; among others.

Selection process: Artists should send slides and SASE.

31 GRAND

31 Grand St., 11211.   **T:** (718) 388-2858.

E: gallery31grand@earthlink.net   **W:** www.31grand.com

Year established: 1999.   **Size:** 2,000 sq. ft.

Open: Sat. and Sun. 1-7 and by appointment.

Owners/Directors: Megan Bush: clothing designer; Heather Stevens, graphic designer; Diane Vasil, photographer; and Karen Flood, costume designer.
Directors: Megan Bush and Melissa Cliver.
Work shown: Contemporary art in all media.
Annual exhibitions: 8.
Selection process: Our doors are always open to receiving materials from artists and curators by mail or email. Artists receive 60% of sales.

URBAN GLASS

647 Fulton St., 11217.
F: (718) 625-3889.
W: www.urbanglass.com
Year established: 1978.
T: (718) 625-3685.
E: urbanglass@aol.com
Open: Mon.-Fri. 10-6.
Director: Dawn Bennett.
Owner: Non-profit organization. This is an artist access space. Artists rent time and the use of the equipment.
Work shown: Glass sculpture.   **Annual exhibitions:** 4.
Selection process: Exhibition selections are made by Dawn Bennett. The gallery is not interested in receiving unsolicited materials from artists.
Additional information: There are classes in stained glass, glass blowing, lampworking, neon, kiln cast glass, kiln fired glass, mold making and mosaic. Urban Glass publishes *Glass,* a critical quarterly magazine.

WILLIAMSBURG ART & HISTORICAL CENTER

135 Broadway, 11211.
W: www.wahcenter.org
Founder: Yuko Nii, painter.
Year established: 1996.
T: (718) 486-7372 or (718) 486-6012.
Owner: Non-profit organization.
Executive Director: Terrance Lindall.
Open: Sat. and Sun. 12-6, Mon. by appointment.
Size: 4 separate galleries comprising 10,000 sq. ft.
Work shown: Contemporary, historical, and performance art. All media including painting, sculpture, photography, film, video, and computer-generated art.
Work by: 1,200 artists each year.   **Annual exhibitions:** 40.
Advertising: *Village Voice* and *New York Times.*
Focus/Mission: To invite emerging local artists as well as nationally and internationally established artists to come together through the universal language of the arts. To serve the community of Williamsburg, the Borough of Brooklyn, the city of New York and beyond.
Selection process: Artists should mail slides, photographs, biography, resumé and SASE. Artists should call for an appointment. **Response time:** 2 months.
Additional information: The Center also presents performances and lectures. It is housed in a landmark structure built in 1867. It is the 7th building in NYC to be given landmark status.

YWCA OF BROOKLYN: SECOND FLOOR

30 Third Ave., 11217.
F: (718) 858-5731.
Open: Mon.-Fri. 9-5.
Year established: 1989.
T: (718) 875-1190.
E: jcook78@aol.com.
Size: 2,200 sq. ft.
Curator: Joe Cook.
Work shown: Contemporary art in various media.

continued

Work by: Exhibitions have featured Joe Cook: cityscapes in oil; Folk art and expressionistic work by Diane Grazzette Collins and Jose James; Linda Gilbert Schneider: travel and nature photography; Jan Hoogenboon's lyric myths in watercolor and Noon Gourfain: surrealistic ceramics and portraits among others. Theme shows of Outsider art, Women's art, African American art and Gay art along with winter and summer group exhibits. **Annual exhibitions:** 12.

Focus/Mission: The Second Floor of the YWCA of Brooklyn is primarily for local emerging artists, in particular women and people of color.

Selection process: Artists should call for an appointment or email Joe Cook.

BRONX

THE BRONX MUSEUM OF THE ARTS

1040 Grand Concourse, at 165 St., 10456. **T:**(718) 681-6000.
F: (718) 681-6181.   **Year established:** 1971.
Director: Jenny Dixon.   **Open:** Wed. 12-9, Thurs.-Sun. 12-6, $3 general admission, $2 seniors students, free for children under 12 and on Wed.

Work shown: Work by emerging, mid-career and established artists, that reflects a broad range of Modernist and Contemporary art tendencies, from Abstraction, Constructivism, and Surrealism to Conceptual and Performance art.

Focus/Mission: To serve the ethnically diverse populations of the Bronx and to stimulate audience participation primarily through the visual arts. Its permanent collection reflects the museum's surrounding communities and constituents, comprised primarily of African American and Latino populations, as well as a growing number of Asian American communities in the metropolitan area.

Selection process: The "Artist in the Marketplace (AIM) Program" is a free seminar program for emerging N.Y. metropolitan artists. Participating artists are featured in an exhibition at the museum. Call: (718) 681-6000 ext. 143.

Additional Information: The museum has a café on the premises

BRONX RIVER ART CENTER

1087 East Tremont Ave., 10460.   **T:** (718) 589-5819.
E: info@bronxriverart.org   **W:** www.bronxriverart.org
Open: Mon.-Fri. 3-6, Sat. 12-5. **Year established:** 1980.
Owner: Not-for-profit organization. **Director:** Gail Nathan.
Annual exhibitions: 5.   **Work shown:** Paintings, photographs, prints, sculpture, and experimental works with culturally diverse themes.

Focus/Mission: To offer emerging and established artists a place to create and exhibit their works. It is a forum where new, experimental, and provocative ideas can be explored and presented for public debate.

Selection process: Artists should call or mail slides, resumé and SASE.

Additional information: The Artist Space Program aims to create a multi-cultural environment where professional artists of all backgrounds can communicate while pursuing their own work. Art Training Programs for the Bronx Community include free after school art classes for youths ages 9-19.

HOSTOS COMMUNITY COLLEGE/CUNY

450 Grand Concourse, 10451.   **T:** (718) 518-6700.
Open: Mon.-Fri. 10-6, Sat. 10-2.   **Year established:** 1985.
Size: 2,000 sq. ft.   **Director:** Wallace Edgecombe.
Work shown: Contemporary art in all styles and media. Painting, photography,
sculpture and installation.   **Annual exhibitions:** 4.
Selection process: Artists should send slides, resumé and SASE to Wallace
Edgecombe.

KRASDALE

400 Food Center Drive, 10474.   **T:** (718) 378-1100.
Year established: 1986.   **Open:** Mon.-Fri. 10-5 by appointment.
Director: Sigmund R. Balka.   **Annual exhibitions:** 6-8.
Work shown: 20th Century Modern and Contemporary art in all media by artists
from all geographical areas.
Focus/Mission: To provide artists museum quality exhibits reviewed regularly by
the *New York Times*. It is considered a leading alternative exhibition space. To
present to the general public as well as employees and visitors challenging art in
a corporate environment, provoking thought, while enhancing the workplace.
Selection process: Artists should mail slides, photographs, CD or video, resumé,
and SASE.

LEHMAN COLLEGE

250 Bedford Park Blvd. West, Lehman College Campus, 10468.
T: (718) 960-8731.   **F:** (718) 960-8212.
E: susan@lehman.cuny.edu   **W:** ca80.lehman.cuny.edu/gallery/web/AG/
Year established: 1984.   **Size:** 4,075 sq. ft.
Director: Susan Hoeltzel.   **Associate Director:** Mary Ann Siano.
Open: Tues.-Sat.10-4. July Mon.-Thurs. 10-4, Aug. by appointment.
Owner: Not-for-profit organization incorporated separately from the college.
Work shown: Contemporary art in all media by emerging artists as well as
leading national and international figures. Also, significant theme shows.
Advertising: *Gallery Guide.*
Work by: Exhibitions have featured Lisa Corinne Davis: mixed media; Monica
Bravo: video installation; and Alice Adams: public art; among others.
Focus/Mission: To exhibit artists with Bronx roots in its ongoing series "The
Bronx Celebrates." To be an important center for the visual arts within a college
community, responsive to the interests of the larger population of the Bronx and
its environs. It is dedicated to the interests of the community residents of all ages.
Selection process: Artists should mail 8-20 slides, resumé, cover letter, press
clippings, and SASE. **Response time:** 3 months.
Additional information: There is an emphasis on education programs for
elementary, intermediate and high school student groups that incorporate gallery
and studio experience related to the shows.

LONGWOOD ARTS PROJECT

965 Longwood Ave., 10459.   **T:** (718) 842-5659.
F: (718) 842-3933.   **E:** longwood@artswire.org
W: www.longwoodcyber.org   **Open:** Mon.-Fri. 9-5, Sat. 12-4.
Year established: 1985.   **Owner:** Bronx Council of the Arts.

continued

Director: Eddie Torres.
Work shown: Work in all media by local and international artists. Solo shows feature local artists. The exhibition program runs in 4 cycles per year.
Annual exhibitions: 4.   **Advertising:** *Bomb* magazine.
Focus/Mission: To raise the profiles and technical/creative ceilings of artists from under-represented groups. Longwood Cyber provides artists access to work stations, visual arts and web design software, hardware, technical consultants and artist honoraria so they may experiment with new technologies as creative tools.
Selection process: Artists do not have to be Bronx residents. Artists should mail slides/photographs, resumé, and SASE to the attention of Eddie Torres.

WAVE HILL: GLYNDOR GALLERY, WAVE HILL HOUSE GALLERY & GENERATED@WAVEHILL

675 West 252 St., 10471.   **T:** (718) 549-3200.
F: (718) 884-8952.   **E:** info@wavehill.org
W: www.wavehill.org   **Year established:** 1975.
Owner: City of New York.   **Executive Director:** Kate French.
Visual Arts Curator: Jennifer McGregor.
Open: Oct. 15-April 14, Tues.-Sun. 9-4:30; April 15-Oct. 14, Tues.-Sun. 9-5:30. Memorial Day-Labor Day open Wed. until sunset.
Admission: March 15-Nov. 14, Wed.-Sun., $4 general, $2 seniors/students; members/children under 6 free. Tues. free. Sat. free 9-12 noon. Free admission from Nov. 15-March 14.
Annual exhibitions: 3 in Wave Hill House Gallery; 2 in Glyndor Gallery, and 1 outdoor installation at Generated@wavehill.
Work shown: Sculpture, work on paper, photography, painting, mixed media and installation. **Work by:** International artists. All ages. All origins.
Focus/Mission: The Arts Program at Wave Hill presents contemporary artists in all fields whose work explores, demonstrates, or otherwise reflects upon the dynamic relationship between human beings and natural phenomenon.
Selection process: Artists should call for information.

QUEENS

AQA

99-10 Metropolitan Ave., Forest Hills, 11375.   **T:** (718) 520-9842.
Open: Tues.-Sat. 1-6.   **W:** www.arts4u.org/gallery.htm
President: Bob Menzel.
Work shown: Many views and styles that reflect the most culturally diverse city in The U.S. This is the gallery of the Alliance of Queens Artists organization.
Work by: George Chau; Richard Finnell; Jacqueline Fogel; Marvin Goldfarb; and Stan Goldstein; among others.
Selection process: Artists should call or visit the web site for membership application.

DORSKY GALLERY CURATORIAL PROGRAMS
11-03 45th Ave., Long Island City 11101. **T:** (718) 937-6317.
F: (718) 937-7469.   **E:** Ndavid@Dorsky.org
Open: Wed.-Sun. 11-6   **Year established:** 1963.
Owners: Non-profit organization.   **Director:** David A. Dorsky.
Size: 2,500 sq. ft.   **Annual exhibitions:** 4 solo/4 group.
Work shown: Contemporary art in all media.
Focus/Mission: To exhibit thought-provoking and interesting art based on
proposals by independent curators. The gallery represents no artists, but instead
offers its space for independent curators to have a venue to examine their visions.
Additional information: Each exhibition is accompanied by a full color brochure
with an essay by the curator(s).
Selection process: Proposals for exhibitions are reviewed quarterly and each
exhibition that is accepted runs for 7-8 weeks.

FISHER LANDAU CENTER
38-27 30 St., Long Island City, 11101. **T:** (718) 937-0727.
Open: By appointment.   **Size:** 25,000 sq. ft.
Year established: 1991.   **Director:** Nicholas Arbatsky.
Work by: Rauschenberg; Twombly; Johns; Rosenquist; Artschwager; Baechler;
Fischl; Gornick; Kruger; Lorna Simpson; Kiki Smith; among others.
Focus/Mission: The Center is devoted to the study of the collection of Emily
Fisher Landau.

GODWIN-TERNBACH MUSEUM
Queens College, 65-30 Kissena Blvd., Flushing, 11367.   **T:** (718) 997-4747.
F: (718) 997-4734.   **Director:** Amy H. Winter.
Open: Sept. 1-May 30, Mon.-Thurs. 11-7.
Work shown: Art from antiquity to the present time.
Annual exhibitions: 4, primarily solo.
Focus/Mission: To exhibit work from the collection in addition to a concentration
of established living and deceased artists.
Selection process: Artists should mail slides, resumé, and SASE.
Response time: 1-2 months.

INDEPENDENT ARTS
Queens Independent Living Center, 140-40 Queens Blvd., Jamaica, 11435.
T: (718) 658-2526 / (718) 658-4720 TTY
F:(718) 658-5295.   **Open:** Mon.-Fri. 9-5.
Year established: 1987.   **Executive Director:** Mark Gardella.
Owner: Queens Independent Living Center, a non-profit, community-based, non-
residential center. It provides services and advocacy by people with disabilities for
people with disabilities.
Work shown: Contemporary art in all media by disabled artists. Photography,
prints, paintings, sculpture and mixed media.
Focus/Mission: To integrate artists with disabilities into the established art
community. The gallery is guided by its own advisory committee consisting of a
majority of artists with disabilities, gallery owners, and art administrators who are
sensitive to both disability issues and the cultural community.
Selection process: Artists must be disabled. Contact Christian Valle by phone or
send resumé, slides with SASE. **Response time:** 1 month.   *continued*

Additional information: The Independent Arts Gallery provides additional resources, support and programs, including poetry readings and performances.

JAMAICA CENTER FOR ARTS AND LEARNING

161-04 Jamaica Ave., Jamaica, 11432.

T: (718) 658-7400
F: (718) 658-7922.
E: kskvirsk@earthlink.net
W: www.jcal.org
Open: Mon.-Sat. 10-5.
Year established: 1972.
Visual Arts Director: Hen-Gil Han. **Annual exhibitions:** 6.
Work shown: Art by emerging NYC and international artists. All styles and media.
Focus/Mission: To offer accessible, diverse programs that foster creative expression and personal growth through the arts.
Selection process: Artists should slides or photographs, resumé, artist's statement, and SASE to the attention of Karina Skvirsky.
Response time: Up to 6 months.
Additional information: There is an Artist-in-Residence program. There are education programs in conjunction with the exhibitions. Call for information.

LA GUARDIA COMMUNITY COLLEGE

31-10 Thompson Ave., Long Island City, 11101.

T: (718) 482-5709.
F: (718) 875-6957.
E: gvollo@lagcc.cuny.edu
Year established: 1972.
Open: Mon.-Sat. 8-9; Summer: Mon.-Thus. 8-9.
Directors: Bruce Brooks and Gary Vollo. **Annual exhibitions:** 20.
Size: 4 galleries on the 4th and 5th floors.
Work shown: Exhibitions feature the work of students and faculty as well as professional artists. They tend to be pluralistic and didactic, ranging from artifacts to contemporary art in all media.
Selection process: Artists should mail slides, photographs, resumé, and SASE to Bruce Brooks or Gary Vollo. The Art and Exhibition Review Committee usually meets in the Fall and the Spring, to review submissions.
Response time: 2 months.

LANGSTON HUGHES COMMUNITY LIBRARY AND CULTURAL CENTER, QUEENS PUBLIC LIBRARY

100-01 Northern Blv., Corona 11368.

T: (718) 651-1100.
E: ajackson@queenslibrary.org
Open: Mon. and Fri. 10-6, Tues., 1-6, Wed. and Thurs. 1-8, Sat. 10-5.
Year established: 1969.
Executive Director: Andrew P. Jackson.
Work shown: Contemporary art in all media by emerging and established artists.
Annual exhibitions: 5-6.
Selection process: Artists should mail slides or photographs, brief biography and SASE. **Response time:** 1 month.

MUSEUM OF MODERN ART

MoMA QNS, 45-20 33 St., Long Island City, 11101. From Summer 2002 through 2005, MoMA will be located at this address, until the building at 53 St. in Manhattan is completely renovated. Visit MoMa web site for information.

T: (212) 708-9400
W: www.moma.org
Director: Glenn D. Lowry.
Size: 160,000 sq. ft.

Work shown: The following exhibitions are planned: "Collection Highlights": Summer 2002; "Wish You Were Here: The Howard Gilman Archive of Visionary Architectural Drawings": Fall 2002; "Contemporary Drawings: Eight Propositions": Winter 2002; and Matisse and Picasso exhibition: Spring 2003.
Additional information: The Museum has a café and design shop.

ISAMU NOGUCHI FOUNDATION AND GARDEN MUSEUM

36-01 43 Ave., Long Island City, 11101; Mailing address: 32-37 Vernon Blvd., Long Island City, 11106.   **T:** 718-204-7088.
F: (718) 278-2348.   **E:** museum@noguchi.org
W:www.noguchi.org   **Open:** Wed.-Fri. 10-5, Sat. and Sun. 11-6.
Admission: Suggested donation $5; seniors and students $2.50.
Year established: 1985.
Work shown: 250 works by sculptor Isamu Noguchi (1904-1988) in 13 galleries and an outdoor sculpture garden.
Additional information: The museum does not have a parking lot and is located in an area with limited street parking. Call for weekend shuttle bus information.

P.S. 1 CONTEMPORARY ART CENTER

22-25 Jackson Ave., at 46 Ave., Long Island City, 11101.
T: (718) 784-2084.   **F:** (718) 482-9454.
W: www.ps1.org   **Year established:** 1971.
Director: Alanna Heiss.
Open: Wed.-Sun. 12-6; Summer: Wed.-Sun. 12-6, Sat. 12-9.
Owner: Non-profit organization.   **Work shown:** All styles and media.
Focus/Mission: To function as a gallery space for art which would not be shown in commercial venues. There is an international and national studio program.
Selection process: Artists should submit materials and SASE to Alanna Heiss.
Additional information: P.S. 1 is an affiliate of the Museum of Modern Art.

QUEENSBOROUGH COMMUNITY COLLEGE / CUNY

The City University of New York, Bayside, 11364.
T: (718) 631-6396.   **F:** (718) 631-6620.
E: QCCGallery@aol.com   **Year established:** 1981.
Director: Faustino Quintanilla.   **Open:** Mon.-Fri. 9-5 and by appointment.
Annual exhibitions: 8-10. One exhibition is of students' work, and the remaining exhibitions are of professional artists.
Focus/Mission: To collect and preserve, present and interpret, educate and motivate research, and stimulate new art production.
Selection process: Artists should mail materials and SASE to Faustino Quintanilla. An executive board makes the decisions.

QUEENS COLLEGE ART CENTER

Benjamin S. Rosenthal Library, Queens College/CUNY, 65-30 Kissena Blvd., Flushing, 11367.   **T:** (718) 997-3770.
F: (718) 997-3753.   **Director:** Suzanna Simor.
Curator: Alexandra DeLuise.   **Annual exhibitions:** 4-6.
Open: Sept.-Dec. & Feb.-May: Mon.-Thurs. 9-8, Fri. 9-5; Jan. & June-Aug: Mon.-Fri. 9-5.
Work shown: Modern and Contemporary art in all media by emerging and established artists.

Work by: Exhibitions have included Eva Fuka; Deborah Harse; and Fulvio Testa; among others.
Selection process: Artists should mail slides, resumé, and other printed information with SASE. **Response time:** 2-3 weeks.

QUEENS LIBRARY
89-11 Merrick Blvd., Jamaica, 11432. **T:** (718) 990-8665.
F: (718) 291-8936.   **W:** queenslibrary.org/gallery
Year established: 1995.   **Exhibitions Manager:** Mindy Krazmien.
Size: 2,500 sq. ft.   **Annual exhibitions:** 4.
Open: Mon.- Fri. 10-9, Sat. 10-5:30, Sun. 12-5. Call for summer hours.
Work shown: Diverse traveling and original exhibitions.
Focus/Mission: Our mission is to foster awareness and appreciation of the visual arts and encourage an understanding and sensitivity for the arts in the greater community. The gallery also enhances recognition of the Library and its collection as well as to reach out to new audiences.
Selection process: An Exhibition Committee reviews submissions. Proposals are always accepted. Shows are scheduled at least 5 months in advance. Individual artists should not apply, rather non-profit organizations or curators may submit proposals for exhibitions that have an interdisciplinary approach. Applicant should provide slides and other documentation, exhibition proposal, budget, letter of interest and a resumé.

QUEENSBOROUGH LIBRARY INTERNAT'L RESOURCE CENTER
Flushing Library, 41-17 Main St., Flushing, 11355.
T: (718) 661-1200.   **W:** www.queenslibrary.org
Year established: 1998.   **Open:** Mon. and Wed. 10-8, Tues. 1-8, Thurs and Fri. 10-6, Sat. 10-5, Sun. 12-5; Summer: Closed Sun.
Annual exhibitions: 4.
Work shown: Art and historical exhibitions with international themes.

QUEENS MUSEUM OF ART, NYC
Building, Flushing Meadows, Corona Park, 11368.
T: (718) 592-9700.   **F:** (718) 592-5778.
W: www.queensmuse.org   **Year established:** 1972.
Interim Director: Carma Sauntleroy. **Open:** Tues.-Fri. 10-5; Sat. and Sun. 12-5.
Admission: Suggested donation: $5 general, $2 student/senior.
Work shown: Contemporary art, design, and architecture.
Focus/Mission: To be at the vanguard in art education in Queens. To show the best art, architecture and design of the 20th Century with relationship to Queens.
Selection process: Call for current policy.

RO GALLERY.COM
47-15 36 St., Long Island City, 11101. **T:** (718) 937-0901.
F: (718) 937-1206.   **E:** art@rogallery.com
W: www.rogallery.com   **Open:** By appointment.
Size: 10,000 sq. ft. warehouse.   **Year established:** 1979.
Director: Robert Rogal.
Work shown: Prints, paintings, and sculpture and other forms of art.
Work by: Miró; Picasso; Chagall; Ralph Goings; and Peter Max; among others.
Prices: $50 and up.

SCULPTURE CENTER

44-19 Purves St., Long Island City, 11101. **T:** (212) 879-3500.
F: (212) 879-7155. **E:** info@sculpture-center.org
W: www.sculpture-center.org **Owner:** Non-profit organization.
Director: Mary Ceruti. **Size:** 2,000 sq. ft.
Open: Call for hours. **Year established:** 1920.
Work shown: Contemporary sculpture.
Work by: Artists are from all origins. Mostly emerging, some mid-career artists.
Focus/Mission: Sculpture Center's mission is to support and encourage experimentation and excellence in contemporary sculpture by providing opportunities for artists to produce and exhibit work in multiple dimensions; to educate audiences about sculpture and its relationship to other art forms and fields; and to act as a catalyst for new ideas in contemporary art and culture.
Work by: Exhibiting artists have included: Beverly Semmes; Robert Chambers; Holly Zausner; Brigitte Nahon; and Lee Boroson; among others.
Advertising: *Gallery Guide.*
Selection process: Most of the artists are selected from slides. Artists should submit 20 slides, biography and SASE anytime. Artists must be emerging or under-exhibited, mid-career sculptors. Good quality slides are important.

SOCRATES SCULPTURE PARK

Vernon Blvd. and Broadway, Long Island City, 11106. **T:** (718) 956-1819.
F: (718) 626-1533. **W:** www.socratessculpturepark.org
Open: Daily 9-sunset. **Year established:** 1986. **Size:** 4.5 acres.
Director: Alyson Baker. **Assistant Director:** Robyn Donohue.
Owner: Not-for-profit organization, NYC Department of Parks and Recreation.
Work shown: Contemporary out door sculpture.
Work by: Exhibitions have included Mark di Suvero; Bill and Mary Buchen; Eduardo Chillida; Elaine Lorenz; Maren Hassinger; and John Ahearn; among others.
Annual exhibitions: 1 group in the Fall / 1 group in the Spring.
Focus/Mission: To provide artists with opportunities to create and exhibit large-scale work in a unique environment that encourages strong interaction between artists, artworks and the public. The Park's existence is based on the belief that reclamation, revitalization and creative expression are essential to the survival, humanity and improvement of our urban environment.
Selection process: The Outdoor Studio Program provides artists with a grant to fund the construction of a new sculpture on site. Sculptors should send SASE and request guidelines. There is also an Emerging Artist Fellowship Program from which half of the exhibiting artists are selected. NY State residents only are eligible.
Additional Information: The Park was an abandoned riverside landfill and illegal dumpsite until 1986 when a coalition of artists and community members, under the leadership of Mark di Suvero, transformed it into an open studio and exhibition space for artists and a neighborhood park for local residents.

ST. JOHN'S UNIVERSITY -- CHUNG-CHENG

Sun Yat Sen Hall, St. John's University, 8000 Utopia Parkway, Jamaica, 11439.
T: (718) 990-7476. **Year established:** 1994.
Open: Mon.-Thurs. 10-3, Fri. 11-2; Summer: Closed Fri.
Directors: Various curators from within the university. *continued*

Work shown: Exhibitions include work by students and faculty members, and national and international artists.   **Annual exhibitions:** 7.

Focus/Mission: To advance the development of aesthetic values which are central to the institution's mission as a University and, in addition, reflects the Catholic, Vincentian, and metropolitan character of the institution. The gallery is committed to the advancement of the visual arts and creativity as they flow from free inquiry and human experience, through an ongoing program of diverse, comprehensive, and thematic exhibitions.

Selection process: Artists are selected from materials sent to the gallery and from the national juried exhibitions. Artists should mail slides/photographs, resumé and SASE to the attention of Belenna Lauto, Chair, Dept. of Fine Arts with SASE.

Additional Information: The gallery has at least one annual exhibit of artwork by Asian artists. It also has national juried exhibitions.

STATEN ISLAND

MUSEUM OF STATEN ISLAND INSTITUTE OF ARTS & SCIENCES

75 Stuyvesant Place, 10301.
F: (718) 273-5683.
Year established: 1881.
children/seniors
T: (718) 727-1135.
Open: Mon.-Sat. 9-2.
Suggested donation: $2.50 adults, $1.50
President: Michael Botwinick.

Curator of Art, VP Collections: Peggy McGuire.

Owner: Staten Island Institute of Arts and Sciences, Staten Island's oldest cultural institution.

Work shown: Exhibitions in art, science, and history, with a strong representation of 19th and 20th Century art in its collections.

Additional Information: SIIS has a library and archives, open to researchers by appointment.

NEWHOUSE CENTER FOR CONTEMPORARY ART/SNUG HARBOR

1000 Richmond Terrace, Staten Island, 10301. **T:** (718) 448-2500.
F: (718) 442-8534.
Open: Wed.-Sun. 11-5, Sat 11-7.
Size: 8,000 sq. ft.
W: www.snug-harbor.org
Suggested donation: $2
Year established: 1976.

Owner: Not-for-profit organization. **Director of Visual Arts:** Olivia Georgia.

Assistant Director: Melissa Hiller.

Work shown: All styles of 2- and 3- dimensional media, literature, and interdisciplinary art by 50-130 artists annually. All ages. All origins.

Annual exhibitions: 3 major group shows/4 solo shows.

Advertising: *Gallery Guide.*

Focus/Mission: To create art programs for the growth and development of artists and the public while servicing both local and regional constituencies. To promote inquiry and learning through exhibitions and artist projects and related education and public programs, publications, and interpretative materials.

Selection process: Artists should send 20 slides and resumé with SASE. We prefer innovative work, particularly by emerging, mid-career and minority artists.

Additional Information: Musical performances are presented.

STATEN ISLAND INSTITUTE OF ARTS and SCIENCES - THE STATEN ISLAND FERRY COLLECTION

Staten Island Ferry Terminal Waiting Room, 10301. **T:** (718) 727-1135. **F:** (718) 273-5683.

Open: Mon.-Fri. 9-1, Sat-Sun. 9-2. **Director:** Michael Botwinck.

Work shown: A permanent exhibition featuring maritime art by local artists and historical publications and ferry memorabilia on the history of the Staten Island Ferry in the terminal on the Staten Island side.

Additional information: SIIAS hosts several tours aboard the ferry that focus on the NY harbor. Call for additional information or to be placed on their mailing list.

ST. GEORGE

22 Fort Pl., 10301. **T:** (718) 448-0553.

E: paweg7@yahoo.com **Open:** Tues.-Sat. 10-6.

Year established: 2001. **Size:** 800 sq. ft.

Owner/Director: Paul Gorlach, artist and designer.

Work shown: Modern, abstract and renaissance paintings, prints, drawings, and design objects by American, Brazil and Polish American artists.

Prices: $100 and up.

Annual exhibitions: 7. **Advertising:** *Gallery Guide.*

WAGNER COLLEGE GALLERY

631 Howard Ave, Staten Island 10301. **T:** (718) 390-3192

Open: Tue.-Sat, 11-4 **Director:** Professor Jebah Baum

Work shown: Students in addition to local and international artists.

Annual exhibitions: 4-5

At press time the following galleries and artists' studios came to our attention. They will be profiled in more detail in the next edition. We recommend you call first before visiting the gallery.

MANHATTAN

A/D
560 Broadway, 10012.
T: (212) 966-5154.
W: www.ADeditions.com.
Open: Tues.-Sat. 10-6.

CARLO ALESSI
157 West 26 St., 10001.
T: (646) 336-9869. Open:
Tues.-Fri. 10-4, Sat.12-4.
Director: Carlo Alessi.

**ARTISTS' MUSEUM
NEW YORK CENTER**
83 Mercer St., 10012.
T: (212) 219-0787. F: (212)
219-3787. E: artists
museumny @aol.com
Open: By appointment.

**BLUE STOCKING
WOMEN'S
BOOKSTORE**
172 Allen St., 10013.
T: (212) 777-6028.

**KENNEDY BOESKY
PHOTOGRAPHS**
535 West 22 St., 2nd floor,
10011. T: (212) 741-0963.
F: (212) 680-9897. E:
marla@kennedyboesky
photographs.com
Open: Tues.-Sat. 10-6.

LINDSEY BROWN
526 West 26 St., 10001.
T: (212) 252-4885. F: (646)
336-6286. Open: Wed.-
Sat. 11-6.

ROBERT BURGE
315 East 62 St., 10021.
T: (212) 838-4108.
F: (212) 838-4390.

E:yaleburge@earthlink.net.
Open: By appointment.

**CENTER FOR
FIGURATIVE PAINTING**
115 West 30 St., #202,
10001. T: (212) 868-
3452. Call for hours.

**CONSULATE GENERAL
OF CHILE**
866 United Nations Plaza,
Suite 601, 10017. T: (212)
980-3366.
W: www.chileny.com

CUCHIFRITOS
Inside the Essex St. Food
Market at South end of
the building, 10003.
Open: Mon.-Sat. 12-5:30.

CULTURE
415 West Broadway, 5th
floor, 10012. T: (212)
226-8921. Open: Tues.-
Sat. 11-6.

THE CULTURE CENTER
410 Columbus Ave,
New York, NY 10024.
T: (212) 362-5087.
F: (212) 724-9102.
E: cultctr@aol.com
Open:By appointment.

**DAKOTA JACKSON, P.A.
(PUBLIC ACCESS)**
43 Mercer St., 10013.
T: (212) 925-4994. F: (212)
625-1933. E: dumbbox
@dakotajackson.com
W: www.dakotajackson.
com. Open Tues.-Wed. 11-
6, Thurs. 11-7, Fri.-Sat. 11-
6.

**LINDA DURHAM
CONTEMPORARY**
210 11TH Ave., 10001.
T: (212) 337-0025.
F: (212) 337-0031.
E:ldca@earthlink.net
W: www.lindadurham.com
Open: Tues-Sat. 11-5.

FORDHAM UNIVERSITY
113 West 60 St., 10023.

**FOURTH STREET
PHOTO**
67 East 4 St., 10003.
(212) 673-1021. E: photo_
direct@hotmail.com
Open: Tues.-Sun 3-10.
Director: Alex Harsley.

**GALERIE THOMAS,
GREENWICH VILLAGE**
41 Perry St., 10014. E:
galeriethomas@aol.com
Open: Tues.-Sun. 2-9.

BRIAN GORMLEY
233 E. 34th Street, 10016.
T: (212) 689-1157.
E: bgorm@hot mail.com
W: www.arnet. com.
Open: By appointment.

INFRAMUNDO
106 Spring St., Suite 65,
10012. T: (212) 431-
7276. Open: Wed.-Sat. 1-
6 by appointment.

LAUMONT EDITIONS
333 West 52 St., 10019.
T: (212) 664-0594. F: (212)
664-1664, E: plaumont
@aol.com. Open: Mon.-Fri.
10-6. Director: Philipe
Laumont.

LIGHTZONES GALLERY
212 Pinehurst Ave., 10033.
T: (212) 928-5634. F: (212)
928-5770. E: montag520
@earthlink.net. Open:
Mon.-Sat. 10-6, Sun. 12-5.
Owner: Simone Song.

LOBBY, EQUITABLE PROPERTIES
850 Third Ave., (Ground
floor lobby) 10022.
Open: Mon.-Fri. 8-7.

JUSTIN OSTEEN
32 Union Square East,
Studio 311, 10003. T:(212)
253-7866. Open: By
appointment.

MODERN CULTURE AT THE GERSHWIN HOTEL
3 East 27 St., 10016.
T: (212) 213-8289. Open:
Tues.-Sat. 10-6. W: www.
bway. net/~modcult

MUNDER SKILES
799 Madison Ave.,10021.
T: (212) 717-0150. Open:
Mon.-Fri. 9-5, Sat. 11-5.
Owner: John Danzer.

PERIMETER
526 West 26 St., 10001.
T: (212) 675-1585.
W: www.perimeter.com.
Open: Tues.-Sat.10-6.

QUESTROYAL FINE ART
903 Park Ave., 10021.
T: (212) 861-6650.
W: www.questroyal
fineart.com. Open: Mon.-
Fri. 10-6, Sat. 10-5, and by
appointment.

RANDEL
49 East 78 St., 10021.
T: (212) 861-6650.
W: www.randelgallery.
com. Open: By
appointment.

SPHERIS
20 Bond St., 10012.
T: (917) 328-3801.
W:www.spherisgallery.com
Open: Thurs.-Fri. 11-6,
Sat. 12-4.

STERILEMIND
230 Mulberry St., 10012. T:
(212) 941-6767. F: (212)
941-6244. E: liesl@sterile
mind.com
Open: Tues.-Sat. 12-7.

BRONX

FOCAL POINT
321 City Island Ave., City
Island, 10464. T/F: (718)
885-1403. Open:Tues.-
Sun. 12-7:30,Fri.-Sat. 12-9.

BROOKLYN

ART LAND
609 Grand St. 11211
T: (718) 599-9706.
Open: Daily 12-4.

BAX
421 Fifth Ave., 11215.
T: (718) 832-0016.

DABORA GALLERY
1080 Manhattan Ave.,
Greenpoint, 11222.
T: (718) 609-9629.
Open: Sat. 12-5.
E:mort66@ earthlink.net
W:www.daboragallery.com

DAM, STUHLTRAGER
38 Marcy Ave., 11211
T: (718) 387-9818.
E:damstuhltrager@alta
vista.com Open: Sat.-Sun.
12-6.

GOOD/BAD ART COLLECTIVE
383 South 1 St., 11211
(718) 599-4962.
E:weber@goodbad.org
www.goodbad.org

PLUS ULTRA
235 South 1 St., 11211
T: (718) 387-3844.
E: info@plusultra
gallery.com
W: www.plusultra
gallery.com
Open: Sat.-Sun. 12-6
and by appointment.

WILLIAMSBURG ART NEXUS
205 North 7 St., 11211.
T: (718) 599-7997.

QUEENS

BELL-BAKER
49-17 Verson Blvd., Long
Island City, 11101. T: (718)
729-0140. E: Laurabel@
eaarthlink.net. Studios of:
Laura Bell and Robert
Baker

FLUSHING TOWN HALL
137-35 Northern Blvd.,
Flushing ,11354. T: (718)
463-7700. W: www.flushing
townhall.org. Open: Mon.-
Fri. 9-5, Sat.-Sun. 12-5.

HOLOCENTER CENTER FOR THE HOLOGRAPHIC ARTS
45-10 Court Square
Long Island City, NY 11101
T: (718) 784-5065.
E: holocenter@mindspring
W: www.holocenter.com
Open: By appointment.

ELINORE SCHNURR STUDIO
10-09 50 Ave., Long Island
City 11101. T: (718) 937-
5229. E: info@elinore
schnurr.com. W: www.
elinoreschnurr.com.
Open: By appointment.

NEW YORK CENTER FOR MEDIA ARTS
45-12 Davis St., Long Island
City, 11101. T: (718) 472.-
9414. W: www.nyc
mediaarts.org

NOTES OR DOODLES

RESOURCE DIRECTORY

COPYRIGHT

- **U.S. COPYRIGHT OFFICE**. Register of copyrights. The Library of Congress, Washington, DC 20559. For forms call (202) 707-9100. For information pertaining to copyright law or procedures call (202) 707-3000.

ADVOCACY, LEGAL & HEALTH

- **ALLIANCE FOR THE ARTS,** 330 West 42 Street, Suite 1701, New York, NY 10036. T: (212) 947-6340. F: (212) 947-6416. W: www.allianceforarts.org. It is dedicated to policy research, information services and advocacy for the arts in NY. It influences the policies and actions of government, funders, and the business of art.
- **AMERICANS FOR THE ARTS**, 1 East 53 St., New York, NY 10022. T: (212) 223-2787. F: (212) 980-4857. W: www. americansforthearts.org. It works with cultural organizations, arts and business leaders and patrons to provide leadership, advocacy, visibility, professional development, research and information to advance support for the arts and culture in our nation's communities.
- **NEW YORK ARTISTS EQUITY (NYAEA)**, 498 Broome St., New York, NY 10013. T: (212) 941-0130. F: (212) 941-0138. W: www.anny.org. It disseminates information regarding legislation and legal rights, in the interest of addressing artists' "survival" issues. It monitors local, state and federal legislation and strongly advocates bills in support of art and artists and it protects the legal rights of artists.
- **NEW YORK CITY DEPARTMENT OF CULTURAL AFFAIRS**, 330 West 42 St., 14th floor, New York, NY 10036. T: (212) 643-7770. F: (212) 643-7780. It helps to oversee, sustain and promote arts and culture in NYC. It is an advocacy agency, a source of funding and a major resource for many arts organizations. Its "Percent for Art" Program offers city agencies the opportunity to allocate 1% of the capital budget of eligible city construction projects for commissioning new art work and/or the conservation of existing public art.
- **RBA INSURANCE STRATEGIES,** T: (800) 722-0160. They have served the arts community for many years. Various insurance plans are available.

- **VOLUNTEER LAWYERS FOR THE ARTS,** 1 E. 53 Street, New York, NY 10022. T: (212) 319-2787. It provides arts-related assistance to low-income artists. Its Art Law Line provides artists with quick answers to arts-related legal questions. (Check your local listings for the VLA branch near you.)

FINANCIAL AID & GRANTS

- **THE FOUNDATION CENTER**, 79 Fifth Ave., 2nd floor, New York, NY 10003. T: (212) 620-4230. W: www.fdncenter. org. This resource center provides complete information on philanthropic support of the arts and other areas, private and public grant, loan and fellowship opportunities.
- **ADOLPH AND ESTHER GOTTLIEB FOUNDATION**, 380 W. Broadway, New York, NY 10012. T: (212) 226-0581. F: (212) 226-0584. It provides financial support to individual artists who have shown a lifetime of commitment to their art. It has an Emergency Assistance Program for a specific emergency.
- **JOHN SIMON GUGGENHEIM MEMORIAL FOUNDATION**, Art Department, Scholarship/ Grant Program, 90 Park Ave., New York, NY 10016. T: (212) 687-4470 F: (212) 697-3248. W: www.gf.org. It offers fellowships to further the development of scholars and artists.
- **NEW YORK FOUNDATION FOR THE ARTS**, 155 Ave. of the Americas, New York, NY 10013. T: (212) 366-6900. F: (212) 366-1778. W: www.nyfa.org. It provides fellowships, residencies, loans, and fiscal sponsorship of organizations, and information services for artists and organizations. Visual Artist Information Hotline T: (800) 232-2789. W: www.nyfa.org/vaih
- **NEW YORK STATE COUNCIL ON THE ARTS (NYSCA),** 175 Varick St., New York, NY 10014.T: (212) 627-4455. F: (212) 620-5911. W: www.nysca. org. It promotes and develops New York's cultural, economic and human resources through support of the arts. It funds non-profit organizations to provide cultural services, and awards grants in the performing and visual arts.
- **POLLACK-KRASNER FOUNDATION**, 863 Park Ave., New York, NY 10021. T: (212) 517-5400. F: (212) 288-2836. The Foundation Grant provides financial assis-

tance to individual working artists of established ability.

- **JUDITH ROTHSCHILD FOUNDATION** 1110 Park Ave., New York, NY 10128. T: (212) 831-4144. W: www.fdncenter.org/grantmaker/Rothschild. It makes grants to present, preserve, or interpret work of the highest aesthetic merit by lesser-known artists' achievements.
- **MARIE WALSH SHARPE** 443 Greenwich St., 7th floor, New York, NY 10013. T: (212) 925-3008. F: (212) 279-0773. E: ISPNYC @concentric.net. It awards rent-free studio space to artists for a period of up to one year at the Space Program.
- **VISUAL AIDS**, 526 West 26 St., #510, New York, NY 10001. T: (212) 627-9855. F: (212) 627-9815. W: www. visualaids.org. It provides grants and photo documentation for artists with HIV / AIDS, and produces exhibitions and publications.

BUSINESS & PUBLIC ART

- **THE AMERICAN FEDERATION OF ARTS (AFA)**, 41 East 65 St., New York, NY 10021. T: (212) 988-7700. F: (212) 861-2487. This museum service organization strengthens the ability of museums to enrich the public's experience and understanding of art. It presents traveling art exhibitions.
- **ART DEALERS ASSOCIATION OF AMERICA**, 575 Madison Ave., New York, NY 10022. T: (212) 940-8590. F: (212) 940-7013. W: www.artdealers.org. An organization of the nation's leading fine art dealers, it promotes the highest standards of connoisseurship, scholarship, and ethical practice within the profession.
- **ARTTABLE, INC.**, 270 Lafayette St., Suite 608, New York, NY 10012. T: (212) 343-1735. F: (212) 343-1430. W: www.art table.org. This organization for professional women in the visual arts provides a forum for the exchange of ideas and information through educational programs and events.
- **THE BUSINESS COMMITTEE FOR THE ARTS, INC. (BCA)**, 29-27 Queens Plaza North, 4th Floor, LIC, N Y 11101. T: (718) 482-9900. F: (718) 482-9911. W: www.bcainc.org. It fosters business/arts alliances through research, publications, seminars and conferences. It guides companies in their investments in the arts.
- **CITY ARTS**, 525 Broadway, Suite 700, New York, NY 10012. T: (212) 966-0377. F: (212) 966-0551. E: tsipi@cityarts.org. W: www.cityarts.org. It presents public art work throughout the NYC area through public,

private and corporate commissions. It maintains a slide registry.

- **CREATIVE TIME**, 307 Seventh Ave., #1904, New York, NY 10001. T: (212) 206-6674. F: (212) 255-8467. W: www. creativetime.org. It helps visual artists, architects, and performing artists bring their work to a wide range of NYC public spaces.
- **MATERIALS FOR THE ARTS**, T: (212) 255-5924. It donates artists' materials to artists organizations.
- **THE PUBLIC ART FUND**, 1 East 53 St., 11th floor, NY, NY 10022. T: (212) 980-4575. F: (212) 980-3610. W: www.public artfund.org. It integrates contemporary art within the urban landscape by bringing together artists, communities and city agencies. It provides artists with opportunities to create art outside the traditional context of museums and galleries.

MEMBERSHIP & SERVICE

- **ALLIANCE OF QUEENS ARTISTS (AQA)**, 99-10 Metropolitan Ave., Forest Hills, NY 11375. T: (718) 520-9842. F: (718) 261-6166. W: www.arts4u.org. Executive Director: Bob Menzel. It promotes the visual arts through exhibitions and other activities.
- **AMERICAN ABSTRACT ARTISTS**, 470 West End Ave., #9D, New York, NY 10024. T: (212) 874-0747. President: Beatrice Riese. It promotes American Abstract art by bringing it before the public, and fostering public appreciation of this direction in painting and sculpture.
- **AMERICAN ARTISTS PROFESSION-AL LEAGUE, (AAPL)**, C/O Salmagundi Club, 47 Fifth Ave., New York, NY 10003. T: (212) 645-1345. U.S. authority on artist's pigments, sets the standards for pigments and artists materials.
- **AMERICAN RENAISANCE FOR THE TWENTY-FIRST CENTURY (ART)**, F.D.R. Station, PO Box 8379, NY, NY 10150.T: (212) 759-7765. F: (212) 759-1922. W: www.art-21.org. President: Alexandra York. It promotes and advances public knowledge and understanding of Western heritage art forms through exhibitions, publications, grants, lectures and special events.
- **AMERICAN SOCIETY OF CONTEMPORARY ARTISTS, (ASCA)**, Joseph Lubrano, President, 130 Gale Place, 9-H, Bronx, NY 10463. T: (718) 548-6790. It represents, through exhibitions of its members, the varied currents of 20th century art.
- **AMERICAN WATERCOLOR SOCIETY**, C/O Salmagundi Club, 47 Fifth Ave., NY, NY

10003. T: (212) 675-8986. It advances watercolor painting, awards scholarships, holds demonstrations and watercolor exhibition in U.S. and other countries.

- **ARTISTS TALK ON ART, (ATOA),** 10 Waterside Plaza, #33D, New York, NY 10010-2608. T: (212) 675-1308. E: Gloria@newtoryartists.net. It presents panel discussions on important art issues led by art professionals.
- **BROOKLYN WATERCOLOR SOCIETY**, Robert Axelrod, 454 2nd Street, Brooklyn, NY 11215. T: (718) 965-3024. W: www.bsw.org. It shares ideas and encourages interest in the transparent watercolor medium, through critiques and exhibitions.
- **BROOKLYN WORKING ARTISTS COALITION**, 499 Van Brunt St., Brooklyn, NY 11231. T: (718) 596-2507. W: www. bwac.org. This 350-member artist group presents exhibitions in Redhook, Brooklyn spaces, open studio tours and other events.
- **BRONX COUNCIL ON THE ARTS**, 1738 Hone Ave., Bronx, NY 10461. T: (718) 931-9500. F: (718) 409-6445. W: www. bronx-arts. org. It provides exhibitions and workshops for artists.
- **BURR ARTISTS**, C/O Fred Schwartz, President, 325 West 86th St., #12B, New York, NY 10024. T: (212) 877-3527. This organization exhibits its members' work of varied styles and media in exhibitions throughout NYC.
- **THE CENTER FOR DIGITAL ART**, 345 East 12 St., New York, NY 10003. T: (212) 982-4712. W: www.centerfordigital art.org. Dedicated to the promotion of digital fine art through exhibitions, lectures and a Website.
- **COLLAGE/ASSEMBLAGE SOCIETY**, Roy Secord, Director, 504 W. 111 St., New York, NY 10025. T: (212) 662-5430. E: Flocord @ aol. com. France Garrido, Director, 215 Angelique St., Weehawken, NJ 07087. (201) 319-1504. E: fgarrido@ world-net.att.net. It is dedicated to increasing awareness of collage / assemblage.
- **COLLEGE ART ASSOCIATION OF AMERICA**, 275 Seventh Ave., New York, NY 10001.T: (212) 691-1051. F: (212) 627-2381. E: newyorkoffice@ collegeart. org. W: www. collegeart.org. It promotes excellence in the practice and teaching aspects of art and art history. Presents annual conference.
- **d.u.m.b.o.**, 30 Washington St., Brooklyn, NY 11201. T: (718) 624-3772. F: (718) 624-8261. W: www.dumboart center.org. It is a multi-media, center with group shows. Artist slide file and video archive. Home of d.u.m.b.o. Art Under the Bridge Festival.

- **EN FOCO, INC.**, 32 E. Kingsbridge Rd., Bronx, NY 10468. Tel/F: (718) 584-7718. W: www.enfoco.org. E: info@enfoco. It is dedicated to producing exhibitions, publications and events which support culturally diverse photographers.
- **GEN ART, Art of The Next Generation**, 145 West 28 St., #11C, New York, NY 10001. T: (212) 290-0312. F: (212) 290-0254. W: www.genart.org. It exposes the work of young emerging artists, filmmakers, and fashion designers.
- **INTERNATIONAL FINE PRINT DEALERS ASSOCIATION**, 15 Gramercy Park So., Ste.7A, New York, NY 10003. T: (212) 674-6095. E: ifpda@printdealers.com W: printdealers.com. President: Robert K. Newman. It encourages and promotes excellence in the fine art print field.
- **NATIONAL ASSOCIATION OF WOMEN ARTISTS (NAWA),** 41 Union Square West, #906, New York, NY 10003. T: (212) 675-1616. The oldest woman artists exhibiting organization. It encourages and promotes the creative output of women artists and presents exhibitions.
- **NATIONAL SCULPTURE SOCIETY**, 237 Park Avenue, New York, NY 10017. T: (212) 764-5645. F: (212) 764-5651. W: www.nationalsculpture.com. It sponsors exhibitions, publishes *Sculpture Review,* provides academic scholarships, and operates the National Sculpture Society gallery.
- **NEW YORK SOCIETY OF WOMEN ARTISTS,** provides a venue for women to exhibit their work. It juries new members in April. Artists who work in 2-d contact Catchi, 2 Grist Mill Lane, Manhasset, NY 11030. Artists who work in 3-d contact Janet Indick, 428 Sagamore Ave., Teaneck, NJ 07666.
- **NURTURE ART**, 160 Cabrini Blvd., PH 134, New York, NY 10033. T: (212) 795-5566. E: grobins@erols.com. It provides exposure and support for artists.
- **PASTEL SOCIETY**, C/O National Arts Club, 15 Gramercy Park, New York, NY 10003. T: 212-533-6931. W:www.pastel society. org. President: Barbara Fischman. It encourages the use of pastel and educates the public. It presents exhibitions, workshops and classes.
- **PRINTED MATTER, INC.**, 535 West 22 St., New York, NY 10011. T: (212) 925-0325. F: (212) 925-0464. To foster the appreciation, dissemination, and understanding of publications made by artists.
- **PROFESSIONAL WOMEN PHOTOGRAPHERS,** c/o Photographics Unlimited,

17 West 17 St., NY, NY 10011. T: (212) 726-8292. W: www.pwponline.org. It educates, supports, and encourages the work of women photographers. It presents exhibitions, workshops and publishes a newsletter.

- **QUEENS COUNCIL ON THE ARTS**, One Forest Park at Oak Ride, Woodhaven, NY 11421-1166. T: (718) 647-3377. F: (718) 647-5036. W: www.queenscouncil arts.org. E: qca@queenscouncilarts.org. It supports, promotes and develops the arts in Queens County by assisting organizations and individual artists.
- **THE SCULPTORS GUILD**, SoHo Building, 110 Greene St., #601, 10012. Tel/F: (212) 431-5669. E: sculptorsguild @earthlink.net W: www.sculptorsguild.org. It promotes and encourages contemporary sculpture by providing a forum and showcase for its members.
- **TWO RIVERS ART GROUP**, 10 Waterside Plaza, #24E, 10010. T: (212) 679-2242. E: susanrobins@rcn.com. Dir: Susan A. Robins and John Spoerri. It features contemporary figurative and landscape art, some abstract, in all media.
- **CATHARINE LORILLARD WOLFE ART CLUB, INC.**, 802 Broadway, New York, NY 10003. An organization of women artists presents exhibitions, open to all artists with professional quality work, regardless of residence and age.
- **WOMEN'S CAUCUS FOR ART/ New York Chapter (WCA)**, #20-B, 340 W. 28th St., NY, NY 10001. It provides information and support of women artists. It holds annual conferences, distributes a newsletter and maintains a slide registry and resource file.
- **WOMEN'S STUDIO CENTER INC.**, Mai to: P.O. Box 56155, Woolsey Station, Long Island City, NY 11105. Location: Wills Art Deco Building, Suite 216, 43 - 01 21 St., Long Island City, NY 11101. T: (718) 361-5649. E: WSC586@aol.com. W: www .womenstudiocenter.org. Melissa Wolf, Executive Director. It offers studio space, classes and workshops to artists and provides information about women in the arts and the business of art to artists.

PHOTOGRAPHY & DIGITAL

- **ART PHOTOGRAPHY BY KRIS VAGNER**, 471 Vanderbilt Ave. #3B, Brooklyn, NY 11238. T: (718) 789-0581 or (646) 339-4605. E: kris@volition.org. W: www.kris.vagner.net. High quality 35mm slides of 2-D and 3-D artwork, scanning, CDs, and digital prints, at moderate rates.

- **PHOTOGRAPHICS UNLIMITED**, 17 West 17 St., New York, NY 10011. T: (212) 255-9678. F: (212) 620-0999. E: photosnyc @earthlink.net. 2-D artwork photographed on their premises. Slides, photographs, slide dupes, other services.
- **PRINT SPACE, INC.**, 151 West 19 St., 7th Floor, New York, NY 10011. T: (212) 255-1919. Custom and self-service color and black & white. Darkroom facility available for hourly rental.
- **ROBERT PUGLISI**, T: (212) 330-0903. Reproduction quality art photography.
- **RAFI IMAGING**, 21 West 46 St., New York, NY 10036. T: (212) 719-2929. W: www.raffi.com. Photo CD Scans and other Digital services.
- **ADAM REICH**, T: (212) 736-5999. All formats, studio or location.
- **SPECTRA DIGITAL ARTS**, 508 LaGuardia Place, New York, NY 10012. T: (212) 477-6767. W: www.podgallery.com. Digital printing of fine art.

WRITING & PUBLIC RELATIONS

- **ED MC CORMACK** 217 East 85 Street, PMB 228, New York , NY 10028. T: (212) 861-0683. E: galleryandstudio@mindspring. com. New York writer and critic who has written catalogue essays for numerous galleries and museums in the U.S. and abroad.
- **FITZ & CO.**, 526 West 26 Street, #916, New York, NY 10001. T: (212) 627-1455. W: www.fitzandco.com. Public relations for galleries and art institutions.
- **MANHATTAN ARTS**, (212) 472-1660. E: info@ManhattanArts.com. W: www. ManhattanArts.com. Writing and editing promotional materials for print and web.
- **CAROLE SORELL INC. (CSI)**, 236 East 47 St., New York, NY 10017. T: (212) 339-0074. F: 212) 339-0075. Public relations firm specializing in the promotion and marketing of the arts and culture. Extensive experience museums, galleries, and established artists.

GRAPHIC & WEBSITE DESIGN

- **STEPHEN BEVERIDGE**, (212) 928-8351. E:scotstyle@scotstyle.com. W: www.scotstyle.com. Website designer and consultant specializing in artists' and art-related organizations' websites.
- **HARRIET REGINA MARION**, M.F.A., (212) 475-7410, F: (212) 375-9027, E: h1r1m@aol.com. W: www.troublegirl. com. Design and formatting of promotional pieces, invitations, press kits, etc.

- **MELISSA ULTO**, Web design and multi-media functionality for conceptual and artistic sites. T: (917) 549-7006. E: webdesign@multo.com. W: www.multo.com.

CAREER GUIDANCE & THERAPY

- **ANDREW ABRAMS AKA AGENT ANDY** Licensing Agent, Career Coach, and Concept Developer. T: (201) 933-8098. W: www.AgentAndy.com
- **ART INFORMATION CENTER** 55 Mercer St., New York, NY 10012. T: (212) 966-3443. Director Dan Concholar counsels artists about NYC galleries and offers direction on appropriate galleries for their work.
- **SANDRA INDIG C.S.W., A.T.R.-B.C.**, T: (212) 330-6787. Artist, arts therapist and analytic psychotherapist. To experience full expression of one's talent is a primary goal.
- **CAROLL MICHELS** 19 Spring Wood La., East Hampton, NY 11937. T: (631) 329-9105. W:carollmichels.com. Career advisor for artists at all career stages. Author of *How to Survive and Prosper As An Artist.*
- **RENÉE PHILLIPS** Manhattan Arts International, 200 East 72 St., New York, NY 10021. T: (212) 472-1660. F: (212) 794-0324. E: Renee@ManhattanArts.com. W: www. ManhattanArts.com. Career guidance and coaching with a focus on marketing strategies and promotion. Private consultations and group workshops.

BOOKS

- *THE ART DEALERS*, by Laura de Coppet and Alan Jones. Published by Clarkson N. Potter, Inc.
- *THE ARTIST-GALLERY PARTNERSHIP: A PRACTICAL GUIDE TO CONSIGNING ART*, by Tad Crawford and Susan Mellon. Published by Allworth Press.
- *THE ARTIST'S FRIENDLY LEGAL GUIDE*, by Floyd Conner et al. Published by North Light Books.
- *ARTISTS' GALLERY GUIDE*, published by Chicago Artists Coalition. (312) 670-2060.
- *THE ARTIST'S GUIDE TO NEW MARKETS: OPPORTUNITIES TO SHOW AND SELL ART BEYOND GALLERIES*, by Peggy Hadden. Published by Allworth Press.
- *THE ARTIST'S RESOURCE HANDBOOK*, Revised Edition by Daniel Grant. Published by Allworth Press.
- *THE ARTIST'S SURVIVAL MANUAL: A COMPLETE GUIDE TO MARKETING YOUR WORK* by Toby Judith Klayman.

Published by Charles Scribner's Sons.
- *ART LAW: THE GUIDE FOR COLLECTORS, INVESTORS, DEALERS, AND ARTISTS*, by Ralph E. Lerner and Judith Bresler. Published by Practicing Law Institute.
- *ART MARKETING HANDBOOK: MARKETING ART IN THE NINETIES*, by Calvin J. Goodman and Florence J. Goodman. Published by Gee Tee Be.
- *ART MARKETING 101: A HANDBOOK FOR THE FINE ARTIST*, by Constance Smith. Published by Art Network.
- *ART OFFICE: BUSINESS FORMS, CHARTS, SAMPLE LETTERS, LEGAL DOCUMENTS & BUISNESS PLANS FOR FINE ARTISTS*, by Constance Smith and Sue Viders. Published by ArtNetwork.
- *ARTSWIRE WEB MANUAL*, published by New York Foundation for the Arts.
- *THE BUSINESS OF ART* edited by Lee Caplin. Published by Prentice-Hall.
- *BUSINESS AND LEGAL FORMS FOR FINE ARTISTS,* by Tad Crawford. Published by Allworth Press.
- *BUSINESS AND LEGAL FORMS FOR PHOTOGRAPHERS,* by Tad Crawford. Published by Allworth Press.
- *THE BUSINESS OF BEING AN ARTIST,* by Daniel Grant. Published by Allworth Press.
- *CARING FOR YOUR ART*, by Jill Snyder. Published by Allworth Press.
- *THE COPYRIGHT GUIDE: A FRIENDLY GUIDE TO PROTECTING AND PROFITING FROM COPYRIGHTS*, by Lee Wilson. Published by Allworth Press.
- *CREATING SUCCESS: THE ARTIST'S COMPLETE GUIDE TO FREEDOM & PROSPERITY*, by Renée Phillips. Published by Manhattan Arts International. *(See order form in this book.)*
- *THE FINE ARTIST'S CAREER GUIDE,* by Daniel Grant. Published by Allworth Press.
- *THE FINE ARTIST'S GUIDE TO MARKETING AND SELF-PROMOTION* by Julius Vitali. Published by Allworth Press.
- *THE FINE ARTIST'S GUIDE TO SHOWING AND SELLING YOUR WORK*, by Sally Prince Davis. Published by North Light Books.
- *FINE ART PUBLICITY: THE COMPLETE GUIDE FOR GALLERIES AND ARTISTS*, by Susan Abbott and Barbara Webb. Published by Art Business News Library.
- *GERRY FRANK'S WHERE TO FIND IT, BUY IT, EAT IT IN NEW YORK* published by Gerry's Frankly Speaking.

- *FOUNDRY GUIDE & DIRECTORY: AN A TO Z COMPARISON OF 100 FOUNDRIES*, published by International Sculpture Center.
- *GRANT-SEARCHING SIMPLIFIED* by S.B. Wolfe. Published by Creative Resources, Clyde, NC.
- *HOW TO PHOTOGRAPH YOUR ART* by Malcolm Lubliner. Published by Pomegranate Press.
- *HOW TO PHOTOGRAPH YOUR ARTWORK* by Kim Brown. Published by Canyonwinds.
- *HOW TO START AND SUCCEED AS AN ARTIST,* by Daniel Grant. Published by Allworth Press.
- *HOW TO SURVIVE AND PROSPER AS AN ARTIST*, by Caroll Michels. Published by Henry Holt and Company.
- *LANDSCAPE WITH FIGURES: A HISTORY OF ART DEALING IN THE UNITED STATES*, by Malcolm Goldstein. Published by Oxford University Press.
- *LEGAL GUIDE FOR THE VISUAL ARTIST* by Tad Crawford. Published By Allworth Press.
- *LICENSING ART 101* , by Michael Woodward. Published by ArtNetwork.
- *MARKETING MADE EASIER: GUIDE TO FREE ORGANIZING ARTISTS* published by National Association of Artists' Organizations.
- *MONEY FOR VISUAL ARTISTS* published by Americans for the Arts with Allworth Press.
- *NEW YORK PUBLICITY OUTLETS* published by Public Relations Plus, Inc.
- *ON EXHIBIT: ART LOVER'S GUIDE TO AMERICAN MUSEUMS* by Judith Swirsky. Published by Abbeville Press.
- *PHOTOGRAPHING YOUR ARTWORK: A STEP-BY-STEP GUIDE TO TAKING HIGH QUALITY SLIDES AT AN AFFORDABLE PRICE* by Russell Hart. Published by North Light.
- *PRESENTATION POWER TOOLS FOR FINE ARTISTS*: Step-by-Step Writing Guidelines, Professional Advice & Samples, by Renée Phillips. Published by Manhattan Arts International. *(See order form in this book.)*
- *PROFESSIONAL'S GUIDE TO PUBLICITY* by Richard Winer. Published by Public Relations Publishing Co.
- *THE PUBLICITY MANUAL* by Kate Kelly. Published by Visibility Enterprises.
- *TAKING THE LEAP, THE INSIDER'S GUIDE TO EXHIBITING AND SELLING YOUR ART*, By Cay Lang. Published by Chronicle Books.

- *ULRICH'S INTERNATIONAL PERIODICALS DIRECTORY* published by R.R. Bowker.

ART PERIODICALS

- *AMERICAN ARTIST,* 1515 Broadway, New York, NY 10036. Monthly art magazine.
- *APERTURE*, 20 East 23 St., New York, NY 10010.
- *ART AND AUCTION,* 440 Park Avenue South, New York, NY 10016.
- *ART BUSINESS NEWS*, 60 Ridgeway Plaza, Stamford, CT 06905. (213) 356-1745.
- *ARTFORUM,* 65 Bleecker Street, New York, NY 10012. Monthly art magazine.
- *ART IN AMERICA*, 575 Broadway, New York, NY 10012. T: (212) 941-2806.
- *THE ARTIST'S MAGAZINE,* 1507 Dana Avenue, Cincinnati, OH 45207.
- *ART NEW ENGLAND*, *A Resource For Visual Artists*, 425 Washington St., Brighton, MA 02135.
- *ARTNEWS*, LIC, 48 West 38 Street, New York, NY 10018. (800) 284-4625.
- *ART NOW GALLERY GUIDE,* 97 Grayrock Rd., PO Box 5541, Clinton, NJ 08809. T: (908) 638-5255.
- *ART SOURCE QUARTERLY,* ArtNetwork, PO Box 1360, Nevada City, CA 95959. T: (530) 470-0862.
- *ART TIMES,* CSS Publications, Inc., PO Box 730, Mt. Marion, NY 12456. T: (914) 246-6944.
- *ART TRENDS MAGAZINE: The Magazine of Fine Art Prints*, 225 Gordons corner Rd., Manapalan, NJ 07726. T: (800) 969-7176.
- *ARTWORLD HOTLINE*, ArtNetwork, PO Box 1360, Nevada City, CA 95959. T: (530) 470-0862.
- *DECOR: THE BUSINESS MAGAZINE OF FINE ART AND FRAMING,* 330 North Fourth Street, St. Louis, MO. T: (314) 421-5445.
- *DIGITAL FINE ART MAGAZINE*, PO Box 420, Manalapan, NJ 07726.
- *ENTREPRENEUR: THE SMALL BUSINESS AUTHORITY,* (800) 274-6229. E: subscribe@ entrepreneurmag.com. W: www.entrepreneurmag.com
- *F.Y.I.,* Foundation for the Arts, 155 Avenue of the Americas, New York, NY 10013. *(See Organizations.)*
- *GALLERY & STUDIO,* 217 East 85 St., PMB, New York, NY 10028. T: (212) 861-6814. E: galleryandstudio@mindspring.com
- *NEW ART EXAMINER,* 314 West Institute Place, Chicago, IL 60610.

- *THE NEWSLETTER,* published by Caroll Michels, 19 Springwood Lane, East Hampton, New York 11937. T: (516) 329-9105. F: (516) 329-9107.E: carollmich@ aol.com.
- *NEW YORK ART WORLD*, MBM Publications, 303 West 42 St., 5th floor, New York, NY 10036. Monthly art magazine.
- *NEW YORK PUBLICITY OUTLETS*, Public Relations Plus, Inc., PO Box 1197, New Milford, CT 06776. T: (800) 999-8448.
- *PHOTOGRAPHY IN NEW YORK*, 64 West 89 Street, #3F, New York, NY 10025.
- *THE PHOTO REVIEW*, Photo Review, 301 Hill Avenue, Langhorne, PA 19047.
- *PICTURE FRAMING MAGAZINE,* 225 Gordons Corner Rd/ PO Box 420, Manalapan NJ 07726. W: www. pictureframe. com.
- *SCULPTURE* MAGAZINE, published by the International Sculpture Center. T: (212) 785-1144.
- *SCULPTURE REVIEW*, published by the National Sculpture Society, 1177 Avenue of the Americas, New York, NY 10036. T: (212) 764-5645.
- *SUCCESS NOW! THE ARTREPRENEUR NEWSLETTER*, Published by Manhattan Arts International. T: (212) 472-1660. W: www.ManhattanArts.com. *(See order form in this book.)*

NYC ART SCHOOLS

- **ART STUDENTS LEAGUE**, 215 West 57 St., New York, NY 10019. T: (212) 247-4510. W: ww.theartstudentsleague.org.
- **CHRISTIE'S EDUCATION**, 55 East 59 St., 15th floor, New York, NY 10022. T: (212) 355-1501. W: www.christies.edu.
- **FASHION INSTITUTE OF TECHNOLOGY**, Seventh Ave. at 27 St., New York, NY 10001. T: (212) 217-7675. W: www.fitnyc.suny.edu
- **NATIONAL ACADEMY SCHOOL OF FINE ART**, 5 East 89 St., New York, NY 10128. T: (212) 996-1908. W: www.nationalacademy.org.
- **NEW YORK ACADEMY OF ART**, Graduate School of Figurative Art, 111 Franklin St., New York, NY 10013. T: (212) 966-0300. F: (212) 226-3665. W: www.nyaa.edu.
- **SCHOOL OF VISUAL ARTS**, 209 East 23 St., New York, NY 10010. T: (212) 592-2100. W: www.schoolofvisualarts.edu.
- **PARSONS SCHOOL OF DESIGN**, 2 West 13 St., New York, NY 10011. T: (212) 229-8987. W: www.parsons.edu.

- **PRATT INSTITUTE**, 295 Lafayette St., New York, NY 10013. T: (212) 461-6000. W: www.pratt.edu.

ART SUPPLIES / FRAMING

- **THE ART STORE:** 1-5 Bond St., New York, NY 10012. T: (212) 533-2444. W: www.artstores.com.
- **DICK BLICK:** T: (800) 933-2542. W: www.dickblick.com
- **CHEAP JOES:** T: (800) 227-2788. W: www.cheapjoes.com
- **ESSEX:** T: (800) 581-0949.
- **SAM FLAX:** 12 West 20 St., New York, NY 10011. T: (212) 620-3038.
- **GRAPHIK DIMENSIONS:** T: (800) 221-0262.
- **JERRY'S ARTORAMA:** W: www.jerryssale.com
- **LEE'S ART SHOP** 220 West 57 St., New York, NY 10019. T: (212) 247-0110.
- **LIGHT IMPRESSIONS:** T: (800) 828-6216. W: www.lightimpressionsdirect.com
- **METROPOLITAN FRAMING** T: (800) 626-3139. W: www.metrofram.com
- **MISTER ART:** T: (866) 672-7811. W:www.misterart.com
- **NEW YORK CENTRAL ART SUPPLIES** 62 Third Ave. NY, NY 10003. T: (212) 473-7705.
- **OFFICE WORLD:** W: www.officeworld.com/worlds-biggest-selection/artist.supply
- **PEARL PAINT:** 308 Canal St., NY, NY 10013. T: (800) 221-6845. W: www. pearlpaint.com
- **UTRECHT:** 111 Fourth Ave., NY, NY 10003. T: (800) 223-9132. W: www.utrechtart.com

PRINTERS

- **ART EDITIONS:** T: (800) 331-8449.
- **BRILLIANT COLOR LINE:** T:(800) 869-8398.
- **COLOR CARD:** T: (800) 875-1386. W: www.afullcolorcard.com
- **CLARK CARDS:** T: (800) 227-3658.
- **COLOR Q:** T: (800) 999-1007.
- **GO CARD:** T: (212) 925-2420.
- **GREAT AMERICAN PRINTING:** T: (800) 440-2368.
- **ORIGINAL CARD COMPANY:** T: (800) 587-2640. W: www. originalcards.com
- **MITCHELL GRAPHICS:** T: (800) 841-6793.

- MODERN POSTCARD: T: (800) 959-8365.
- POST SCRIPT PRESS: T: (800) 511-2009.

PACKING/SHIPPING/ WAREHOUSE/INSURANCE

- CARLSON'S VAN LINES: T: (415) 583-1694.
- COOKE'S CRATING AND FINE ARTS TRANSPORTATION: T: (323) 268-5101.
- CRATERS AND FREIGHTERS: T: (303) 399-8190.
- DAD TRUCKING: T: (212) 226-0054.

- DIETL INTERNATIONAL SERVICES: T: (718) 244-6954.
- FORTRESS F.A.E. WORLDWIDE: T: (718) 937-5500. W: www. fortressfae.com
- HAHN BROTHERS ART SERVICES: T: (212) 926-1505.
- MASTERPAK: T: (800) 922-5522. W: www.masterpak-usa.com
- NEW YORKER ARTS: T: (212) 222-6169.
- OCS: T: (212) 226-1052.
- SOHO CRATES: T: (212) 219-2383.
- THOMSON & PRATT INSURANCE ASSOCIATES, INC: T: (877) 334-6327
- TRANSCON INTERNATIONAL, INC: T: (718) 585-1600.

INDEX

Workshops Presented by Renée Phillips

Artists HOW TO SELL YOUR ART

Also known as "How to Break into New York Galleries"

An insider's comprehensive 3-hour workshop

- Learn how different NYC galleries operate and select their artists.
- Obtain successful strategies to approach and obtain the appropriate gallery.
- Acquire simple steps on how to price and increase the value of your work.
- Find out which galleries are more accessible and where to exhibit *now*.
- Learn how to prosper *without* a gallery.

Held every month in NYC. Course #888.
For reservations call The Learning Annex, NYC (212) 371-0280.

CREATING SUCCESS

Small Group Workshops

In these series of workshops you will learn how to:

- Plan and Attain Your Financial, Career and Creative Goals
- Develop Powerful Professional Relationships
- Increase Sales, increase income, and increase the value of your artwork
- Create Polished Promotional Materials
- Attract the Press and Get Publicity

"Renée is all about helping artists become successful." Cornelia Seckel, *Art Times*

"Renée Phillips completely de-myths the NYC gallery system. She delivers a wealth of information with clarity and inspiration." Dr. Henry Jablonsky

"I traveled from San Francisco to attend your workshop and I am so pleased that I made the effort. I have already made progress in several areas as a result of what I learned."
M. Loncola

Renée Phillips lectures and conducts workshops throughout the U.S.   Contact us for a current schedule.

T: (212) 472-1660   E: info@ManhattanArts.com   www.ManhattanArts.com

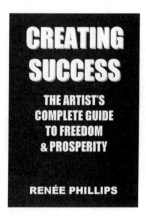

In **CREATING SUCCESS** Renée Phillips offers unwavering encouragement, sage advice and a wealth of innovative and practical career strategies in art marketing and promotion.

She shares 20 years experience as an artist career advisor, coach, curator, critic, and motivational speaker. You'll learn the myths that sabotage an artist's career and how to avoid them, and how to develop career goals and attain them step-by-step. You'll learn many secrets and strategies of successful artists. Renée's motivational voice and inspirational quotes will lead you to freedom, prosperity, and power. $19.95   ISBN 09646358-0-1

"I have never met anyone in the art world like Renée Phillips who is so singularly focused in her pursuit to help artists establish and further their careers."
Edward Rubin, NY critic, *New Art Examiner* and *Theater Week*

This book will help you achieve a polished, professional approach to dealers, critics and collectors.

"A must read for professionals and students."
– Diane Leon, New York University

"Renée inspires, guides and encourages artists to reach their goals through sound advice on the business of art."
Regina Stewart, NY Artists Equity Association

PRESENTATION POWER TOOLS FOR FINE ARTISTS is a vital resource for any Fine Art professional engaged in promoting and selling Art. Step-by-step writing guidelines and expert advice are designed to save time, frustration and costly mistakes in the preparation of promotional materials. Samples of **Business Letters, Resumes, Biographies, Artist's Statements, Promotion Pieces, Comment Sheets, Bill of Sale, Invoice, Certificate of Authenticity** and **Press Releases** are provided. The book also contains an **Artist/Gallery Agreement** checklist, **Workforms** and more documents.   ISBN 0-9646358-5-2 $19.95   81/2" x 11"

Both books are available at www.Amazon.com, www.BN.com and major bookstores.

HOW TO ORDER THESE BOOKS
Use the order form on page 303 or contact
Manhattan Arts International (212) 472-1660 or go to www.ManhattanArts.com

Thank you for purchasing this copy of
NEW YORK CONTEMPORARY ART GALLERIES

To show our appreciation please accept this
$5.00 Discount Per Item
on the purchase of any of our publications.

Where did you purchase this copy of
NEW YORK CONTEMPORARY ART GALLERIES?

___ book store   ___ gallery   ___ workshop   ____ museum   ___ It was a gift

___ www.Amazon.com   ___ www.BarnesandNoble.com   ___ www.ManhattanArts.com

Name _____

Address _____

City _____ State_____ Zip_____

Tel: _____ Email: _____

Name as it appears on the credit card: _____

___ MC ___ VISA ___AE Card # _____

Expiration date_____

# copies	Item	Cost per copy	Total
_____	New York Contemporary Art Galleries	$25	_____
_____	Presentation Power Tools For Fine Artists	$25	_____
_____	Creating Success: The Artist's Complete Guide	$25	_____
_____	One year subscription to SUCCESS NOW! newsletter	$25	_____
_____	New York Contemporary Art Gallery Mailing List labels	$75	_____
Rush charge to receive Mailing List Labels by Next Day Air		Add $10	_____
		TOTAL	_____

DEDUCT $5.00 FOR EACH ITEM ORDERED
Number of items _____ x $5.00 = Total Discount   _____

YOU PAY ONLY   _____

All costs include shipping and handling charges.

If paying by U.S. check or money order please make it payable to Manhattan Arts International,
200 East 72 Street, New York, NY 10021. U.S. shipments only. Sorry, no foreign orders.
Tel: (212) 472-1660   Fax: (212) 794-0324
Email: info@ManhattanArts.com   Web site: www. ManhattanArts.com

Thank you for your order!